Landscape ecology and land use

Landscape ecology and land use

A. P. A. VINK

TRANSLATED BY THE AUTHOR

ENGLISH TRANSLATION EDITED BY

D. A. DAVIDSON
UNIVERSITY OF STRATHCLYDE

LONGMAN
LONDON AND NEW YORK

Longman Group Limited
Longman House
Burnt Mill, Harlow, Essex, CM20 2JE, England
Associated companies throughout the world

Published in the United States of America
by Longman Inc., New York

English translation
© Longman Group Limited 1983

First published as *Landschapsecologie en landgebruik*
by Bohn, Scheltema & Holkema Utrecht, 1980
© 1980 Scheltema & Holkema BV
English edition first published in 1983

British Library Cataloguing in Publication Data
Vink, A. P. A.
  Landscape ecology and land use.
  1. Environmental education
  I. Title II. Davidson, D. A.
  333.7'07 GF26

  ISBN 0-582-30077-0

Library of Congress Cataloging in Publication Data
Vink, A. P. A.
  Landscape ecology and land use.

  Translation of: Landschapsecologie en landgebruik.
  Bibliography: p.
  Includes index.
  1. Land use – Planning. 2. Land use – Environmental aspects.
3. Environmental protection. 4. Ecology. 5. Agricultural ecology.
6. Landscape protection. 7. Physical geography. I. Title.
HD108.6.V5613 1983 333.73'13 82-10030
ISBN 0-582-30077-0 (pbk.)

Set in 10/12 pt Linotron 202 Times
Printed in Singapore by Selector Printing Co Pte Ltd

Contents

Preface

This book is based on a book published in the Dutch language with the same title. It is meant to provide undergraduate students in geography with a sufficiently detailed as well as comprehensive view on the landscape and its use. Hopefully it will also be of interest to students in such disciplines as agriculture, planning and environmental sciences. It has no pretension to be complete nor to contribute to the development of basic theories. Where possible, examples from various countries have been used to give a picture to those who for the first time come into closer contact with these subjects.

The author is a Dutchman and an agronomist. He may be excused for using a rather large number of examples from the Netherlands and for putting more emphasis on agriculture than on other land uses. However, emphasis on agriculture is warranted because of the crucial role of agriculture in feeding the continuously increasing populations of the world.

Very special thanks go to Dr D. A. Davidson of the Department of Geography, the University of Strathclyde, Glasgow, for his initiative with regard to this English version and for his continuous and agreeable cooperation in correcting and editing this English text. Mr C. J. Snabilié, Mrs M. C. G. Keijzer-v.d.Lubbe and Miss G. J. M. Scholts are offered particular thanks for their help and work on the figures and the final manuscript.

A. P. A. Vink
Amsterdam, October 1981

The material published by the Soil Survey of Scotland is reproduced by permission of the Macaulay Institute for Soil Research and the Authors.

1

Introduction

With these preliminary considerations in mind the study of the landscape may be summarized as the study of the relationships in space and in time between phenomena which are active in the landscape or geosphere including the communities of plants and animals on earth.

LANDSCAPE

The purpose of this book is to analyse the significance of the landscape for man and to identify his positive and negative effects. The landscape is thus interpreted as the basis of the human environment. However, as will be demonstrated in the book, human existence is impossible without plants and animals. Plants and animals live in communities. These communities may have little or no human influence, or they may be more or less strongly influenced by man. In the former case we often speak of 'nature' to indicate the more natural environments of plants and animals, which have not been markedly influenced by man. Such terms as 'landscape', 'nature', and 'environment' can be interpreted in a number of ways. In general, these are not mutually exclusive, but they do give different emphasis to various aspects of these interpretations. However, it is important to give an outline of the viewpoint from which this book has been written. This does not mean that we have less respect for other viewpoints which do not coincide with the adopted approach.

Landscape may be visualized in the first instance as a sphere within which a range of processes are active. More generally used terms are cosmosphere, atmosphere, biosphere, hydrosphere, lithosphere, pedosphere and anthroposphere or noosphere, i.e. the sphere in which human knowledge (Greek: *noos*) is active. However, it is also possible to identify a landscape-sphere or geosphere which can be defined as the natural characteristics of the surface of the earth and of the space near to this surface. These characteristics are not static since this is the environment in which most of those processes take place which influence the conditions of life for human beings and for all other organisms. It is the sphere in which other spheres interact. The landscape may also be seen as the continuously changing result of the interactions between processes in the various types of spheres. At a specific locality, then, the landscape is an expression of the relationships between these spheres. The study of a landscape over a certain period of time reveals the processes in a given landscape or geotope, i.e. a part of the geosphere which is relatively homogeneous with respect to its form and processes. There are also processes which result from the interactions between groups of organisms. These interactions may be a function of biological as well as of social relationships. These kinds of processes have in general either a direct or indirect influence on the geosphere. Some of these consequences will be indicated during the discussion of various topics in the book. However, the systematic treatment of these processes exceeds the scope of this book.

With these preliminary comments in mind, the study of the landscape may be summarized as *the study of the relationships in space and in time between phenomena and processes in the landscape or geosphere including the communities of plants, animals and men.*

Other ways of approaching the landscape as a complex phenomenon are not excluded from this interpretation. An alternative approach, which is often used successfully, puts less emphasis on the processes and more on those phenomena which are observable at a given moment or in a given period. In this case, a further two different main uses of the term 'landscape' may be recognized:
1. The surface of the earth with all its phenomena, including landforms, vegetation and man-influenced attributes, which are collectively indicated by the term *physiography*. This term has strong connections with physiognomy, which is used in particular for indicating the visual, or architectural, characteristics of a landscape. For this purpose physiognomic landscape surveys are carried out. As an example, landscape architects carry out various types of physiognomic survey. In Chapter 4 some consideration will be given to these surveys.
2. The region, a defined and delineated area of the surface of the earth, sometimes indicated as a geotope or a complex of geotopes, depending on the dimensions of the landscape and on the mapping scale. Such a region is delineated because of its own specific landforms, vegetation and also in many instances man-made attributes. The delineation of landscapes as regional units is often very helpful for practical as well as for theoretical purposes.

Examples of physiographic regions with their own visual and ecological characteristics are perhaps less common in the English language than it is in some other Germanic languages, such as German 'Landschaft' or Dutch 'landschap'. However, physiographic regions as practical units have been used by all rural populations from earliest times. In general, these physiographic regions have a number of distinguishing characteristics with regard to relief, vegetation, soils and human land use. Large river valleys such as the Thames, or the Vale of Eden present distinct physiographic regions. Examples such as the Weald, the Cotswolds, or the Cairngorms generate images of contrasting physiographic types. In the Grand Duchy of Luxembourg, the division between the 'Guttland' (the good agricultural land area) and the 'Oesling' (the rougher Ardennes) is rather typical. The Netherlands appears to the untrained visitor as a very flat homogeneous country. In the 1860s, W. C. H. Staring, the father of geology as well as of soil survey in the

Netherlands, made a map of the different landscapes or physiographic regions. He recognized such landscapes as the young seaclay landscape, the old seaclay landscape, the riverclay landscape, the lowland-peat landscape, and the coversand landscape. This subdivision into landscapes still corresponds with the present day main subdivisions on the soil maps of the Netherlands. In other countries – for example, France – the agrogeologists of the nineteenth century had a very similar approach. In more recent periods, the land systems approach of the Australian CSIRO and a similar approach for surveys in developing countries used by LRDC (Land Resources Development Centre of the Ministry for Overseas Development), London, have proved to be useful for modern agricultural planning.

Landscape has different meanings to varying groups of people according to their interests and background. This can be demonstrated by considering the average person living in a town, the landscape architect and the ecological landscape planner. The average person living in a town, on making a trip into the countryside, looks at the landscape primarily as if he or she were looking at an attractive picture. If the view from a hotel or from a holiday house is considered, it is even seen within a frame, similar to that of a picture. A wider view prevails from the top of a hill, but still the picture-viewing impression often remains. This view leads directly to landscape-painting. The landscape as a painting, from the sixteenth century masters to Van Gogh and until today, is an expression of this kind of approach, with the result that landscape painting has influenced many people's approach to the landscape. A similar influence, although perhaps less direct, may be discerned in descriptions of landscapes in literature.

The older schools of landscape architecture, strongly connected with urban architecture, resemble in their approach the view of the landscape as a picture. The picture preferably shows depth, but this only increases the similarity to many good landscape paintings. Even a walk around a garden or park reveals a different spot from each picture. The analogy with a painting may be applied to a sculpture, made from natural materials. In general, ecological problems are seen as difficulties to be solved by the application of human technology, although good landscape architects consider the suitability of climate and soils for the growth of plants. This may arise from the cost of establishing and maintaining gardens or parkland. Working with nature is in general cheaper and often more effective than working against nature.

During the last decades, and in particular since the late 1960s, landscape architects such as McHarg in the USA have started to develop better techniques of designing with nature. Such developments coincide with a general tendency towards the provision of landscapes for recreation and for various kinds of conservation, based on ecological principles. New landscapes are being created which are designed to encourage beneficial ecological processes and thus provide a better environment for men. This development has already led to important changes in our decisions on major aspects of land

use planning; for example, in projects of land reclamation and land reallocation. Until ten years ago, intensive technology was applied to create as much
land as possible for agriculture and other directly productive uses. Now
there is a tendency to try to save certain areas such as small woods or lakes
as habitats for birds, fishes and other animals. A typical decision, as part of
the Delta Enclosing Project in the Netherlands, was to create in the Oosters-
chelde, north of the Isle of Walcheren in the Netherlands, not a fully closed
dam but a partly open one. In this case the ecological need was to retain the
open link between the water system of the estuary and the North Sea.

LANDSCAPE ECOLOGY

The term *landscape ecology* was introduced by the German geographer Carl
Troll who later used the term 'geo-ecology'. He views the birth of landscape
ecology as the outcare of the marriage of geography (landscape) and biology
(ecology). The geographer's point of view stresses that concern is not only with
natural landscapes, but also with landscapes including man. This implies that
cultural landscapes and socio-geographical aspects have also to be considered.
As a result Troll visualized the application of landscape ecology to human
purposes such as land development, regional planning and urban planning.
Troll introduced his term in 1938 and at this early date already applied air-
photo interpretation to his methodology. In the last few decades the development of landscape ecology is partly due to the increased use of air-
photo interpretation in various kinds of surveys for land use planning. Air-
photo interpretation, more than other survey methods, gives an opportunity
to study a landscape as a whole, including all aspects seen in the stereoscopic
image such as relief, vegetation, water, land use, soil surfaces. Although it
must never be seen separate from the essential, and often specialised, field
observations, it does promote a more holistic approach to the geosphere.

Landscape ecology is the discipline which has the landscape or geosphere
as the key foundation of the environment for plant communities, animals
and man. The landscape, including all its phenomena and processes, may
also be viewed as supporting ecosystems (see Ch. 2). As a subject, it therefore belongs to the environmental sciences, a topic introduced in the next
section. It may, as is the case with other environmental sciences, also be
seen as an interdisciplinary subject between several sciences; for example,
between physical geography, biology and human geography. This does not
exclude other interdisciplinary contacts, such as with medical geography.

From the physical geography viewpoint, the landscape is a very intricate
complex of phenomena and processes, which may have been initiated in the
distant past. These phenomena and processes, which will have varied in
space and time, still have an influence on present day landscapes. As an
example, the geomorphologist first applies himself to the various shapes
which the abiotic elements of the landscape have obtained, with emphasis on
topography or relief and on the materials constituting the various landforms.

In particular the process geomorphologist studies the geomorphological processes which are currently prevailing in a given landscape and the resultant
forms and materials. Increasing attention is being paid to the influences of
various organisms (plants, animals, man) on these processes and as a result
contributions are made to some essential aspects of landscape ecology. If a
geomorphologist executes a systematic and accurate description and mapping of landforms, the results are directly applicable to morphographic and
physiognomic landscape surveys (see definitions at end of chapter). These
surveys have strong affinities to the work of the landscape architect and
provide him with useful basic data.

In general landscape ecology concentrates on the relationships between
individual or groups of organisms and a given area on the surface of the
earth. In theory it might be possible to develop for any particular locality a
complete and well-balanced model including the ecological relationships. In
such a model all the different components of the system, including man and
their functional inter-relationships, would have to be specified. In practice,
model-building necessitates simplification of the real situation. Thus the
need is for an approach which includes a degree of simplification, but which
also provides results relevant to land management and land use planning.
The phytocentric approach is often the adopted simplified approach. In this
approach, landscape–vegetation relationships are taken as the standard of
measurement. This is very often useful for the management of natural or
semi-natural ecosystems and for their conservation against outside influences. Another worthwhile approach is the zoocentric one in which the
significance of landscape phenomena and processes are assessed with reference to animal communities. The combination of the two could be called a
biocentric approach. For our purpose, emphasis is given to the relationships
within landscapes as seen from a human viewpoint and an anthropocentric
approach is thus adopted. This includes those relationships between plants
and animals and the landscape which clearly impinge upon present and future human existence. It has been argued (Vink 1981a) that an anthropocentric approach to landscape ecology does not only concentrate on the
short-term needs of human beings. A proper anthropocentric approach gives
full emphasis to the long-term as well as short-term needs, and to the responsibilities of human beings for the landscape and all its organisms.

Plants and animals are therefore of no less importance to us than if a
biocentric approach was adopted, but they are taken together with all
aspects in the landscape and are considered from a human viewpoint. The
anthropocentric approach seems therefore to be a better tool for many operational purposes. In essence, neither man nor animals can live without
plants. This is true in the most literal sense since only plants are able to
produce organic compounds from carbon dioxide gas in the atmosphere with
sunlight as the energy source. Animals and man therefore are completely
dependent both for energy and for matter on the life and production of
plants. In addition, plants and other organisms need water and mineral nu-

trients, the latter being supplied mainly by the soil through the weathering of rocks. Plants are the only organisms which assimilate minerals in their elementary forms, as ions, and the resultant proteins are essential nourishment for all other organisms. Man is dependent upon animals as a source of some proteins though these may not always be essential. Less direct, but perhaps more vital, is the role which animals play in the cyclical processes in ecosystems. Life is a continuous process of construction and destruction, in which new life grows from destruction. Plants as well as animals are essential for this.

Man is a component of many different ecosystems, but unlike other components, he has the most serious potential impact on these ecosystems. At one extreme he is able to completely destroy ecosystems, including much of the abiotic parts of the landscape; for example, through accelerating soil erosion. But man is also able to build new ecosystems which are called *cultural ecosystems* or *land utilization types*. In these cultural ecosystems man is the controlling agent and his goal is to obtain materials for food, clothes, luxuries or energy or space for recreation. In other words, the land use is a reflection of man's needs. The protection and conservation of natural ecosystems through nature reserves is, in this sense, seen as a specific kind of land use, reflecting not only human needs but also human responsibilities.

Landscape ecology and land use are therefore inseparable. In this world of growing human populations with increasing interference in all localities, it is unrealistic to undertake ecological analysis without also considering human impacts and human management. However, there exist countless different ecological aspects of the landscape and countless different ways by which man tries to control the various processes and phenomena in the landscape. It is the intention of this book to indicate, and to describe more fully wherever possible, several of the complex relationships and systems involved. It will be understood that an exhaustive treatment of all aspects is impossible. Figure 1 is a very simple diagram of the various factors and components which have to be taken into account in an ecological analysis.

A distinction can be drawn between fundamental and applied landscape ecology. Fundamental landscape ecology describes and investigates, for example by survey techniques, the phenomena, processes and relationships in the landscape with regard to human beings and other organisms. The applications of this are, for example, to land evaluation, impact studies, landscape design, and to land use planning. The land resources of an area are those components of the landscape which have a particular importance for human life and living standards. Land resources can be viewed as including vegetation resources, water resources, soil resources, etc. These resources have varying magnitudes and different potentials in different landscapes. They also have different relationships depending on the kind of landscape in which they are considered. Some aspects of these will be indicated in Chapter 3. In Chapter 4 the inventories and other investigations of land resources, often done with land resources surveys, are discussed. Their man-

Fig. 1 Relationships between man and the landscape

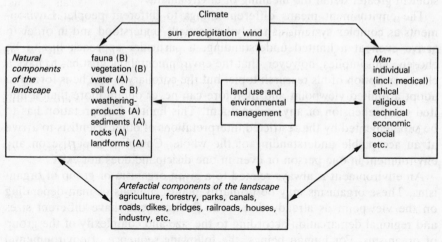

A = abiotic; B = biotic; ◄──► = reciprocal influences

agement and use is treated in Chapter 5, with special emphasis on agricultural land use, which in a global context is by far the most important use. To date urban land use has often been neglected in ecological studies as well as in publications on land use. Towns and cities ought to be viewed as cultural ecosystems and urban ecology may be able to make important contributions to providing man with a better urban environment in the future. For this reason, Chapter 6 is devoted to those aspects which properly may be said to belong to landscape ecology. Chapter 7 examines degradation as well as the improvement of the land for human uses. Finally, in Chapter 8 some aspects of landscape ecological investigations with regard to their evaluation for land use planning are discussed.

ENVIRONMENT IN A GEOGRAPHICAL CONTEXT

It has already been indicated that landscape ecology belongs to the environmental sciences. Environments as very complex systems can only be properly studied using a multidisciplinary, and better still with an interdisciplinary, approach. This involves the systematic cooperation of several sciences on an integrated basis. In practical daily life we try wherever possible from the backgrounds of our own discipline to learn of the complex problems involved. In this way separate branches of science such as environmental biology, environmental chemistry, and environmental geography have been developed. Landscape ecology may be considered to belong to environmental biology or to environmental geography, depending on the particular viewpoints of the scientists involved in the project. In this book we are taking the geographical viewpoint. It will be made clear in the following chapters that the biological aspects are also essential. However, it seems advisable to consider in greater detail the meaning of environment.

The environment means different things to different people. Environments as complex systems can only be partially understood and in order to arrive even at a limited understanding, a particular approach has to be chosen. This implies, however, that the environmental scientist has to have a clear perception of his research topic, but the corollary is that he is forced to adopt a limited viewpoint and therefore can never obtain more than a limited comprehension of any environment. This limited interpretation has to be supplemented by the restricted interpretations of other scientists to arrive at an acceptable understanding of the whole. Complete expertise on any environment in one person or even in one disicipline does not exist.

An environment is always related to a given organism or group of organisms. These organisms may be primarily plants, animals or man depending on the viewpoint as already discussed. Environments have different sizes and regional demarcation according to the size and complexity of the group of organisms. For human beings, the following sequence of environmental magnitudes may be given:

- a person – a family – the occupants of a house
- of a town . . . of a region . . . of a province . . . of a country
- of a group of countries (for example, EEC) . . . of a continent . . . of the whole world.

Such sequences can also be given for other organisms, based on their autecology (the particular needs of the given organisms) as well as on their synecology (their interactions with other kinds of organisms). But it is also possible to begin the sequence with the environmental factors and then lead to complexes of these factors which form the environments of the organisms. The following two examples indicate this approach:
1. Drop of water – small pond – small stream – lake – river – sea – ocean.
2. Soil aggregate – soil horizon – soil (pedon) – soil series – soil region or soil landscape.

Within each of these environmental ranges, organisms may be considered to range from micro-organisms to complex associations and communities of micro-, meso- and macro-organisms. The various components and types of landscapes have particular significance not only for man but also for most other organisms. The grouping of the complexes of environmental factors in land units and landscapes or physiographic regions then leads again to landscape ecology.

The geographical or landscape approach to environments is indeed an excellent way to give full value and extensive treatment to the various attributes of environments. This is done by producing different kinds of maps (for example, maps of vegetation, soils, water, physiography) at a number of scales. Such scales can range from 1 : 100 (very large scale) to 1 : 5 000 000 (very small scale) and to 1 : 20 000 000 (scale of maps in atlases). In Fig. 2

Fig. 2 A farm in one of the sandy regions of the Netherlands, the 'Gelderse Vallei', depicted on different map scales (after Vink and Van Zuilen 1967). The numbers of the legend refer to different soil mapping units which differ primarily in their water conditions: from 1 (excessively drained) to 6 (poorly drained); in addition, there are differences in soil texture: 6 = loamy sand, all others are slightly loamy sand. Soil groups (profile development) according to De Bakker and Schelling 1966: 1 and 2 are 'enkeerd' soils (plaggen soils), 3, 4 and 5 are podzols, 6 is a 'beekeerd' soil (humose gley soil)

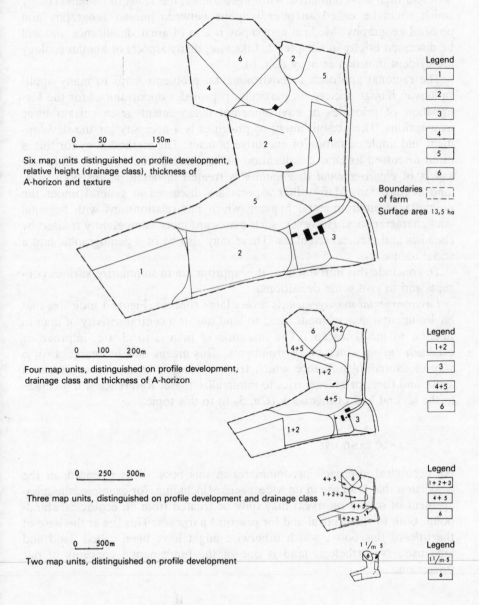

Six map units distinguished on profile development, relative height (drainage class), thickness of A-horizon and texture

Legend
1
2
3
4
5
6
Boundaries of farm
Surface area 13,5 ha

Four map units, distinguished on profile development, drainage class and thickness of A-horizon

Legend
1+2
3
4+5
6

Three map units, distinguished on profile development and drainage class

Legend
1+2+3
4+5
6

Two map units, distinguished on profile development

Legend
1 1/m 5
6

an example is given of the use of several map scales for the representation of a farm in one of the sandy regions of the Netherlands.

The regional approach to environmental problems leads to the separation and delineation of different environmental complexes in relation to the nature, the quantity, the intensity and the interactions of the component factors. This regionalization may then be combined with a regionalization of the groups and communities of the organisms themselves, by means of which a better understanding is arrived at of the relationships between the organisms and their environments. Within geography, this leads to human ecology which could be called an interdiscipline between human geography and physical geography. Medical geography is also of great significance and will be discussed briefly in Chapter 2. Likewise, many aspects of human ecology are evident in urban ecology (Ch. 6).

The regional approach to environmental problems leads to many applications in human society. In particular it provides opportunities for the formulation of priorities in environmental management given certain basic assumptions. The establishment of priorities is a necessity for the development and implementation of executive policies. The methodology for this is often discussed as land classification or land evaluation (Ch. 8). Only one aspect of *environmental degradation* is treated in detail in this book, viz. land degradation. Many other aspects are discussed in general under the umbrella of environmental hygiene which has relationships with regional land characteristics. However, such issues are more competently treated by chemists and medical scientists. These may also be of a demographic and a social nature.

To conclude this introduction, it is appropriate to summarize various concepts and to give some definitions.

Environmental management is a very large concept. Figure 1 indicates that environmental management, next to land use, is a central activity of man in relation to the landscape. The intention of man is to create, improve or establish certain kinds of environments. This means that he searches for a way of exercising influence which tries to prevent harmful side-effects in space and time, or at least tries to minimalize these. Reference will be made in the second half of this book (Ch. 5–8) to this topic.

LAND, LAND USE

An ecological approach predominates in this book. This is based on the conviction that land use in its widest sense (including, for example, the management of nature reserves) may only be treated from an ecological standpoint, both for theoretical and for practical purposes. This lies at the base of the title of this book, which otherwise might have been called 'land and land use'. Nevertheless, land is one of the fundamental concepts of our discussion.

Given an anthropocentric approach to landscape ecology, land use and land become two important operational concepts. 'Land' is not a unity with a fixed dimension nor is it related to a particular scale of operations or of mapping. In general we can treat it as a part of the larger regional concept which is called landscape. Landscape may also be defined as 'a natural arrangement of mutually related tracts of land'. A tract of land is used to indicate demarcated units of land in several ways. It is used for a unit of land use as well as a unit of land mapping; for example, in landscape ecological surveys; and finally a land evaluation unit for the applications of the surveys. The terms 'land use unit', 'land mapping unit' and 'land evaluation unit' are used to distinguish these three concepts. These have strong mutual relationships, but in many cases their characteristics do not fully coincide. A land use unit may consist of several land mapping units, but it may also be only a small part of one mapping unit, depending on the scale of land use operations as well as on the scale of the map used in a particular case. In general, a land evaluation unit is based on one or more land mapping units; under ideal circumstances, it should also be the basic unit for current or future land use. The dimensions of each of these three kinds of units may vary from a few square metres to thousands of hectares.

Land must thus remain a rather abstract concept. Given our anthropocentric viewpoint the following definition developed by the Food and Agriculture Organization (FAO) of the United Nations is very satisfactory:

Land is an area of the earth's surface, the characteristics of which embrace all reasonably stable, or predictable cyclic, attributes of the biosphere vertically above and below this area including those of the atmosphere, the soil and underlying geology, the hydrology, the plant and animal populations, and the results of past and present human activity, to the extent that these attributes exert a significant influence on present and future uses of the land by man (FAO 1976).

During the last few years a large amount of research has been done using this interpretation of land. Such work will be reviewed in Chapter 8.

One consequence of this definition of land is that many, and perhaps all, water bodies on the surface of the earth have to be considered as land. In fact this is an advantage with regard to landscape ecology as well as to land use. With the former, too little attention is often paid to the essential relationships between the terrestrial and the aquatic ecosystems. Sometimes this leads to a rather unbalanced approach to research as well as to evaluation and to planning. Good examples are found in the Netherlands, where land use and land reclamation have an important impact on the larger aquatic systems; for example, in the Wadden Sea, the former Zuyderzee (now IJssel Lake) and the estuaries of the southwestern delta. It is also applicable to many other river or marine systems such as the North Sea and the Mediterranean. Sometimes water is treated as that part of the earth's surface which is left after land has been considered. But there is good reason to consider fisheries and other uses of aquatic systems by man as kinds of land use which should be treated on an equal basis with the terrestrial land utilization types which will be discussed in Chapter 5. Brief reference to the land uses of aquatic surfaces will be made in Chapter 2.

Our definition of land includes the urban areas and other highly urbanized parts of the earth's surface such as industrial complexes and motorways. The merit of this approach is most evident in many industrialized areas of the world including those in developing countries. In general the boundary between an urban area and surrounding rural areas is much less clear than is sometimes assumed. Furthermore, one present-day problem is the encroachment of urban land uses into rural localities. Some aspects of urban land use and its connection with rural areas will be outlined in Chapter 6.

It can thus be appreciated that *land use*, if approached in this manner, is a very comprehensive concept. If consideration is limited to terrestrial conditions, it embraces land use in all its forms from agricultural uses to nature conservation in addition to all kinds of urban and industrial land uses. The formal definition given at the end of the chapter states that land use is an expression of man's management of ecosystems in order to produce some of his needs. The Universal Declaration of Human Rights specifies many of mankind's needs. Those which are directly related to land use are food, clothing, housing and health. According to the World Health Organization, health is 'a state of complete physical, mental and social well-being, and not merely the absence of disease or infirmity'. Health is therefore closely connected with food as well as with many other environmental factors, many of which are largely determined by the landscape, but not all these considerations are easily treated within the subject of landscape ecology. Medical geography is a major subject in itself and is only briefly considered in Chapter 2.

A systematic examination of the mental and social well-being of man is outside the scope of this book though some attention will be paid to recreation and to nature conservation. As already indicated, however, urban ecology is certainly concerned with the well-being of man and is discussed in a separate chapter. Urban land uses, from industrial uses and high-rise buildings to parkland, are as integral to landscape ecology as rural land use forms. The background and interests of the present author however lead to a more extensive treatment of agricultural land use. Such a particular focus can easily be justified by our present global situation. The provision of food and clothing is and will remain for the next few decades the major task which mankind has to tackle. These needs can only be provided by agriculture which is interpreted in this book to include animal husbandry and forestry.

DEFINITIONS

Artefactial attributes of the landscape: landscape attributes which at some time in the past have been created as artefacts by man.

Ecosystem: a particular assemblage of living organisms and the environment in which they exist within a spatial unit of any magnitude.

Environment: this can only be defined in relation to an organism or a group of organisms. It is then the collection or complex of external factors to which the organism(s) is (are) directly or indirectly related. The result is that there are many different environments. Each organism has its own environment which is more or less influenced by other organisms. In any environment, abiotic, biotic and psychological environmental factors may be distinguished. From a biological standpoint, man is just one of these organisms. Man can, however, exert a disproportionate influence on the environments of other organisms, sometimes favourable (agricultural crops), but often injurious.

Environmental management: **1.** The details of such management depend on the initial conditions and on the particular objectives. It may be carried out in order to conserve certain natural ecosystems (nature reserves), but increasingly it is also applied to permit the management of industrially developed human communities. **2.** Intentional human activities to prevent or lessen harmful environmental impacts.

Environmental science: the science which studies those ecological processes which dominate the relationships between man and his environment. Integral to these analyses is often the aim to modify these processes for man's benefit.

Geosphere, see landscape-sphere

Geotope: part of the geosphere which is relatively homogeneous with respect to its form and processes.

Human environment: the environment within which man exists and it includes a solid substratum (including topography), water areas, atmosphere, vegetation and fauna with their biotic as well as psychological factors. The environment of individual human beings and their groups should also be seen in terms of socio-cultural and medical-hygienic conditions. Political, religious, economic and technological factors can be included within the socio-cultural group.

Land: an area of the earth's surface, the characteristics of which embrace all reasonably stable, or predictably cyclic, attributes of the biosphere vertically above and below this area including those of the atmosphere, the soil and the underlying geology, the hydrology, the plant and animal populations, and the results of past and present human activity, to the extent that these attributes exert a significant influence on present and future uses of the land by man.

Land use: the expression of man's management of ecosystems in order to produce some of his needs.

Landscape: **1.** The surface of the earth with all its phenomena including land – forms, soils, vegetation and attributes influenced by man – (synonomous with physiography); **2.** The region, a delineated area on the earth's surface with its own characteristic landforms, soils, vegetation including properties which are frequently influenced by man; **3.** A natural arrangement of mutually related tracts of land with a structure which is characterized by certain internal processes.

Landscape ecology (*geoecology*): **1.** An approach to the study of the landscape which interprets it as supporting natural and cultural ecosystems; **2.** The science which investigates the relationships between the biosphere and anthroposphere and either the earth's surface or the abiotic components.

Landscape-sphere (*geosphere*): the zone of interaction on or near the earth's surface of atmosphere, hydrosphere, biosphere, lithosphere, pedosphere and noösphere or anthroposphere.

Morphographic landscape surveys: surveys which map the landforms in a descriptive manner (height, slope, shape) without any genetic connotations.

Morphometric landscape surveys: as morphographic but with greater emphasis on a quantitative approach.

Nature management: a part of environmental management including those human activities which have as their goal the production or maintenance of natural or semi-natural geotopes in a desirable condition.

Noösphere: the sphere in which human knowledge is active.

Physiognomic landscape surveys: as morphographic but with emphasis on the image the landscape creates in man's mind.

INTERNATIONAL ORGANIZATIONS

Investigations and applications of landscape ecology and land use are carried out in many institutions in many countries, sometimes under such headings as land classification, land system surveys, vegetation surveys, soil surveys, etc. Reference is made in the text to the work of particular institutions. For Great Britain, mention must be made of the work of the Soil Survey of Scotland, the Soil Survey of England and Wales, the work of several universities (University of Aberdeen, University of Reading, University of Strathclyde in Glasgow) and by the Land Resources Development Centre (LRDC, Surbiton, Surrey) of the Ministry of Overseas Development. For the USA, reference must be made to the research by the US Soil Conservation Service and by the US Bureau of Reclamation. Examples could also be quoted from many other countries, but there are too many to cite in full. Exceptions are made for the Land and Water Use Division of the Agriculture Department of Sri Lanka at Peradeniya and Environment Canada, Ottawa.

Some international organizations are listed below in order to indicate their activities related to the subject matter of this book as well as to explain the abbreviations used in the text.

FAO   Food and Agriculture Organization of the United Nations, Rome.

IUCN   International Union for the Conservation of Nature and Natural Resources, Morges, near Geneva, Switzerland.
UNEP   United Nations Environmental Programme, Nairobi.
UNESCO United Nations Educational and Scientific Organization, Paris.
UNU   United Nations University, Tokyo.
WHO   World Health Organization, Geneva.
WMO   World Meteorological Organization, Geneva.

2
Ecosystems

GENERAL

The term 'ecology' was introduced by the German biologist Ernst Haeckel in 1869, who defined it as 'all the relationships between an animal and its organic as well as its inorganic environment'. This concept evolved as one of the many aspects of biology until the 1930s, when scientific development in this subject started to transgress monodisciplinary boundaries. These new ideas were crystallized by the British biologist Sir Alfred Tansley, who introduced the term 'ecosystem'. He wrote:

Our natural human prejudices force us to consider the organisms (in the sense of the biologist) as the most important parts of these systems, but certainly the inorganic 'factors' are also parts – there could be no system without them, and there is constant interchange of **the most various kinds** within each system, not only between the organisms but between the organic and the inorganic (Tansley 1935 as reproduced by Colinvaux 1973).

The ecosystem approach is an essential part therefore of ecology and thus for landscape ecology. It is particularly useful because a systems approach is the only manner of presenting the various kinds of relationships in this subject as it tries to describe 'nature' and the landscape. As indicated in Chapter 1, Carl Troll followed Tansley a few years later with his development of the concept of 'landscape ecology'. It could be said that 'ecosystems' bridge the gap between biology and physical geography with a biological emphasis and that 'landscape ecology' bridges the gap between physical geography and biology as well as between physical geography and social geography. The bridging of these gaps between related sciences is essential for scientific development and applied research as related to land use planning. Often only planning is mentioned, but the execution of projects and land management are integral to the research progress as well as to actual practice. All three – planning, execution and management – should be seen in their widest sense, including not only rural land use, but also urban and industrial uses; and also including in rural areas not only agricultural and related land uses, but nature conservation as well. In the application of landscape ecology there are instances of very good preparatory planning, but execution of projects as well as management may make great mistakes. On the other hand, rather poorly planned projects may still lead to reasonable results with careful execution and good management.

Ecosystems as well as unit areas of landscape ecology may be depicted at many different map scales as has been discussed in Chapter 1 (Fig. 2). It is even possible to see the whole world as one ecosystem, as is more or less the case in the GEMS-project (Global Environmental Monitoring System) of UNEP. Large regions may also be seen as ecosystems, such as tundra, arid, and humid tropical regions. For regional planning within a country, we often think in terms of landscapes which can be mapped and shown on scales of between 1 : 100 000 and 1 : 25 000. The smallest units are often called 'ecotopes'; these are in general seen as existing on small tracts of land, from hectares down to square metres, which may be depicted on large map-scales (1 : 10 000 to 1 : 500). This implies the same dimensions for the related ecosystems. Sometimes the term 'geotope' is used in the sense of the landscape component of an ecotope. To some extent a landscape or geotope and the related ecosystem may be used as synonyms, the difference being mainly one of emphasis on either the geographical (landscape, geotope) or the biological (ecosystem, ecotope) aspects. The larger animals and men cannot be said to belong to a certain landscape. They do quite definitely belong however to the ecosystems within which they live.

ECOSYSTEMS AS A SYSTEM

In order to obtain some idea about the working of ecosystems, the proper significance of the term 'system' should first be considered. According to Chorley and Kennedy (1971), 'A system is a structured set of objects and/or attributes. These objects and attributes consist of components or variables (i.e. phenomena which are free to assume variable magnitudes) that exhibit discernible relationships with one another and operate together as a complex whole, according to some observed pattern.'

Ecosystems are open systems, which means that these systems exchange mass, energy and information with their environment. Information includes intangible but often essential knowledge and thought. Within open systems, ecosystems belong again to a specific kind termed control systems. Control systems are those systems where certain variables, called key variables, can be partly or wholly controlled by the application of some intelligence; for example, human intelligence. Similar influences may however also be distinguished in natural ecosystems which exhibit homeostasis due to self-regulating feed-back mechanisms. Land use, which consists of a multitude of different cultural ecosystems, is characterized by the continuous or regular and intermittent guiding of organisms and other variables in order to obtain certain human goals and to effect certain human responsibilities. Chorley and Kennedy (1971) write in a similar context of a geographical control system which results from the interaction of a decision-making system and a

Fig. 3 Schematical comparison of the structure of a terrestrial ecosystem (grassland) and an ecosystem in open water (fresh or marine). Components are: I. Abiotic materials; II. Producers (plants); III. Macroconsumers (animals): A. herbivores (grasshoppers, meadowmice, etc., on land, zooplankton, etc., in water); B. indirect or detritus consumers or saprovores (soil invertebrates on land; bottom invertebrates in water); C. carnivores such as hawks and large fish; D. decomposers such as bacteria and fungi (after Odum 1963). *Note*: although in aquatic ecosystems there are no 'soils in the pedogenetic sense', there are, certainly in shallow waters, 'soils' in the ecological sense, meaning the habitats of plant roots.

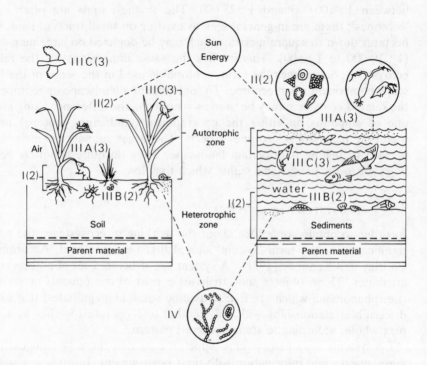

physical process response system. Some of the relationships in these systems will be discussed with particular reference to ecosystems. The essential kinds of relationships are: energy flow, chains of organisms and of food, and cycling of water, carbon and of nutrients. (Fig. 3).

The central and most fundamental concept of ecosystems is that of *energy flow*. Nearly all energy for ecosystems is directly produced by the sun. Approximately half of the energy of the sun is transformed into heat energy and temperature plays an essential role in ecology. About 23 per cent of the sun's energy which penetrates to the earth's surface is used for evapotranspiration by plants and for evaporation of water from other surfaces. Only approximately 0.2 per cent of the energy of the sun received at earth's surface, in the order of 40×10^{12} Watt-years, is used for photosynthesis. This small energy input is however the key to all life, as this is the energy which enters directly into the chains of living organisms. The amount of energy available for the various kinds of processes depends on latitude. The highest total production of biomass as expressed in carbohydrates ($C_6H_{12}O_6$ glucose and related compounds) amounts to 124×10^3 kg carbohydrates per hectare per year and is found between 10° and 20 °N. This is 59×10^3 kg at 50 °N, 12×10^3 at 50 °S and at 70 °N (De Wit 1966; Starr *et al.* 1971). The transport of energy in the chains of organisms and of food is schematically indicated in Fig. 4.

Figure 4 shows the large loss of energy which results from transfers to

Fig. 4 Simplified diagram of energy flow through ecosystems. The heavily lined partly dashed areas indicate the successive kind of organisms on the three main trophic levels (levels of nutrition): 1. producers of autotrophic organisms (green plants); 2. primary consumers or herbivores; 3. secondary consumers of carnivores; the latter two are also taken together and called 'heterotrophic organisms' (auto = self, hetero = other). The channels or 'pipelines' represent the energy streams through the ecosystems. L = sunlight, L_a = part of sunlight absorbed by plants, P_b = the gross production of biomass, P_n = net production of biomass, A = assimilated energy, NA = not assimilated energy, NU = un-used energy (may be stored e.g. in trees), R = the loss of energy by respiration (and therefore e.g. by movements of animals). The figures at the bottom of the figure indicate the order of magnitude of the energy levels in kcal per m^2 per day (after Odum 1963 and 1975).

3000 kcal = 1.26×10^4 kJ
1500 kcal = 6.28×10^3 kJ
15 kcal = $6.28 = 10$ kJ
1.5 kcal = 6.28 kJ
0.15 kcal = 6.28×10^{-1} kJ

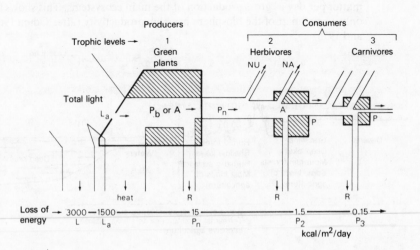

higher trophic levels, from plants to herbivores to carnivores. The chains of organisms in nature are in general more complicated than is suggested in this diagram. Food, for example as proteins, is transferred from one level to the next. Therefore deficiencies and excesses of certain nutrient elements are also transferred, leading respectively to deficiencies or excess quantities, the latter causing toxicity of certain elements. The excess of heavy metals caused by air, water or soil pollution is an example. Iodine deficiency causing goitre in human beings was used as an example by the Dutch ecologist Baas Becking (1934), and this general subject is now being studied by medical geography and environmental medicine (Melvyn Howe and Loraine 1973). It is possible to indicate an order of magnitude of the biomass production of the main groups of ecosystems in the world (Fig. 5).

Some special attention must be given to the cycling of water and to the main plant nutrients. The hydrological water cycle is of particular importance because water is involved with the movement of all nutrients. Of course water is also a much-needed substance. Most organisms consist of more than 90 per cent water, and water is the solvent for all materials within the organisms. Furthermore, water is essential for regulation of the temperatures of most organisms. Finally, of course, large groups of organisms live in the water of streams, rivers, lakes, seas and oceans. Some aspects of water will be discussed in subsequent parts of this book. For present purposes reference should be made to Fig. 6, which indicates the nature of the hydrological cycle.

Next to water, the plant nutrients have a central position in ecology. Plants consist of three main groups of organic compounds: proteins, carbohydrates (including celluloses, lignins, etc.) and fats. Proteins are the most active and typical substances of the tissues of organisms. Some proteins

Fig. 5 Distribution over the earth of primary production, in grams dry matter per day as gross production of the main ecosystems. This shows that only a small part of the biosphere has high productivity (after Odum 1963 and 1975)

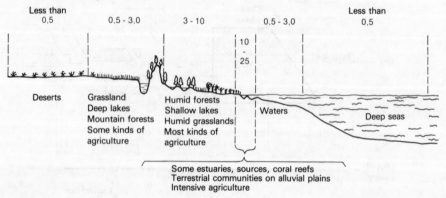

Fig. 6 Hydrological cycle (partly after Teune 1976)

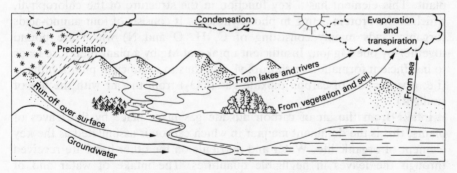

such as chlorophyll (photosynthesis) and proteins of the nuclei of living cells (DNA etc., genetic and regulating) have a very specific function for growth and reproduction. All three groups of organic compounds consist in varying quantities of carbon (C), hydrogen (H) and oxygen (O). The carbohydrates and many celluloses consist completely of these three elements. The proteins have however in addition often considerable quantities of nitrogen (N), sulphur (S), sometimes phosphorus (P) and of one or more metals, in particular magnesium (Mg), iron (Fe), calcium (Ca), manganese (Mn) and occasionally of the so-called micronutrients (e.g. copper, cobalt, etc.). A plant needs rather large quantities of potassium (K) and sometimes of sodium (Na), elements which are essential for internal transport processes. Table 1 gives some chemical data of agricultural crops to exemplify this point in a more quantitative manner.

Table 1. Chemical analyses of selected agricultural crops

(a) Contents of organic compounds and of ash (combined minerals) in g per 100 g digestible matter

Plant	Water	Proteins	Fats	Carbohydrates	Ash
Wheat (*Triticum vulgare*)	11	12	2	73	2
Rice (*Oryza sativa*)	10	9	2	77	2
Groundnuts (*Arachis hypogaea*)	5	26	43	23	3

(b) Contents of some plant nutrients (in kg per 1000 kg product)

Plant	N	P	K	Ca	Mg	S	Remarks
Wheat (*Triticum vulgare*)	28	11	17	5	2	2	
Rice (*Oryza sativa*)	17	4	23	5	2	n.d.	irrigated
Groundnuts (*Arachis hypogaea*)	70	4	23	13	9	n.d.	
Potatoes (*Solanum tuberosum*)	7	2	10	0.1	0.3	0.3	

Magnesium provides a good example of the function of metals in the plant. This element has a key function in the structure of the chlorophyll, which is the protein acting in photosynthesis. It consists of four amino-acids (organic acids mainly consisting of C, H, O and N) which are bound together by one Mg ion. Insufficient uptake of Mg by a plant therefore leads to insufficient formation of chorophyll and thus to insufficient photosynthesis (i.e. assimilation of carbon dioxide gas (CO_2) from the air with the use of sunlight).

Intake from the air of carbon dioxide gas takes place by the leaves of plants; this is the dominant manner in which carbon is assimilated as the key element of organic life. Water and nutrients on the other hand are received through the leaves in negligible quantities. The intake of water and of mineral nutrients, cations as well as anions, takes place within the soil. This intake is achieved by a complicated set of processes via a system of membranes, with membranes between the roots and the soil as well as between the various parts of a plant. The transport via the semi-permeable membranes requires energy. The energy is obtained by respiration, which is the oxidation of carbohydrates. This means that a regular stream of oxygen to the roots of any plant is an essential prerequisite to plant life, equivalent to the presence of carbon dioxide and oxygen in the air as well as sunlight. During the night, when no sunlight is available, the parts of the plants above the surface also change from carbon dioxide-assimilation to respiration; that is, intake of oxygen and production of carbon dioxide. In the extreme, this is the cause of oxygen-deficiency of fishes due to 'eutrophication' (excessive plant growth) in waters.

The quantity of oxygen which is at present available in the atmosphere is almost completely of biogenic origin, i.e. has been originated by photosynthesis of plants. An increase of the carbon dioxide content of the air induces enhanced plant growth and has been demonstrated in hothouse experiments. There exists therefore a feed-back mechanism in the biosphere via all green plants and this mechanism may prevent the development of too high a carbon dioxide content of the earth's atmosphere. Nevertheless, it is necessary to regularly monitor the $O_2 : CO_2$ mechanism of our atmosphere. The actual composition of the atmosphere (excluding water vapour) is:

- nitrogen (N)   78%
- oxygen (O)   21%
- carbon dioxide (CO_2) 0.03%
- other gases   0.07% (hydrogen, argon, neon, etc.)

In the atmosphere above industrialized regions, for example north-western Europe (from France to Sweden), a varying percentage of sulphur dioxide (SO_2) and sometimes of oxides of nitrogen is found due to industrial fumes.

Nutrient cycling provides a good illustration of important relationships, processes and feed-backs in nature. They exist in large ecosystems as well as

Fig. 7 The nitrogen cycle with emphasis on soil processes (after Brady 1974)

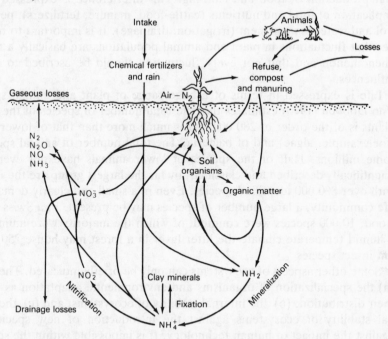

in ecological subsystems such as in soils. An example of the nitrogen-cycle, with emphasis on soil processes, is given in Fig. 7.

COMMUNITIES

It is important to appreciate that there are many relationships within ecosystems in addition to those already outlined. This results from the fact that organisms form communities within the ecosystems, in which different organisms have various populations (numbers of plants or animals per unit surface area). This causes the development of feed-back mechanisms between the various organisms. Populations of organisms always fluctuate, even under completely natural circumstances. The classical example is provided by the lemmings, small rodents of northern areas; their populations increase approximately every four years to such quantities that multitudes destroy themselves in the sea. But other populations also show regular or irregular fluctuations due to annual variations of the weather or of available quantities of food. These fluctuations respond again to complex regulating mechanisms in nature; for example, caused by parasites.

In general human interference in ecosystems has as its object the increase of certain populations which are useful for men (crops, cattle) at the expense of other populations (weeds, parasites). In addition man tries to prevent excessive fluctuations in his preferred populations in order to receive a regular production of food and clothing. This interference is expressed in the application of food and nutrients (cattle-food, manure, fertilizers), pest control and water management (irrigation, drainage). It is important to remember that fluctuations in plant and animal populations are basically a natural phenomenon and that not every fluctuation should be ascribed to human influences.

Life is expressed in terms of a huge range of plant and animal species. Van Dobben (1970) estimates that the total number of species of the higher plants is of the order of 280 000 and is much more than that of lower plants (for example, algae) and of bacteria. The total number of animal species is some millions. Half of the species of lower animals have not even been scientifically described and classified; by far the largest group are the insects, with over 800 000 identified species. Even in a small and clearly demarcated life community, a large number of species may be present. In a Swiss beechwood, 10 000 species were counted, of which the majority were animals. In a humid temperate climate the litter layer in a forest may house 250 different insect species

Some other aspects of ecosystems can only be briefly indicated. These are: (a) the specialization of organisms and environmental adaptation as well as their distribution; (b) the internal stability of ecosystems; and (c) the external stability of ecosystems against the introduction of new species and against the impact of human technology. It is impossible within the scope of this book to systematically treat these, as well as various other aspects of ecology. Instead some additional information on the working of ecosystems can be given by comparing a grassland ecosystem with a forest one.

Under favourable ecological conditions, the growth of a grassland vegetation and associated other vegetation types depends on the quantity of light which shines on the leaves. As the grass grows, there is an increasing shadow on the lower leaves. The growth of a grassland vegetation will eventually stop, assuming no interference from other organisms or from man. The growth will start again after mowing or due to grazing. The situation in a close deciduous forest is completely different. In contrast to the grassland situation, respiration caused by the lack of light plays only a minor role. Additional growth of a forest is stored in the stems and other wooden parts which show virtually no respiration. A deciduous wood on sufficiently humic soils in the Netherlands produces as much dry matter as a heavily manured grassland, approximately 20 tonnes per hectare per year.

In a grazing ecosystem, the production strongly depends on the density of the cattle as well as on the grazing system and on the effect of the cattle walking on the vegetation. In an average grazing land ecosystem, approximately 11 per cent of the nett primary production is assimilated by the herbivores; the remaining 89 per cent is consumed as little by micro-organisms and soil fauna, these two components being in a ratio 81 : 8. In a Dutch forest ecosystem measurements were made by Van der Drift (1970) of the various kinds of primary production. The total production of the 'Meerdink Wood' on sandy soils in the Eastern Netherlands was found to be of the order of 13.4 tonnes/ha/year, equivalent to 6000 kcal/m^2/year or about 25×10^3 kJ/m^2/year. This is approximately $0.7 \times$ the total radiation energy consumed by the system. The consumption of 0.3 is mainly by the respiration of micro-organisms (over 3000 kcal, approx. 12.6×10^3 kJ) and by the soil fauna (150 kcal, approx. 630 kJ). The main difference between the grassland and the forest is found in the regular accretion of the biomass of the wood, which of course is absent in the grassland.

PATTERN, PROCESS, GRADIENTS

The above terms were introduced by the Dutch ecologist Van Leeuwen (1966). They resulted from the introduction of cybernetical principles in ecology, in which the different kinds of relationships expressed by 'pattern' and 'process' respectively are of special importance. Pattern indicates the spatial variation in a community at a given moment, whereas process indicates the variation during a period of time. Both are evident in the development of a community. A simple pattern is found in a pioneer vegetation and will develop during the succession into a more intricate one. With growing ecosystem complexity many feed-backs develop, so that the process of succession is increasingly retarded. This produces the internal, and to some extent the external, stability of ecosystems which sometimes tend towards a stable final stage termed 'climax'.

A second important aspect of Van Leeuwen's theory is indicated by the term 'gradient'. Gradients in this sense are transition zones where varied ecological conditions lead to special communities often very rich in species. Two different kinds of gradients are distinguished: (1) convergent zone – a sharp transition in the landscape such as may occur between sand and peat, between high and low, between dry and wet, between rich and poor; (2) divergent zone – a gradual transition of ecological conditions which occur in most landscapes. Convergent zones are relatively poor in species, whereas the divergent ones tend to show a very variegated pattern with great internal stability and are rich in different species. True convergent zones are rather an exception in most landscapes. Divergent zones vary in different dimensions and these will be depicted on different map scales. They are very important for many landscape ecological considerations.

The third point to be discussed from Van Leeuwen's work regards the influence of man on the landscape. This influence on the variability and stability of the landscape can be seen throughout the centuries. Old agricultural systems were characterized by the following:

1. The methods used did not vary very much throughout the centuries;

this strongly localized stability of impacts led to an increasing variation in pattern.

2. The influence of man on the landscape was greatest near his settlements and minimal at some distance from these centres with all kinds of variations between these extremes.

3. Our ancestors used technologies which resulted in gradual change and the scale of operation was small.

This impact of man through time induced a growing complexity in landscape pattern. A strong contrast is shown by the influence of human technology since around 1900, and in the Netherlands even more since 1945, with the start of large-scale mechanization in agriculture and in land reclamation. The result has been the uniformity of landscape and of land use over large surfaces. This process still continues in many areas of the world and is clearly seen, for example, in some regions of Italy. Since around 1970, however, a healthy change is gradually being introduced into land use planning, whereby the ideas of Van Leeuwen and of other ecologists are starting to have an influence.

SOME ADDITIONAL REMARKS ON ECOLOGY

A few more ecological principles require to be introduced. The terms *autecology* and *synecology* indicate two different approaches to ecology. Autecology has as its focus the needs of individuals and of species on a separate basis with regard to food, nutrients, water and other direct requirements for sustenance. In the next chapter climatic needs will be indicated. Investigations in autecology may often be done by special experiments, either in the field or in controlled artificial environments; for example, greenhouses. Curves of optimal plant or animal growth, indication of limits of growth with low or high concentrations of elements and measures of tolerance of toxic elements or compounds are examples of autecological investigations. Some species have narrow limits for certain ecological conditions, for example temperature (stenothermal), and others have wide zones between the limits of their growth (eurythermal). If stenothermal species can only live at low temperatures they are called oligothermal, if only at high temperatures polythermal. Other examples are: *water*: stenohydric, euryhydric; *salts*: stenohaline, euryhaline.

Synecology is the study of populations of organisms and of the composition of plant and animal communities. It also studies the fluctuations which are found within these communities of the component species; for example, animals and their predators, such as wildebeests and lions, weevils and wasps (Colinvaux 1973). This line of research also leads to investigations on the mutual tolerance of species or subspecies. In this context the study of niches also has to be mentioned. These niches may be considered as vacant positions within an ecosystem in which a migrating species may find its ecological home.

SOME RELATIONSHIPS IN THE LANDSCAPE WITH REGARD TO MAN

So far in this chapter the main concern has been biotic relationships. However, there also exist many relationships in the landscape which are the result of abiotic processes. Processes of erosion-colluviation and of denudation-accumulation are of great importance in all areas of the world where there is some amplitude of relief (see also Ch. 3). Most landscapes of the world, including subaquatic ones, possess these attributes. Even in relatively flat countries such as the Netherlands, much erosion is active on the slightly more hilly areas. Our recent investigations have shown that in the wooded sandy hills of the Veluwe, the central area north of Wageningen and Arnhem, erosional processes in semi-natural vegetation have a considerable impact on the ecosystems.

Hydrological processes are a dominant feature of many landscapes. A process which is of particular importance in the Netherlands is seepage from higher areas into lowlands or from waterbodies into polders. This process of sub-surface flow is a very general feature in areas with permeable rocks and dissected topography. This may lead to increased salinity, to pollution and to other less favourable effects in the lowlands. It may also lead to enrichment of nutrients in lowland ecosystems. In Fig. 8 a simplified example is given from the Netherlands. This example is deriven from the Zuyderzee polder area. To the left is the remaining water body of the former Zuyderzee (now IJssel Lake), to the right of the figure are the Pleistocene sandy hills of the Veluwe complex which was mentioned above.

Man may also cause, by continued land use throughout the centuries, the transport of materials. This may to some extent counteract natural processes in the landscape with regard to the concentration of nutrients and organic matter. In Fig. 9 an example is given of the farming system which occurred, with minor variations, in the sandy areas of the Netherlands, Belgium and north-west Germany, from the ninth century into the early decades of the

Fig. 8 Seepage from a hilly area and from open water to a polder

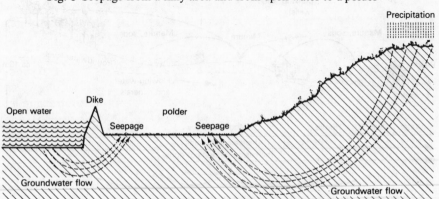

twentieth century. The system is well known to soil scientists with regard to one of its results, the formation of plaggen soils on the arable land areas (central part of Fig. 9). Cattle and sheep, grazing on the meadows and the moors respectively, dropped most of their manure in barns and pens and to this were added sods cut from the moors and forest litter. The mixture was brought onto the arable land each spring, causing an addition of approximately 1 cm of humic A horizon per 10 years (see also Pape 1970). This resulted in the soils having a humic A horizon of thickness ranging from 50 cm to over 100 cm, on top of the original soil profile which is in general a podzol. In the US Soil Taxonomy (Soil Survey Staff 1975) these soils are now called *Plaggepts*. In older publications, only the enrichment of these soils was stressed. Seen within the ecological context of the whole landscape, however, this enrichment was only possible by the impoverishment of a much greater area from which litter, sods, animal food and manure had been extracted. The natural sequence from very dry and relatively poor soil conditions in the higher areas to soils which were wet and relatively rich in nutrients in the low areas was partly counteracted and partly enhanced by human activity.

Transformations of certain compounds into others continuously take place in any landscape. Most of these processes have micro-organisms as an intermediary and these organisms live mainly in the soil. Transport of the new compounds in the landscape is again achieved by throughflow. It is possible to monitor these processes and to combine the results in budgetary calcu-

Fig. 9 Example of systematic and long-lasting transport of materials in a landscape by human action: a farming system on the sandy soils of northwestern Europe before the application of chemical fertilizers (Vink 1975a)

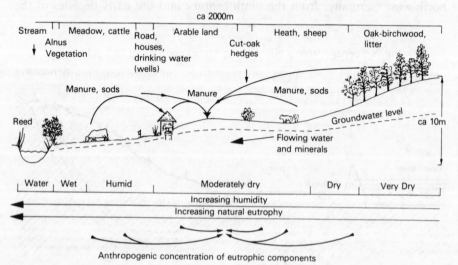

lations. This can be done for soil-budgets as well as for landscape-budgets, as has been shown by Schlichting (1972, 1975a and b). These quantitative investigations are of fundamental importance for calculation of the potential productivity and the carrying capacity of a landscape. In order to use these process data for the prediction of landscape patterns, such analysis should be done with appropriate landscape ecological surveys (see also Ch. 4).

A detailed study of the ecological influences and relationships of man in a particular landscape was made by Soemarwoto (1977) in Indonesia. He studied the rural cultural ecosystem of the Bandung basin, a former lacustrine plain at approximately 500 m above sea level in the mountains of western Java. This ecosystem contains four subsystems: the village (with houses, homesteads and fishponds), the terraced and irrigated rice fields (sawahs, paddys), a river, and the surrounding forest area. The four subsystems have mutual connections through natural transport processes of materials as well as through biological relationships and human intervention. The intricate character and the importance of these relationships only becomes clear when large development projects start to interfere with the system. According to Soemarwoto, improved education for example may lead to more intensive rice-production, higher fuel needs, increases in erosion and forest clearance and larger fluctuations in river-levels. Modern hygiene may lead to less production from the fishponds because the offal from the villages supplies the food for the fishes via biological processes in the ponds.

There are many difficulties with the investigation of cultural ecosystems with respect to processes, relationships and budgetary calculations of energy and materials. Nevertheless, more research of this kind is urgently needed (see also Rappaport 1971).

LANDSCAPE ECOLOGY OF AQUATIC LANDSCAPES

Submarine 'landscapes' are frequently neglected by physical geographers and other scientists. The older tradition was to view oceanography as part of physical geography and today this is to some extent still true. But the present-day forms of oceanography tend to be on sedimentological investigations of deltas, and lake and sea floors. In this text other aspects of the aquatic landscapes are more relevant. As an example, emphasis is given to the mutual relationships between the aquatic and the terrestrial landscapes. The pollution of surface waters is an instance of irresponsible land use. An important theme is the harvest of freshwater areas, seas and oceans for proteins for human consumption. Another topic is the use of surface waters for transport and recreation, but this subject will not be discussed in this book. The use of water for irrigation will be dealt with in Chapters 5 and 7. An interesting type of aquatic ecosystems are the aquacultures in Japan and in other asiatic countries where fish and paddy-rice are grown together on irrigated fields. This fish, together with the fish from village-ponds, gives an important addition of proteins to the human diet.

Internal freshwaters, from rivers to small ditches, are in direct contact with the ecology of terrestrial landscapes. Research on these themes has been done by Macan and Worthington (1968), Worthington (1977), Ringelberg (1976) and Barnes and Mann (1980).

Physico-chemical variables in fresh waters have their own nature and characteristics. The radiation of the sun is reflected by the water and partially absorbed or dispersed. Therefore the intensity of the radiation rapidly diminishes with depth and this is accompanied by a change in wavelength. Temperature also changes with depth; at a certain zone, partly dependent on the season of the year, temperature markedly drops – the thermocline (Macan and Worthington, 1968). In the Sloterplas, a small lake near Amsterdam, the depth of the thermocline in spring was found to be about 10 m, compared with around 30 m in autumn. In Windermere, the largest lake of the English Lake District, the thermocline was at 10–15 m depth in summer, whilst in winter the temperature was uniform from top to bottom (Mortimer, cited by Macan and Worthington, 1968). Variations in temperature are the prime cause of the differences in oxygen (O_2) and carbon dioxide (CO_2). The latter is also influenced by the pH of the water. The pH value depends on the relative concentrations and kinds of ions which are in solution. Typical cations in the water are several metals (Ca^{2+}, Mg^{2+}, Fe^{2+}) and ammonia (NH_4^+). Typical anions are phosphate (PO_4^{3-}) and sulphate (SO_4^{2-}). These and other environmental factors determine the growth conditions of organisms in the water and the ecology of populations is of course related to them.

The plants in aquatic ecosystems consist, for example, of algae and higher order water plants; snails are examples of herbivores. In general the carnivores in fresh water have three successive foodchain stages; for example: (1) larvae of insects; (2) roach and carp; (3) perch and pike. In addition, large numbers of saprovores (detritus-consumers) and of microbes are active in these ecosystems. Many investigations on the abiotic factors of the aquatic environment are of a sedimentological or geochemical nature. A better integration of these with ecological investigations is necessary to obtain a more detailed insight into the phenomena and processes of complete aquatic ecosystems.

Aquatic ecosystems, and therefore aquatic landscapes, can be plotted on the same maps on which are mapped the adjoining terrestrial ecosystems. This does not require special techniques if done in a fairly simple manner, although additional specialized research would be used either as basic data or added at a later stage. We have found that even a simple statement, giving for example the water depth, coastal vegetation and tidal influences where necessary, helps to integrate the two kinds of ecosystems. This promotes better nature conservation in coastal areas as well as better planning for aquatic recreation, both along the coasts and beaches (fishing, bathing) and on the waters themselves (sailing). A more systematic approach is being developed by Environment Canada for the same purpose and this will be discussed in Chapter 4. Human impact may be of the utmost importance for nature conservation as well as for coastal recreation. Many examples of this are to be found in the area of the Delta Project in the south-western Netherlands, where dams have stopped the original tidal movements and have de-salinized the waters as well as made certain stretches of water open for large shipping whilst others have been closed for this use. The influence of shipping on the coastal zones of large waters in the Delta area has been indicated in recent work (Kwakernaak et al. 1979). The Netherlands Ministry of Traffic and Water Management have created a separate division for studying these and similar impacts in the Delta area.

An indication of marine landscape ecology may be given by the work of the Department of Fisheries of FAO (1972). The differentiation of seas and oceans is largely controlled by the differences in water temperature and by depth. Temperature differences are caused mainly by the differences in latitude and by the presence of colder or warmer currents. The most significant element of sea bed topography is the occurrence of the continental shelf on which by far the largest quantities of fish for human consumption are to be found. The shelf areas can be considered to occur where the depth of the sea is less than 200 m. Other ecological influences on the marine landscape are caused by processes resulting from the adjoining terrestrial and coastal areas. These include the inflow of nutrients from river mouths and delta areas, which may have an influence on marine areas some hundreds of kilometres from the coast.

The above-mentioned factors and some other ones not specified here determine the presence, composition and growth of the 'phytoplankton', the autotrophic organisms of the seas. Linked with the phytoplankton are the zooplankton, the small animals which drift in large quantities near the surface of the sea. These have a direct influence on the populations of the various fishes. Finally, man has an enormous influence on the ecology of the sea-landscapes by fishing (which may be over-exploitation as well as under-exploitation) and pollution. The results of this combination of aquatic landscape ecology and of aquatic land use may be depicted on maps such as have been produced by FAO (1972). Certain areas of the seas and oceans have been depicted on a world map. Although this has primarily been done for statistical purposes, this map can be considered to be the first broad landscape ecological map of the world's seas.

The study of marine fauna in their landscape ecological context is used as a means for indicating the potential yields of the various waters without over-exploitation. Some very general data on this are given in Table 2. There exist large differences with regard to over- and under-exploitation of the various regions of the world, but the general picture does not seem to have greatly changed during the last decade. There is a lack of data on some types of fauna; for example, on cuttle-fishes. These animals might become an important source of proteins for human consumption in the near future.

Table 2. Potential world production and catches of some sea animals

(a) Potential world productions and catches in 1968 of some selected groups of fish, crustaceae and molluscs (in millions of tonnes)

Group	Potential production	Catches in 1968
Large pelagic fishes (salmon, tuna, etc.)	4.3	2.0
Demersal fishes (cod, haddock, etc.)	43.8	22.4
Fishes of coastal waters (anchovy, herring, sardine, mackerel, etc.)	56.7	26.4
Crustaceae (lobster, crab, shrimp, etc.)	2.3	1.4
Molluscs	generally cultivated	2.2

(b) Catches and potential production of marine fish, crustaceans and cephalopods by major marine area

	Catch (thousand tonnes)					Estimated potential	Utilization 1975 (%)
	1965	1970	1972	1974	1975		
N.W. Atlantic	3 242	3 697	3 833	3 461	3 230	7 000	46
N.E. Atlantic	9 090	10 140	10 045	11 222	11 499	14 600	79
W.C. Atlantic	1 192	1 208	1 298	1 334	1 350	6 400	21
E.C. Atlantic	1 216	2 981	3 350	3 758	3 493	5 600	62
Mediterranean and Black Sea	940	1 040	1 077	1 305	1 236	1 800	69
S.W. Atlantic	489	1 032	774	886	824	8 500	10
S.E. Atlantic	2 213	2 453	2 954	2 876	2 535	5 000	51
W. Indian Ocean	1 238	1 583	1 737	2 141	2 029	9 600	21
E. Indian Ocean	628	779	799	1 010	1 042	5 300	20
N.W. Pacific	9 540	11 634	13 061	14 825	15 201	17 400	87
N.E. Pacific	1 420	2 609	2 725	2 293	2 206	4 600	48
E.C. Pacific	575	861	923	1 023	1 233	6 000	21
S.W. Pacific	101	144	249	396	258	1 300	20
S.E. Pacific	8 054	13 621	5 445	5 232	4 516	13 300*	34
Total	42 498	57 705	52 775	56 289	55 289	116 800	47

* Assuming full recovery of anchoveta stock
Sources: (a) After Gubland 1971; (b) FAO 1978.

MEDICAL GEOGRAPHY AND ENVIRONMENTAL HYGIENE

From an anthropocentric viewpoint, the medical aspects of landscape ecology have a special meaning. More data have come available in recent years for several kinds of land use in specific areas of the world. The influence of irrigation in arid countries has received special attention (Worthington 1977). Investigations in Kenya give data on the populations of mosquitoes in irrigated areas. In an experiment where mosquitoes were systematically caught, it was found that in irrigated areas over 14 000 mosquitoes were caught in the same time as less than 3000 in non-irrigated areas. This is a very important finding, as mosquitoes are known to be vectors of malaria and some virus diseases and are suspected of also carrying unknown diseases. In irrigated areas of Sudan, investigations have been carried out on the occurrence of schistosomiasis (or bilharziasis), a very dangerous parasitic disease of men. This disease may have fatal results, but in general, similar to malaria, it causes a lowering of the life activities of the infected people. The parasite is an amoeba-like animal, which is transported by snails and transferred to men. The snails live in and near irrigation water and their influence in irrigated areas of some countries is therefore particularly serious. Balanced against these dangers of irrigated agriculture are all the benefits of irrigation.

A particular branch of environmental sciences relevant to the present discussion is *environmental hygiene*, which has strong ties with medical geography. According to Kuenen *et al.* (1976) environmental hygiene is:

1. The care for the condition of air, water and soil and for the prevention of noise insofar as they are relevant to the health of people.

2. That part of medical science which studies the influences of environmental factors on the health of man.

3. The maintenance of a healthy environment for man.

Environmental hygiene pays particular attention to the relationships between the amount and effect of various types of pollution including noise on different groups of people (adults, children, old people). It is most relevant to urban and industrial situations since relationships with specific kinds of rural landscape are less evident. Environmental hygiene has close links with urban ecology (Ch. 6).

Medical geography as a branch of geography pays particular attention to the regional distribution of diseases, a topic examined by Melvyn Howe (Ed.) (1977). Some diseases are directly related to specific kinds of land use, to particular climates, to particular landscapes or to combinations of these. Schistosomiasis (bilharziasis), which has already been mentioned, is a disease of warm climates, especially in parts of Africa and in the irrigated areas of Egypt and of Iraq. The risk of infection is greatest in areas of high population with a relatively small quantity of available water. Filariasis (Loa loa c.a.) is associated with tropical rainforest areas where there are large areas of fresh water. Malaria is probably the best known disease which is related to specific landscape circumstances. In particular it occurs where the temperature ranges between approximately 16 °C and 35 °C, temperatures which are very favourable to the most common carriers of the disease. For certain diseases such as cholera the influencing environmental factors are to some extent known. For diseases such as diseases of the heart and of bloodvessels, mental diseases and various kinds of cancer, the spatial occurrence is known. These distributions are partly, and perhaps largely, dependent on genetic factors and on factors which are studied by the social sciences, including human geography. It is thus very difficult to determine whether there are also influences related to the physical factors as studied by landscape ecology.

Diseases due to deficiencies in one or more nutrients for human beings are partly the result of poverty. Lack of proteins (for example, kwashiorkor) is perhaps the most important of this group of diseases. It is a disease prevalent in many developing countries. Given the global need to produce most of the food near areas of consumption, there is a clear relationship between the occurrence of deficiency-diseases and particular landscapes. The production of sufficient quantities of protein for local consumption is often a difficult problem in land use planning, especially in densely populated tropical countries. In addition, deficiencies of vitamins and of particular mineral elements may constitute a major problem. We have already made reference to goitre, the deficiency of iodine, one of the earliest discussed examples in ecology (Baas Becking 1934). Today this is still an important problem in various regions of the world.

3

Factors in landscape ecology

CLIMATE AND PHENOLOGY

In this chapter, climate is treated as the first land resource or environmental factor. Emphasis is given to the relationships between climates and various kinds of landscapes. Solar radiation provides the ultimate source of energy for all life on earth as well as for physical processes, including climatic and meteorological ones. It could be concluded, therefore, that all climatic influences on ecosystems are in fact influences of radiation. However, this is not a satisfactory approach for treating this subject. In addition to radiation, therefore, the following factors will be considered as more or less independent variables:

- temperature
- precipitation
- evapotranspiration
- wind.

These four, together with radiation, determine the type and rate of growth and reproduction of organisms at any locality. Within the context of landscape ecology, it is therefore very appropriate to speak of *landscape climatology* as has been done by several German authors. Landscape climatology studies climate variables within a landscape or regional context. The relationships between climate and plants, such as agricultural crops, will be discussed as crop ecology in Chapter 5.

Mountains have a definite impact on the nature and variations in the climate of a region. This can be expressed in two ways: (1) the climate differences within a mountainous area; and (2) the influences which mountains have on the adjoining areas. A typical example of the former is the influence of altitude on air pressure, radiation and temperature. Also in this category is the influence of slope angle and orientation on the amount of received radiation. With regard to the influence on adjoining areas, the influence of mountains on air flow and consequently on precipitation is well known. Other influences are warm 'föhn'-winds (e.g. in areas surrounding the Alps) and the cold descending winds such as exist in the area adjoining the Jura Mountains of Switzerland.

For Scotland systematic bioclimatic investigations have been carried out by Birse (1971) and his co-workers (Birse and Dry 1970; Birse and Robertson 1970). Some aspects of their approach are described here. They paid attention to two groups of factors: (1) accumulated temperature and potential water deficit; and (2) exposure and accumulated frost. Accumulated temperature is in this case obtained by calculating the average monthly accumulated temperature in day degrees above a datum of 5.6 °C. The potential water deficit is the excess of potential evapotranspiration in relation to the precipitation in any given period. Exposure is defined according to the influence of wind over a long period on the development and survival of organisms. It is the combined result of the velocity of the air currents together with other related data such as the salt content of the air near a coast, temperature at high altitudes and relative humidity, factors which may enhance or diminish the effects of the wind. The Scottish method however only takes wind speed into account. Wind velocity is taken as the average of the velocity in metres per second over a year. Accumulated frost is the integrated deficit of temperature with regard to a fixed datum (0 °C) over one year. This approach has produced a bioclimatic classification of Scotland which is of value for land use planning at the national scale.

In landscape climatology phenology is of particular relevance since this refers to the effect of climate on the timing of ecological processes. The following factors are of phenological importance: temperature, occurrence of frost (e.g. late night-frosts in spring with regard to fruit trees), precipitation, various kinds of winds and exposure with regard to the incidence of radiation.

Phenology has also been indicated as the study of the dates, c.q. periods of development of plants. The major periods of development of plants may be found in the field on different calendar dates in different areas. For example, some plants in the south of England will bloom in the spring several weeks in advance of the same plants in northern England or Scotland. This spatial variation depends on the local climate as well as on the weather conditions in any given year. Investigations on cereal crops distinguish the following stages of development: tillering (increase of the number of shoots per plant), height growth, formation of the ears, flowering, and finally ripening of the corn. Given certain general ecological conditions, the dates of occurrence of these different stages are primarily determined by the temperature. The French botanist De Candolle introduced in the nineteenth century the concept of accumulated temperature; that is, the product of the number of days times the temperature, taken above 0 °C or any other relevant temperature. This temperature sum may also be handled as accumulated frost with regard to the need for low temperatures by many groups of plants. As was shown above, these concepts are incorporated in the climatic classification of Scotland, where accumulated temperature is used with 5.6 °C as the reference temperature and accumulated frost is also calculated. The choice of any given reference temperature depends on the nature of the crops to be considered. For maize as an example, the best reference temperature might be 7 °C, as this crop in general does not show any development below this temperature.

This approach may be applied in various manners. First, phenological observations can be made in order to define and map climatic zones. This leads to landscape climatological maps based on the development stages of specific plants. Additional information on potential frost damage to certain sensitive crops such as fruit trees may be included. Surveys in this manner have been carried out by German landscape climatologists as demonstrated by the work of Schreiber (1970). Second, field observations together with experiments in hothouses may be used to calculate the accumulated temperature needed for the various stages of growth of certain crops. Thus it should be possible to delineate the areas where certain crops may be grown. Third, these data may be combined with other information on the requirements of certain plants; for example, light and water. This leads to crop ecology which is discussed in Chapter 5.

Another aspect of phenology is the form of trees as conditioned by strong winds. This is very clearly seen in coastal areas and in localities near to deserts. Slope orientation is of particular importance in any area where a crop is near to its growing limit. Such a situation is frequent with orchards on slopes as in Belgium or with vineyards as in Germany, Switzerland and

Fig. 10 Ombrothermograms of some stations in the mediterranean zone (from: Bioclimatic Map of the Mediterranean Zone, Explanatory Notes, Arid Zone Research XXI, with permission of UNESCO 1963)

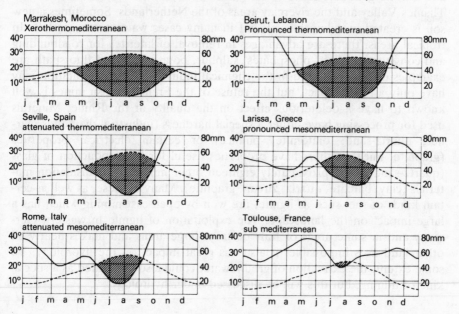

northern Italy. Such orchards and vineyards produce best on southern-oriented slopes. Night frosts occurring late in spring are particularly frequent in valleys where cold air from the hills drains towards the lower areas. The results can be disastrous for fruit crops.

There is a number of techniques for the presentation of climatic data. Ombrothermograms are often used as one of the simplest forms. These display annual fluctuations of temperature (dotted line) as well as variations in precipitation (drawn line) (UNESCO 1963). The result gives an indication of the period of effective drought (dashed area). In addition the 'xerothermic index' may be calculated from the number of days per month which are considered to be dry in a biological sense. Some examples of ombrothermograms are given in Fig. 10.

GEOLOGY

The phenomena and processes of the earth's mantle which are studied by geologists have various kinds of impacts on ecology. Mineral exploitation leads to considerable impacts, as is the case when oil is extracted from below shallow water areas. An obvious example is the debris from coal mining which often has been dumped on the land with little thought to the consequences. The exploitation of valuable minerals by mining companies is mostly concentrated on relatively small areas. Many of the less valuable minerals are extracted on a more extensive basis. Examples are minerals for the construction, chemical and processing industries. The first group includes limestone, clay, gypsum, and sand and gravel. The exploitation of clays, sands and gravels generally leads to soil removal in extensive areas, such as the Thames Valley and the riverclay areas of the Netherlands. Sometimes a new soil is created at a lower level, but in many cases water areas are left. In tropical areas, there are advantages in removal of laterites for roadbuilding and construction. Salt, phosphates, sulphur, potash-salts and fluorspath are examples of minerals used in the chemical industry. Their exploitation may have only a local impact, but the refuse of the French potash mines is well known to have a deleterious effect on the quality of the Rhine. Minerals used for processing have either a special hardness (industrial diamonds, garnet, quartz-sand, diatomite, pumice) or certain electrical properties (graphite, mica). Others have properties useful for the production of glass (quartz-sand and approximately eighteen other minerals) or insulation materials (clay, bauxite, quartz, zircon, graphite). Many of these, as well as certain kinds of fuel such as lignite, are won by open-cast mining which has a large impact on the landscape. The exploitation of lignite in western Germany and in some areas of Italy destroys large areas and makes nearly all other land uses impossible; it also has great impact on the hydrology. To some extent, the extraction of groundwater could also be treated as a special kind of mining, but this will be discussed under hydrology.

A special kind of geology with relations to technical applications in land and water use is 'Rock mechanics', the mechanics of consolidated rocks. The latter is a rather new discipline within geology which has very important implications, e.g. for the building of dams, bridges, etc.

The materials, structures, forms and processes of the consolidated or unconsolidated upper 1000 m or more of the earth's crust are of general relevance to landscape ecology and land use. Geological formations are often considered the most typical abiotic parts of ecosystems. However, it would be preferable to consider them palaeo-biotic. Most of them contain the remnants of old ecosystems and of organisms, sometimes in low concentrations or in microscopic forms. Palaeontology looks at first sight to have little relevance to landscape ecology, apart from the study of those materials (coal, lignite, oil) which have a biogenic origin. But in general palaeontology and other disciplines which study more in particular the genesis of landscapes and their components are of great importance for a better understanding of the present-day phenomena and relationships; this understanding is essential for inventories, surveys and other investigations of the latter. The ecological conditions of today are a result of processes which started in the past.

Special emphasis needs to be given to *Quaternary Geology*. The Quaternary is the shortest of all geological periods, lasting approximately 2.5 million years, whilst the total geological record extends to 5 billion years. Even the Tertiary Period, which preceded the Quaternary, lasted 60 million years. However, the Quaternary is the period in which most present-day landscapes received their characteristic forms and materials. This is true not only for north-western Europe, including Great Britain and Ireland, but also for Canada and northern parts of the USA. The highly dissected mountain chains of today – for example, the Alps, the Himalayas and the Rocky Mountains – were initially formed in the Tertiary Period, but the effect of glaciers and of other processes, such as isostatic changes, continued during the Quaternary and still to some extent continue today. Movement along the well-known San Andreas Fault in California illustrates the active processes of today, but there are other, less spectacular tectonic processes now in various parts in the world.

The Pleistocene, the period of the great Glacial Ages, has shaped and influenced many landscapes above a latitude of approximately 45 °N. In other parts of the world, local glaciations, for example in the Andes, and the Pluvial Ages, which have rather complex correlations with the Glacial Ages, often had a similar, although more restricted, influence. Some examples of landscapes which were largely or wholly formed by glacial processes are (Flint 1971):

- Glacially sculptured terrain: glaciated valleys, areas sculptured by mountain ice-sheets and areas sculptured by piedmont glaciers and by lowland ice-sheets (Canada, several parts of Scandinavia).
- Glacial drift areas: tills (groundmoraines, tills or 'boulder clays')

and stratified drifts (Canada, Scandinavia, large parts of Britain, most parts of Ireland, northern USA).

- Areas covered by aeolian sediments (wind-blown deposits), in particular the loess-covered areas of northern USA, of western and central Europe, and the related and adjoining coversand areas of north-west Germany, the Netherlands and Belgium.
- Old sea levels and old river terraces largely developed due to the changes in sea levels during the Glacial Ages (coastal areas of the Mediterranean, several coastal areas in Asia and in Latin America).

During the last 10 000 years, the period known as the Holocene, many of the alluvial landscapes of today have developed. These include the youngest terraces and the floodplains of all the major rivers in the world as well as the lowlands of such countries as the Netherlands, consisting partly of marine and estuarine sediments and partly of peat. Most of the hill peat areas, for example in Ireland and in Scotland, have also been formed during this period. In all these areas, some of which belong to the most highly productive parts of the world, Holocene deposits are of fundamental importance to landscape ecology.

Separate attention must be given to volcanic activity during the Quarternary Period. In certain regions the modern landscape is largely the result of extensive volcanism which still partly continues. The island of Java in Indonesia as well as the well-known volcanism of Hawaii and parts of Japan are obvious examples. In Africa, large areas of Kenya as well as the region around Mount Cameroon can be mentioned. In Italy the region from south of Leghorn to south of Naples along the coast of the Tyrrhenian Sea and also the island of Sicily are further examples where volcanism has had a major landscape impact. One beneficial product from volcanism can be ash – a material which can be of marked significance to ecosystems because of its high nutrient content.

To conclude this section on geology, it is important to note that during the Holocene man has increasingly exerted his influence on geological processes.

GEOMORPHOLOGY

Geomorphology is the study of the forms, structures, materials and processes on the surface of the earth. In particular these have the following landscape impacts:

1. The general form of the landscape: plains, hills, plateaus, mountains, high mountain ranges.
2. Processes resulting from the form of the land as expressed in: erosion, denudation, sedimentation, accumulation and the resultant landforms and materials.
3. Processes resulting from the lithology as expressed in the structures and

the specific shapes of landforms, e.g. mass-movements along the dipslopes of formations rich in shales.

4. Subsurface processes: water movement, (a) in limestone; for example, leading to karst phenomena; (b) water movement in other kinds of rocks and determined by their permeability, the latter being often due to, or its direction of flow depending on: (1) the occurrence of faults; (2) the slope and alignment of formations; (3) the occurrence of unconformities.

5. Tectonic movements along faults in deeper situated formations resulting in changes of landforms and related processes on the surface.

6. The nature and impact of soil-forming factors: parent material, topography and water conditions and the related influences of the other soil-forming factors: vegetation, fauna and land use, on the nature and variations of soils.

7. The topoclimatic aspects such as altitude and exposure to radiation and to winds, with their influences on ecosystems.

Geomorphology as the science which studies the nature and genesis of the earth's surface is one of the fundamental sciences for landscape ecology. In some respects its contributions are closely related to those of Quaternary geology. Geomorphology may also be characterized with the ecological terms of 'pattern' and 'process'. 'Pattern' indicates the diversity of phenomena in space and 'process' indicates the diversity in time. In this context only the abiotic phenomena will be discussed (see also Ch. 2). This is in most cases a simplification apart from the extreme conditions of cold or hot deserts. In most landscapes the variations of abiotic phenomena in space as well as in time are accompanied by related variations in the biotic aspects both in natural and in cultural ecosystems.

In the study of the variations in space and time the differences in scales have to be carefully considered. If spatial variations of very large-scale phenomena are studied, and they are delineated on maps of very small scales (e.g. 1 : 200 000 to 1 : 1 000 000, see Fig. 2), only the very large differences can be considered; these are caused by epeirogenic tectonic and orogenic processes such as the formation of mountains and basins, folding and faulting of geological formations, movement of large blocks creating horst and graben. In connection with these the large river basins, plains and deltas may be indicated. In cold or formerly glaciated regions, the areas sculptured by ice-sheets and large glaciers are of the same dimensions. Looking over large distances in time, similar phenomena may have occurred under comparable conditions in different regions or in different areas of the same large regions. The reconstruction of the landforms, materials and processes resulting from Glacial Ages in Europe and Northern America for example contributes very much to the understanding of the landscape patterns found today in these regions. Geomorphology and Quaternary geology clearly are combining their results in such cases. The knowledge of processes from older periods is very often the best means for understanding the landscape of today.

The study of separate landforms and their components with their arrangement in typical patterns leads to a more precise study of the processes as they occur in a shorter period of time. Detailed geomorphological investigation is exemplified by *geomorphological mapping* of areas on scales ranging from 1 : 2000 to 1 : 50 000.

Another approach of the detailed scale is the monitoring of geomorphological processes over several years. Process studies are increasingly being carried out in vegetated areas subject to human influence. In these cases the research is concerned with the biotic as well as with the abiotic factors in the landscape, including interactions between landforms, soils and vegetation (see for example Imeson and Jungerius 1976, 1977). The study of geomorphological processes therefore has many contributions to make to landscape ecology for natural as well as for cultural ecosystems, including the various kinds of forestry.

Examples of *geomorphological surveys* are given by the French geomorphologist Tricart (1965), in the Geomorphological Map of the Netherlands (scale 1 : 50 000) by Maarleveld c.s. and in the work of Verstappen c.s. of the ITC (Enschede, the Netherlands). The latter is particularly directed towards the needs of developing countries.

In this latter system, different kinds of geomorphological maps are distinguished: (a) preliminary maps, made for the preparation of fieldwork and based only on airphoto-interpretation; (b) general purpose maps which are the outcome of pure geomorphological research and are generally applicable only if put in the hands of a competent geomorphologist; (c) special purpose maps, which are the results of applied geomorphological research, and two types can be recognized: (1) morpho-conservation maps (for engineering and conservation surveys); and (2) hydromorphological maps (for hydrological purposes). These various maps are produced over the full range of map-scales. The general purpose maps indicate the following types of features:

> landform types
> structural
> volcanic
> denudational
> pluvial
> marine
> glacial/periglacial
> aeolian
> karst
> morphometry
> lithology
> chronology
> topography

Special purpose maps contain a selection of the relevant characteristics extracted from the general purpose maps. In addition, the morphoconservation maps contain information on slopes (gradients, forms, length), cover types (vegetation, land use, terraces) and on processes of erosion and denudation (creep, landslides). The hydromorphological maps give special information on surface water (natural and artificial) and on groundwater (Verstappen and Van Znidam 1968).

These and comparable maps are in the first place essential for obtaining a more precise knowledge and a better understanding of the landscape as a complex of natural phenomena. In addition they are of fundamental value for the production of landscape ecological maps. It is often useful therefore to make a geomorphological map as the basis for the production of a landscape ecological map. In the Netherlands, where minor variations in geomorphological features often are of considerable importance for landscape ecology, geomorphological survey is used as a basic study which is produced as an essential prerequisite for the subsequent landscape ecological survey. In other cases where lack of time or other factors prevent such geomorphological survey, extra attention is paid to all geomorphological features and processes during the landscape ecological survey. This is the case in the landscape ecological surveys which have been carried out in western Switzerland and which are still underway in Tuscany, central Italy (Vink 1973, 1975b; Vink and Van de Weg 1982). If landscape ecological surveys are carried out as integrated surveys by a multidisciplinary team, the active involvement of a geomorphologist, who may be at the same a good soil surveyor, is an essential part of the work.

The monitoring of geomorphological processes (sometimes called 'actuogeomorphology') provides essential data for landscape ecology in all areas where processes are clearly observable in the landscape. In many cases existing active processes are accelerated by human activity. This is in general true in landscapes where considerable erosion by wind and water occurs along with the associated processes of sedimentation (see Ch. 7). The latter are often even more deleterious than the erosion processes; for example, the silting-up of irrigation systems. Processes of mass movement require special mention: these refer to large amounts of materials ranging from landslides to mudflows (plate 13). Under periglacial conditions this phenomenon is often described as solifluction – the downward movement of surface regolith over the permanently or seasonally frozen subsoil. In temperate and even in subtropical and tropical climates *mass movements* are a dominant feature in certain landscapes. There are several kinds of geological formations which have a particular tendency to these movements. These include formations which consist of alternating clayey and sandy or silty layers, which may be unconsolidated or consolidated. The former may also consist more or less exclusively of silty clays. The latter are most typically exemplified by the 'Flysch' formations which are characteristic of Alpine border zones. They are found extensively along the northern and western border zones of the Alps in Switzerland and Austria, in the Appenines and Abruzzi of Italy and in the North African Atlas Mountains, but they are also found in several other areas of Europe, Africa and Asia. In these regions the ecosystems are often dominated by the mass movements creating a continuous instability with regard to topography, soils and hydrology as well as to the related vegetation and types of land use. In a small area of the Appenines (approx. 200 km^2) we counted some years ago a total of nearly 2000 mass movements with surface areas varying from 1 ha to some tens of hectares and most seemed to have occurred over the last 5000 years. In similar areas, comparable land slides have often caused fatal effects, e.g. in 1963 in the Italian town of Longarone in the valley of the Piave river, when approximately 300 people were killed by one landslide.

Mass movements may contain one or more of the following processes: (a) flow – slow streaming of materials with often high clay contents which may have stones and large blocks floating in them due to the high specific gravity of the flowing material; (b) landslides – the movement of coherent masses over a slip plane with relatively high rapidity; (c) falls – the plunging down of more or less large quantities of materials: debris fall, rock fall, avalanches; (d) subsidence due to settling of materials caused by drainage and/or heavy overburdens, c.q. by subterranean solution or mining. The intensity and manner in which mass movements occur depends to a large extent on the moisture status of the materials and on the nature of the subsoils. Many kinds of flow and slide are caused by water contents, e.g. after heavy rainfall or as a result of melting snow.

Old mass movements, which originated in the Pleistocene Period, may be triggered anew by human action such as forest cutting or the construction of a road. In general such areas of former mass movements remain potential areas of instability.

It can be appreciated that geomorphology pays special attention to the processes which result in slope development. These processes consist not only of mass movements but also for example of deep tropical weathering, soil formation and erosion.

WATER

Next to the energy of the sun, water is the most essential prerequisite for life on earth. All organisms consist mainly of water (plants approx. 90 per cent, fishes approx. 75–80 per cent, man approx. 60–70 per cent) and their nutrition as well as their secretion is in the form of solutions. Approximately 98 per cent of all water is saline, with the remaining 2 per cent accounting for global freshwater resources. Figure 6 (Ch. 2) illustrates the hydrological cycle.

Plants vary in their water requirements. Table 3 gives some data for agricultural crops in Iraq (Vink 1975a). These figures for the desert climate of Iraq are slightly higher than those in more humid climates, but still they give a sufficient order of magnitude for general use. They are given in millimetres

bearing formations and into the movement of groundwater. Such research is required for the planning of water resources, but it is also used for predicting drainage needs. In addition concern may be with groundwater pollution and with the effect of naturally saline waters on the regions in which outflow may take place. The need for better data on the total available quantities of water is of prime significance in all arid and semi-arid countries. In industrial countries where there is the ever increasing consumption of water for industrial and related purposes, the calculation of water-budgets has become essential. Even in the Netherlands, the country perhaps with the greatest freshwater resources per unit surface area and possibly per 1000 inhabitants, projections for the water budget for the year 2000 indicate potential summer deficits (Table 5).

The budget has been made for a rather dry year, but not the driest possible. In summer, plants consume large quantities of water and therefore the positive balancing item of 111 mm does not appear too serious. But there are two reasons why any possible optimism should be avoided:

1. The overall conditions of a dry summer are rather theoretical because of the fluctuations in relative drought which may occur over varying periods; the drought incidence also shows large regional differences, even in this small country.

2. In dry periods water quality is often poor, causing the actual availability of useful water to be much lower than is shown in the budget. Again, local

Table 5. Water budget for the Netherlands in *c.* 2000 assuming a rather dry summer half year, surface area approximately 30 000 km², precip. per annum 700 mm

Available after subtracting evaporation	in 10^9 m³	in mm	%	Requirements	in 10^9 m³	in mm	%
From Rhine	21.1	527	82	Urban use	0.7	18	3
From Meuse	0.7	18	3	Industrial use	1.3	33	5
From small rivers	0.5	13	2	Water management in agriculture	3.3	82	13
From drainage	0.5	13	2	Flushing of polders*	6.1	152	24
From groundwater	0.8	20	3	Control of saline water	9.9	247	38
Water storage basins	1.0	25	4	In estuary			
Purified sewerage water	1.1	27	4	Balancing item	4.4	111	17
Totals	25.7	643	100		25.7	643	100

Source: Blumenthal 1977.

* Flushing of polders is necessary to counteract saline groundwater and local pollution; precipitation during the summer half year is approximately 350 mm, evapotranspiration approx. 500 mm.

conditions are very relevant such as the influence of salt water invading into the estuary of the rivers Rhine and Meuse.

Figure 8 (Ch. 2) is a diagram showing the influence of seepage. This seepage is found in many areas of the world where precipitation on higher areas results in groundwater flowing through permeable geological formations to lower areas. This groundwater flow may cause considerable local differences in the actually available quantities of water. Furthermore, the quality of the groundwater may differ due to weathering of different formations and to human pollution. Typical examples of the influence of weathering processes are found in the saline groundwaters descending into the Mesopotamian Plain from adjoining Tertiary hills with saltbearing formations. In Germany and in some areas of the Netherlands, leaching of iron and aluminium may cause high contents of these cations in groundwater. Groundwater flow not only causes influx of water into lower areas; the excessive drainage from the higher areas may lead to excessive drought for natural as well as for cultural ecosystems and this may be aggravated by human interference.

Groundwater conditions of soils, one of the most useful means of indicating water conditions for plant growth and land use, may be indicated in various manners. A very effective but purely descriptive system is found in drainage phases as defined in the US Soil Survey Manual (Soil Survey Staff 1951, 1963), of which a completely new edition is in preparation. The Soil Survey of Scotland includes the drainage of the soils in their characterization of soil series. A more quantitative approach is used by the Netherlands Soil Survey Institute, based on measurements of water conditions with the mapping units of the soil survey. This is especially necessary in this country because water conditions have been, and still are, changed by artificial drainage and polder management. In Table 6 this classification, based on groundwater table classes (GT) indicating the 'mean highest water table' and the 'mean lowest water table', is given.

The hydrological conditions of urban areas need special attention as they show marked differences from rural localities where plants consume large quantities of water by evapotranspiration. In addition, the land in urban areas is covered to a large extent with impermeable buildings and roads which do not allow water to penetrate into the soils. Stone, brick, laterite or gravel-covered roads are preferable in this respect to fully metalled roads.

Table 6. Groundwater table classes (GT) in the Netherlands according to the system of the Netherlands Soil Survey Institute in cm below soil surface (see also Vink 1975a)

GT classes	I	II	III	IV	V	VI	VII
Mean highest water table (winter) (GHW)	—	—	<40	>40	<40	40–80	>80
Mean lowest water table (summer) (GLW)	<50	50–80	80–120	80–120	>120	>120	>120

Gardens and parks with vegetation are therefore an essential means of promoting a certain regulation of water conditions in urban areas. In an average town the proportion of the precipitation penetrating into the soil is often estimated at two thirds of the total precipitation. The other one third has to be drained by fully artificial means unless high temperatures cause rapid evaporation from roofs, pools and roads. The growing of large trees in strongly urbanized areas may provide difficulties because their growing conditions may lead to a lack of water, compared with the same trees on the same soils in rural areas.

Hydrology is a very comprehensive science and only some aspects have been indicated. For more information the reader is referred to the many books on hydrology (see e.g. Kovda *et al*. 1973).

SOILS

In conventional ecological texts soils are only discussed as the products of soil formation and as the growth medium of plants. In this text, which adopts a broader ecological stance including man, the science which is called soil mechanics or engineering soil science has at least to be mentioned. This approach to soil science has a different definition of soil from that normally used in soil science. The definition used in engineering considers soils as all the unconsolidated materials used in engineering construction either as the foundations or as materials to be used; for example, in road building. Some applications are the construction of airfields, roads, houses and dykes. The capacity of soil to support these structures is often determined by engineering soil surveys as well as by special physical tests, some of which are carried out in the field and others in laboratories. Determination of plasticity and of shear strength belong to this category. Soil depth in engineering investigations may be some tens of metres and in areas with thick sedimentary covers to more than 100 m depth. Initial surveys are often done by airphoto-interpretation; this technique is very effective in many kinds of land resources surveys, but it has special significance in those areas where the presence of surveyors in the fields might induce an increase of land prices. Similar surveys, either with or without systematic ground control, are also called terrain evaluation surveys. Although many concepts of the two different approaches to soil science differ rather strongly, there are several techniques in common, in particular those related to landforms and parent materials. Areas with high instability due to active or potential mass movements (for example, landslides) are of particular importance in engineering soil surveys as well as in landscape ecological surveys.

The *soil in a broad ecological sense*, including its consideration for land use, is a very complex phenomenon. Soil is the focus of many research institutes concerned with various kinds of land use. It is also studied on a theoretical basis with emphasis on soil formation (pedogenesis) and soil classification. National soil science societies exist in most countries, and there is also

the International Society of Soil Science, which concentrates its efforts mainly on world soils. A current definition, to some extent adapted by the author, is given as follows:

A soil is a three-dimensional body occupying a part of the uppermost part of the
earth's crust, in which plants grow or are able to grow, and that has properties which
differ from the underlying consolidated or unconsolidated rocks or parent materials
as a result of the interactions between climate, living matter (including human activity), parent material and topography over various periods of time. One soil is distinguished from others on the basis of internal characteristics and of observations
related to the slope, the complicated structure, the microtopography or the stoniness
of its surface.

In addition, other differentiating criteria may be used; for example, the
groundwater level, which is often decisive in low-lying areas. There is one
particular reason why soil has a key position in landscape ecology: according
to the definition it is the site for the growth of plants.

The nutrient cycles of plants and animals were discussed in Chapter 2, and
it was indicated that essential parts of these occur within all soils. A soil,
seen as an entity within which plants and animals live, may itself be considered as an ecosystem. As such it is also a part of a larger ecosystem to
which the plants and animals living on the soils belong. Some soil organisms
are moles, earthworms, termites (in tropical regions), insects, nematodes,
algae, fungi and bacteria. The significance of the number of animals living in
soils in temperate regions may be indicated by the fact that the total weight
per hectare of the earthworms living in a grassland soil equals the weight of
the cattle grazing on these soils, which in intensive grazing systems may be
taken as 2000 kg per hectare.

A soil is also 'a tract of land', a three-dimensional body with its own
surface, including the shape of that surface. The soil profile, although very
necessary for the determination and classification of a soil, gives only two of
these dimensions. The soil profile and its classification are needed for the
determination of taxonomic classes and for the study of pedogenesis; soil
characteristics such as depth and drainage indicate the suitablity of soil for
plants and related ecological factors. But the three-dimensional nature of
soils should always be remembered, a point illustrated in Fig. 11 (see also
Ch. 5, Fig. 18).

The study of certain groups of soils in detail in order to consider their
properties with regard to ecology and land use may be particularly useful
and this can be demonstrated by considering the following soils: saline soils,
soils of tropical regions, heavy clay soils, gleysoils (hydromorphic soils).

Saline soils are, and have been for a long time, of considerable research
interest because of their serious limitations to all aspects of land use. They
cover large surface areas especially in arid and in semi-arid regions. On the
Soil Map of the World (FAO/UNESCO 1974) the following groups of saline
soils are indicated:

Fig. 11 Block diagram, soil map and soil profiles, three soils in the landscape

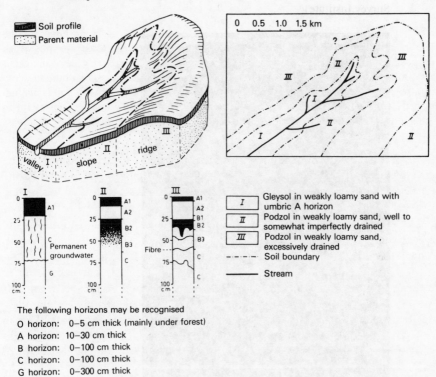

The following horizons may be recognised

O horizon: 0–5 cm thick (mainly under forest)
A horizon: 10–30 cm thick
B horizon: 0–100 cm thick
C horizon: 0–100 cm thick
G horizon: 0–300 cm thick

Solonchaks: 'Soils, exclusive of those formed from recent alluvial deposits, having a high salinity and having no diagnostic horizons other than (unless buried by 50 cm or more of new material) an A horizon, a histic H horizon, a cambic B horizon, a calcic or gypsic horizon' (FAO/UNESCO, 1974).

Solonetz: 'Soils having a natric B horizon; lacking an albic E horizon which shows hydromorphic properties in at least a part of the horizon and an abrupt textural change' (FAO/UNESCO 1974).

It is instructive to compare these descriptions with those given below for planosols. The classification used in the legend of the *Soil Map of the World* is based on quantitatively described diagnostic horizons and diagnostic properties. For more information the reader is referred to the original text (FAO/UNESCO 1974) and to the US Soil Taxonomy (Soil Survey Staff 1975). The terms solonchak and solonetz are derived from the Russian system of soil classification. The third group of saline and related soils is the *solod*, which can be formed from the other saline soils. The solonchak is a soil which has various kinds of salts in the whole of its profile, including sodium, calcium and magnesium chloride ($NaCl$, $CaCl_2$, $MgCl_2$). The solonetz may be de-

Plate 1 Old alluvial soil with very distinctive and thick A horizon, 'Tuineerdgrond', 'Umbraquept', 'Humic Gleysol' (photo: Netherlands Soil Survey Institute)

rived from the solonchak by leaching of the chlorides together with clay towards the lower parts of the soil profile, forming a 'natric B horizon', i.e. a horizon with illuviated clay and sodium. The solod is then formed by further eluviation during which clay from the upper parts of the soil profile (the A horizon) is destroyed and eluviated (leached) towards the B horizon, whereas salts are moving even further down to below the B horizon. This process is called 'solodization' and it leads to the formation of a thick white (albic) E horizon (leached A horizon) which contains nothing but silt to mean that it is poor in fertility. The solods are considered, according to the *Soil Map of the World*, to belong to *planosols*. These are 'soils having an albic E horizon overlying a slowly permeable horizon within 125 cm of the surface (for example, an argillic or natric B horizon showing abrupt textural change, a

Plate 2 Humuspodzol, a classical example of the leaching of humus and iron from the topsoil, an age-old process (photo: Netherlands Soil Survey Institute)

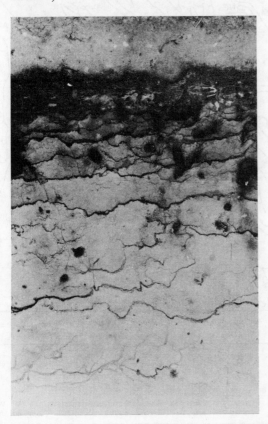

heavy clay, a fragipan), exclusive of a spodic (podzol–) B horizon; showing hydromorphic properties at least in a part of the E horizon'. An argillic horizon is a B horizon containing a certain minimum of illuviated clay.

It is clear that saline soils, including solods or planosols, present major constraints to ecosystems. These result from high contents of easily soluble salts (Na, Mg, Ca, Cl, SO_4 and sometimes NO_3) and from the destruction of soil structure which results from the leaching of these ions. Therefore in general the chemical as well as the physical conditions of these soils are poor for plant growth. The hydromorphic properties of the E horizon of planosols give an indication of poor drainage in the upper parts of the soil profile. Planosols occur, for example, over a large area of the Agro Pontino, the former 'Pontine Marshes' south of Rome, as well as in coastal areas of Portugal and in several areas of the USA. The full development of these soils

Fig. 12 Soil map of an area 25 km south south west of Edinburgh in Scotland (scale c.1:73 000)

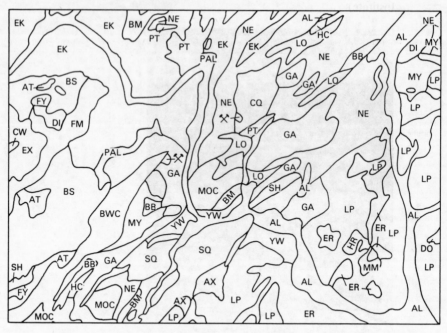

Soil associations and series

Associations	Parent material	Humus iron podzols Freely drained	Peaty podzols Freely drained below iron pan	Brown forest soils Freely drained	Imperfectly drained	Non-calcareous gleys Imperfectly drained	Poorly drained	Peaty gleys Very poorly drained
Bemersyde	Stony drift derived from rhyolite and trachyte.	DI		BM				
Eckford	Fluvioglacial red and reddish brown sand and gravel derived mainly from Old Red Sandstone sediments.			EK				
Ettrick	Silurian and Ordovician greywackes and shales and derived drifts.	MM	DO	LP	AX			
	Clayey till derived from Silurian and Ordovician greywackes and shales.						ER	HR
Mountboy	Drifts from lower O.R.S. grits sandstones and conglomerates with some basic and intermediate lavas.	CQ		GA		MY	BB	HC
	As above but with partially sorted surface layers.			NE			LO	

Associations	Parent material	Humus iron podzols Freely drained	Peaty podzols Freely drained below iron pan	Brown forest soils Freely drained	Brown forest soils Imperfectly drained	Non-calcareous gleys Imperfectly drained	Non-calcareous gleys Poorly drained	Peaty gleys Very poorly drained
Sourhope	Drifts derived mainly from andesitic lavas. Stony drift derived mainly from andesites overlying clay till of mixed origin.	FY		SH	BS EX		AT	
Symington	Sand and gravel derived mainly from andesites.			SQ				
Yarrow	Gravels derived from greywackes of Silurian and/or Ordovician age.			YW				

Soil complexes

Ettrick Ordovician and Silurian Greywackes and shales	Peat rankers, brown rankers, rock outcrops, screes and severely eroded phases of the DO, LP and MM series					TZC		
Mountboy Lower O.R.S. sediments and lavas of variable lithology	Unnamed soils with peaty and MOR Humus surface horizons Unnamed mineral soils					BWC MOC		

Alluvial soils

Peaty	PAL	
Undifferentiated	AL	

Miscellaneous soils

Peat	PT
Mixed bottom land (unlabelled)	〰
Quarry	✗

requires several thousands of years, but the soils may display these serious ecological constraints after only 1000 years of development.

Within the great soil group of the solonchaks, various kinds of soils can be distinguished:

1. Internal solonchaks: little salt on the surface but which nevertheless are completely saline.

2. External solonchaks: salts very clearly on their surfaces, sometimes even as a continuous salt crust (photo 3), mainly consisting of $NaCl$, Na_2SO_4 and $MgSO_4$.

3. Flooded solonchaks: a salt crust of a few centimetres on their surfaces.

4. Puffed solonchaks: a surface resembling a soufflé due to the escape of carbonates in the form of CO_2-gas (consisting of Na_2CO_3, Na_2SO_4 with admixtures of $CaSO_4$ and $NaCl$).

Fig. 13 A part of a Physiographic Soil Map of an area in Italy (the Minturno area, between Rome and Naples) (after Sevink *et al.* 1982). Scale 1 : 100,000 (top of the map is towards N)

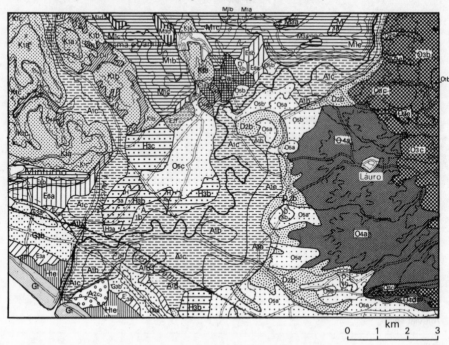

A. Soils in meandering stream deposits

1. *Fluvial deposits s.s*
A1a – Association of calcic cambisols and calcaric fluvisols (1/4-5/a)
A1c – Calcic cambisols (2/3-4/a)
A1e – Eutric cambisols (2/3-4/a)

2. *Other, related, deposits*
A2c – Chromic vertisols (3/1-2/a)

C. Soils in alluvial fans

1. *Large alluvial fans*
C1a – Calcaric regosols (1-2/5-6a)

D. Soils in colluvio-alluvial valley-fills

2. *Deposits mainly derived from volcanic rocks*
D2b – Association of eutric cambisols and gleyic cambisols (2-3/4/a; 2-3/3/a)

4. *Deposits of other origin°*
D4a – Calcaric fluvisols (2/2-3/b)
D4e – Calcic vertic cambisols (3/2-4/b)
D4f – Calcic cambisols (2/2-4/b)

Note: * the code between brackets indicates:
– soil texture (1 = coarse, 2 = medium, 3 = fine)
– soil drainage (from 0 very poorly drained to 6 excessively drained)
– slope classes (a = level to gently rolling to c = steeply dissected)

E. Soils in colluvial and related deposits

2. *Fluvio-colluvial basinfills*
E2f – Chromic vertisols (3/2-3/a)*

3. *Colluvial slope deposits derived from marine and eolian deposits*
E3a – Eutric regosols (2/2-3/a)

6. *Colluvial slope deposits of mixed origin*
E6a – Calcaric fluvisols (2-3/3-4/a)
E6b – Calcaric regosols (2/4-5/a)

G. Soils in littoral-eolian deposits

1. *Recent dunes and beach ridges*

G1 – Calcaric regosols (1/5-6/a-c)

3. *Beach ridges of the Minturno level*
G3a – Chromic luvisols (2/4/a)
G3b – Association of eutric cambisols and orthic luvisols (2/3-4/a)

°) Note: i.e not marine, not eolian, not volcanic and not limestone derived.

H. Soils in lagoonal deposits

1. *Deposits of Terracina level*
H1e – Eutric fluvisols (3/1-2/a)

3. *Deposits of the Minturno level*
H3a – Chromic vertisols (3/2/a)
H3b – complex of chromic vertisols and calcic vertic cambisols (3/2-3/a; 3/2-3/a-b)
H3c – Orthic luvisols (3/2-3/a)

K. Soils on sandstones

1. *Miocene sandstones*
K1a – Calcaric regosols (1-2/4-5/c)
K1b – Complex of calcaric regosols and calcic cambisols (2/4-5/b-c)
K1c = Calcic cambisols (2/4/b-c)

M. Soils on limestone

1. *Soils on limestone*
1. *Slopes*
M1b – Complex of lithosols and rendzinas (3/5-6/a-c)
M1c – Complex of rendzinas and lithosols (3/5-6/a-c)

3. *Karstbasins*
M3a – Chromic luvisols (3/4/a)
M3d – Complex of chromic vertisols and lithosols (3/4/a-b; 3/6/a-b)

O. Soils on Volcanic rocks of the Roccamonfina

1. *Lava outflows and domes*
O1b – Vitric eutric regolsols (2/4-6/b-c)

3. *Higher tuff slope*
O3b – Vitric eutric regosols (2/4-6/b-c)
O3c – Vitric eutric regosols (2-3/4-5/a-b)
O3e – Vitric eutric regosols (2/4-6/c)

4. *Middle tuff slope*
O4a – Complex of eutric regosols, ochric andosols (2/4-5/a-b) and ferric luvisols (2-3/4/a-b)
O4d – Association of mollic andosols and ochric andosols (2/3-4/a)

5. *Lower tuff slope*
O5a – Association of vitric eutric regosols and ochric andosols (2/3-4/a)
O5b – Association of ferric luvisols and ochric andosols (2-3/3-4/a)
O5c – Association of ferric luvisols and luvic phaeozems (2-3/33-4/a)

Plate 3 Solonchaks in Iraq. White: external solonchaks; dark: sabagh soils; in foreground, puffed solonchaks.

5. Sabagh soils (a term for Iraq): a high content of hygroscopic salts ($MgCl_2$, $CaCl_2$) and of $MgSO_4$, which produce a dark surface colour (see Plate 3).

In addition to these soils, in many saline areas there are also 'takyrs', a Russian term indicating saline soils which have a glossy surface crust of fine soil materials formed by peptization and desiccation.

The problems of salinization and desalinization will be discussed in Chapter 7.

Tropical regions contain many different groups of soils, some of which are comparable, for example, to soils in Mediterranean regions. Contrary to soils of more northerly parts of the world, they have not undergone rejuvenation by glacial and periglacial processes in the Pleistocene Period and in general have not been covered by extensive windblown sediments (loess) as have been deposited in the glacial fringe areas. This lack of rejuvenation over large areas means that in tropical and subtropical areas relatively large surfaces of older soils (1 million years or more) are found. To these older soils belong, for example, the nitosols and the acrisols: soils with thick and well developed 'argillic horizons' (clay-illuviation B horizons). Also the vertisols, very heavy claysoils, which are the result of alternating wet and dry warm seasons over long periods are found over large surface areas in tropical and subtropical regions.

There exist also large areas of soils which are more truly typical of the tropical regions themselves. In particular the more typical tropical soils which are called oxisols of ferralsols are found. Formerly these soils were called latosols or lateritic soils. These soils are characterized by the presence of a thick (often over 10 m thickness) 'oxic B horizon' (FAO/UNESCO 1974), which consists predominantly of the clay mineral kaolinite and has a very low adsorption capacity for nutrient minerals. Due to the age of these soils, they are almost completely weathered and have no reserve of weatherable minerals (see also Ch. 5, Fig. 17). These ferralsols, using the terminology of the *Soil Map of the World*, are very poor in nutrients but they have in general very favourable physical conditions for plant growth and provide a deep soil for plant roots. Some aspects of their use will be discussed in Chapters 5 and 7.

The *Vertisols* provide the most typical example of heavy clay soils. They have at least 30 per cent of clay (particles smaller than 2 microns) in all their horizons up to approximately 120 cm depth below the soil surface and often to much greater depth. The clay in these soils consists almost exclusively of minerals of the montmorillonite or smectite group which have a high nutrient adsorption capacity and a strong potential for shrinking (under dry conditions) and swelling (under wet conditions). In dry seasons this causes very wide cracks (more than 1 cm width at 50 cm depth). On the surface these cracks usually show a polygonal pattern and a particular microrelief. This gilgai or 'cauliflower' relief is a result of the same process of shrinking and swelling which causes the 'self-mulching' nature of these soils: the dry particles fall into the cracks and a new surface is formed from the soil material below. The vertisols have also been called 'black tropical soils'; in India they are called 'regurs'. In some cases the name 'black cotton soils' has also been used. They are very common in arid and semi-arid regions of the tropics and in the subtropics; for example, in Mesopotamia and in Sudan. Extensive areas of these soils are found in tropical regions with monsoonal climates; for example, in India, Indonesia and some parts of tropical Africa. The special properties of these and similar heavy clay soils merits their inclusion in a separate group with regard to plant growth and land management. Many tree crops do not grow or only poorly in these soils (many varieties of citrus, cacao) although several varieties of irrigated crops (paddy, sisal, cotton, sugarcane) may grow reasonably well if grown with sufficient care. In general heavy clay soils are difficult for all tillage operations and often provide poor foundations for houses and roads. The latter is especially the case with strongly swelling vertisols.

The many different *sandy soils* of the world all have in common their high contents of relatively coarse particles (more than 50 micron and often more than 150 micron diameter) and a lack of silt (2 to 50 micron) and clay (smaller than 2 micron) parties. This textural composition leads to a combination of poor properties for plant growth including a low water retention capacity (50 to 80 mm available for plants as compared to over 200 mm for a deep soil in loess) as well as a low adsorption capacity for nutrients. The humus content of these soils, if relatively high, may partly but not wholly compensate for these negative factors. In addition many sandy soils have a high quartz content and therefore have almost no weatherable minerals which might supply some nutrients. The generally high permeability of sandy soils is sometimes a disadvantage since the result is the rapid leaching of plant nutrients, but occasionally the high infiltration may be an advantage as it prevents surface run-off of rainwater. In areas of serious water deficiency sandy soils may, under certain management systems, be irrigated with brackish water and give acceptable rates of plant growth.

Many of the large areas of sandy soils consist of aeolian (wind-deposited) sands and these occur to a large extent in semi-arid and arid regions of south-western Asia and of northern and eastern Africa. For example, in Somalia, with a total area of approximately 20 million hectares of cultivable land, there are 3 million hectares of sandy soils. These soils need special measures for their conservation and use; in particular soil conservation from wind erosion, extra applications of manure or fertilizers, irrigation by gravity or with the use of drip or sprinkler systems. Some plants, for example wheat and beech (in temperate regions), grow very poorly on sandy soils. Many crops grow less well on sandy soils than on soils with higher contents of clay or silt, though possible exceptions are coconut trees and, to some extent, tobacco plants.

The *Gleysols* and other *hydromorphic soils* are an ecological group with very different properties for plant growth and land use. In older soil classification systems they were also treated as a separate category at the highest level of classification. For several reasons, this system has to some extent been abolished although the gleysols, the most characteristic wet soils, still are a separate group on the *Soil Map of the World*. Their main characteristic is the more or less continuously high level of the groundwater table, which means water is always available in abundance, but at the same time air, necessary for the respiration of the roots, is often deficient. For various human uses, such as the construction of roads and the building of houses, their properties pose a number of problems. The incidence of flooding, often an annual event, may aggravate these difficulties, although this may be beneficial for irrigation under certain conditions. The peaty soils, now called histosols, have more than 40 cm peaty material within the first 120 cm of the soil profile, and they present additional difficulties for their use, although several species of plants are adapted to these circumstances. Peat soils, as well as other hydromorphic soils, show, in addition to their general waterlogging, deleterious chemical effects such as poor availability of nutrients or toxicities. Some effects may be reduced by artificial drainage, but this may also induce shrinkage, leading to a lowering of the surface by 1 to 3 metres. In certain coastal marshes the oxidation caused by drainage may produce strongly acid clay soils (acid sulphate soils) which have very unfavourable conditions for plant growth due to pH values of 4 and lower.

VEGETATION: SOME RELATIONSHIPS BETWEEN VEGETATION AND OTHER
LANDSCAPE CHARACTERISTICS

The following definition of 'vegetation' is appropriate:

Vegetation is any plant cover in which a number of plant species have adapted to the growth conditions with regard to the combination of plant species as well as to their spatial arrangement. A crop of wheat, therefore, is not vegetation, but the weeds which may occur in this crop if their eradication is not achieved by man (e.g. by herbicides) may be a vegetation including its adaptation to a certain amount of cultivation such as harrowing. The definition of vegetation is not limited to climax vegetation, the kind of vegetation which is often considered to be the typical natural vegetation. In the development of vegetation under natural circumstances, a succession of various vegetation types is the result. A succession starts with a rather simple pioneer vegetation and develops increasing complexity with regard to structure and number of species, which finally may reach an optimal stage called the climax vegetation. Eventually the climax vegetation may deteriorate and a new cycle may start. Pioneer vegetations are found for example on fresh deposits of fluvial, estuarine or marine origin once they have reached a sufficient height for the first plants to grow. They are also found as a first stage of natural regeneration after erosion or landslides. The pioneer stage has often been described as the first phase in the succession of an ecosystem which follows a diminution of the environmental dynamics (tidal movements, erosion). Climax vegetations often indicate the theoretical optimum of a succession during which a maximum variation within the ecosystem is found.

In most ecosystems vegetation plays an indispensable role as the autotrophic organisms (plants) are the only ones which can make the energy of the sun and the inorganic nutrients available to the other heterotrophic organisms such as animals and men. Urban industrial systems cannot exist without plants, even if concern is limited to human nutrition. In addition fossil energy is the product of previous ecosystems.

It is not the purpose of this section to give a comprehensive discussion of vegetation. Reference is made to the many publications by biologists. In many of these the various plant communities and their relationships with climate and landscape are discussed. In addition several methods of mapping vegetation are described. Of the latter some special attention should be given to the mapping of vegetation structure as has been described for example by Dansereau (in Colinvaux 1973), as this can easily be done by nonbiologists. In this system the following categories are distinguished: (1) lifeform (trees, shrubs, herbs, bryoids = mosses, epiphytes and lianas), (2) size (tall, medium, low), (3) coverage (barren, discontinuous, in tufts or groups, continuous), (4) function (deciduous, semi-deciduous, evergreen, evergreen-succulent or evergreen-leafless), (5) leaf shape and size (needle or spine, graminoid, medium or small, broad, compound thalloid), and (6) leaf texture (filmy, membranous, sclerophyll, succulent, fungoid). For most local surveys only a limited number of these criteria are necessary. A relatively satisfactory initial characterization of the vegetation may be given even if the investigator has only limited knowledge of plant species. The mapping of vegetation structure may be combined with the mapping of plant communities to produce much more comprehensive results, but this is not always necessary.

In this text the animals, or fauna, and their relationships with plant communities are not described. This is not done because no value is attached to them. On the contrary, the function of animals in ecosystems, which was briefly indicated in Chapter 2, is essential. For regional examples readers are referred to Nelson and Chambers (1969), Van Dyne et al. (1969) and more recent publications based on the results of the International Biological Programme (Di Castri and Mooney 1973, and other publications in the same series).

To summarize one example, Zonneveld (1980) describes some of the relationships between climate and vegetation in the Sahel and adjoining regions. Mention is made of some of his conclusions on the influence of vegetation on climate relevant to development planning:

1. The vegetation cover has a reciprocal relationship with the macro- and the micro-climate, soil, water and human activity.

2. Reduction of rainfall in the Sahel also influences the adjoining Sudan zone because of intensification of the dry NE winds blowing from the desert (Sahara) during the northern hemisphere winter.

3. Increase of albedo, for example by destruction of vegetation, south of the Sahel, even to the Guinea zone, may influence the Sahel zone.

4. An aggressive human impact is moving gradually southwards in these zones due to intensive clearing by ploughing and burning.

Some indications of the relationships in Iraq between vegetation, topography and soils are given in Table 7.

There exist many intricate relationships between vegetation and soils, including soil formation, some of which are investigated in plant ecology as well as in soil science. Distinct differences in vegetation may be ascribed to ostensibly slight variations in soils, e.g. small differences in clay content. Differences in the development of vegetation also cause contrasts in soil development and this may be the result of human activities over a long period. There are for example differences in soil formation on the sandy soils of the Netherlands due to partial clearance of forest from the Neolithic or the Bronze Age onwards through to the Middle Ages and later. The soil profile where forest remained developed into an acid brown forest soil (cambic arenosol) and does not show a very distinct differentiation of horizons. Where forests were cleared and the area was grazed by sheep, heather moors developed, causing the formation of typical humuspodzols with a clear differentiation of an A horizon, leached E horizon, humus B horizon

Table 7. Grassland vegetation types in Iraq

| Topography | Soil | Vegetation type | |
		Western desert	Southern desert
Plain	Sandy	*Haloxylon salicornicum* *Artemisia herba-alba*	*Rhanterium epapposum* *Haloxylon salicornicum*
	Fine gravel + gravel	*Haloxylon salicornicum* *Ephedra alata*	*Haloxylon salicornicum* *Ephedra alata*
	Fine gravel and sand, somewhat saline subsoil	*Haloxylon salicornicum* *Zygophyllum coccineum*	*Zygophyllum coccineum* *Cyperus conglomeratus*
Wadi*	Loamy	*Artemisia herba-alba* *Haloxylon articulatum*	*Achillea fragrantissima* *Anvillea garcini*
	Sandy	*Haloxylon salicornicum* *Artemisia herba-alba*	*Anvillea garcini* *Artemisia herba-alba*
	Saline, loam	*Halocnemum strobilaceum* *Nitraria retusa*	*Halocnemum strobilaceum*
Old terraces with gravel surface (Hamada)	In areas of sand accumulation	*Haloxylon salicornicum* *Artemisia herba-alba*	*Haloxylon salicornicum* *Artemisia herba-alba*
Dunes	Sand	*Haloxylon ammodendron* *Calligonum comosum*	*Haloxylon ammodendron* *Panicum turgidum*

* Depressions which only carry water after rainstorms.

and iron B horizon. Where farmers concentrated their cultivation and added manure through the ages, thick humic A horizons developed and led to the formation of plaggen soils (Plaggepts according to the US Soil Taxonomy).

Figure 14 and Plate 4 illustrate the influence of human activity on natural vegetation in Central Africa. Natural 'zones of weakness' may occur at the boundaries between different climax vegetations. In these zones, as indicated in Fig. 14, the felling of trees is easiest to initiate and therefore can be done by primitive means to permit subsequent human activities. This leads gradually to a further opening up of the adjoining areas.

Soil and vegetation surveys permit the identification and demarcation of important ecological factors. In general these survey types give valuable additional information to each other. In some cases vegetation surveys indicate factors (for example, availability of nutrients) which cannot be mapped in soil surveys. In other cases vegetation surveys are able to add refinements (details of water condition, effect of different kinds of humus) which are not given by soil surveys. On the other hand soil surveys may show characteristics, for example of the subsoil, which are not indicated by differences in

64   *Factors in landscape ecology*

Fig. 14 Zones of weakness in a natural vegetation (Verboom 1977)

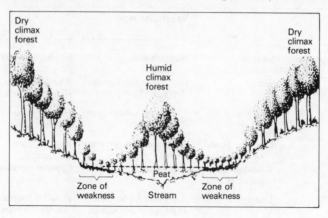

Plate 4 Air-photo of zones of weakness in Central Africa. 1 = Miombo, grass savanna; 2 = Dambo, humid grassland; 3 = zones of weakness (Verboom 1977)

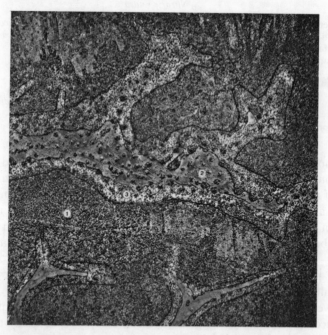

vegetation but which may be highly important for indicating potential use, after drainage or reclamation, and for uses other than are current in the area.

Surveys of grassland vegetation are of special land use relevance in many areas of the world, from the Swiss Alpine meadows to the semi-arid grazing

Table 8. Temperature zones in mountainous areas of Switzerland

Relative temperature	Phenological temperatures zones	Possibilities for land use
	Mountainous zone*	
Very cold	Upper Alpine meadow zone	Alpine meadows with a short grazing period (70–80 days)
Cold	Middle Alpine meadow zone	Zone of competition of the upper limit of trees
Fairly cold	Lower Alpine meadow zone	Middle grazing area
Very raw	Upper mountain grassland zone	Border climate for meadows grazed twice
Raw	Middle mountain grassland zone	Lowest area of mountain grazing†
Fairly raw	Lower mountain grassland zone	Border climate for cultivation of cereals

Source: After Schreiber 1970.
* Only this upper zone is given in this example; for lower zones, see the original publication.
† With a grazing period up to 150 days in an average summer.

lands. In semi-arid areas, these surveys have to be accompanied by investigation of drinking water availability for cattle. In Switzerland, grassland vegetation surveys are important not only for grazing but also for recreation including skiing in winter. Surveys in Alpine areas show strong correlation between vegetation and altitude, as expressed in temperature zones. This is indicated in Table 8.

In landscape ecological surveys the relationships of the various types of plant cover, including true vegetations and agricultural crops, have to be noted as parts of the survey. In Fig. 15 an example is given of a cross-section of the valley of the River Arno (Tuscany, Italy).

HUMAN INFLUENCES

Mention has been made in several places in the foregoing text about the influence of man on landscapes and ecosystems, and it is appropriate to pay more systematic attention to this theme. Human influences are largely unavoidable because of the population increase due to the special characteristics of 'homo faber', man with his tools. Without the wide spectrum of human activities the world would only be able to carry a sparse human population not exceeding a few million people. Even in the Roman period (approximately AD 50 to AD 400) the total population of England did not exceed about 250 000 persons. Great Britain and Ireland had around the year AD 1 a total of approximately 400 000 people, which increased to 4 millions by AD

Fig. 15 Example of a cross-section of the valley of the river Arno (Tuscany, Italy)

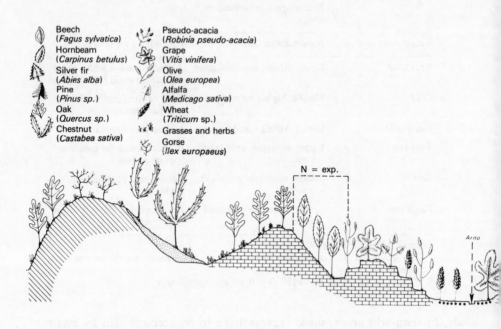

	Beech		Pseudo-acacia
	(*Fagus sylvatica*)		(*Robinia pseudo-acacia*)
	Hornbeam		Grape
	(*Carpinus betulus*)		(*Vitis vinifera*)
	Silver fir		Olive
	(*Abies alba*)		(*Olea europea*)
	Pine		Alfalfa
	(*Pinus sp.*)		(*Medicago sativa*)
	Oak		Wheat
	(*Quercus sp.*)		(*Triticum sp.*)
	Chestnut		Grasses and herbs
	(*Castabea sativa*)		Gorse
			(*Ilex europaeus*)

1500, to 10.7 millions for Great Britain around AD 1800 and 54.5 millions in 1970. The figures for Ireland are 5.2 millions around AD 1800, and 4.5 millions in 1970 (data cited from Broek and Webb 1973). Around the year AD 900, the present province of Friesland in the Netherlands was a relatively densely populated and prosperous area in Western Europe and had approximately 15 000 inhabitants; today its population is over 500 000 people (150 inhabitants per km^2).

Human influences are generally greatest on vegetation and fauna. The resultant impacts have caused several species of animals to become extinct since the Upper Palaeolithic. Human vegetational impact is evident during the Neolithic and increased in the subsequent Bronze Age. Many of the heather moors of north-western Europe have originated from burning, grazing and occasional cultivation of original forest areas through the ages. In tropical regions today, large areas are cleared by burning for such purposes as hunting, grazing, the systems of shifting cultivation or 'slash and burn' agriculture and for arable cultivation. In Central Cameroun the author observed an area of at least 50 km^2 of savanna being burnt in one day in order to shoot four wild cows. The great lack of proteins in human diets explains in part the effort put into such a hunt. Vegetation which is regularly subjected to fire often develops into fire-climax types consisting largely of species which are resistant to some extent to repeated burning.

Fig. 15 cont

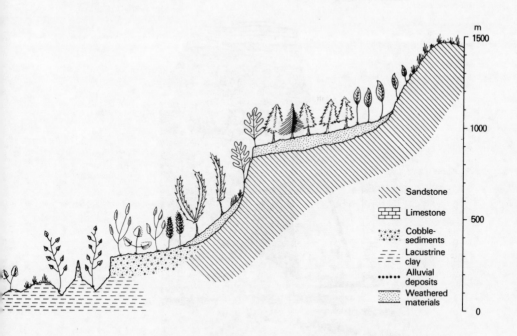

⧹⧹⧹⧹	Sandstone
⊞⊞	Limestone
∴∴∴	Cobble-sediments
− −−	Lacustrine clay
••••••	Alluvial deposits
⠿⠿	Weathered materials

Massive landscape erosion in primitive systems of agriculture is generally negligible as long as the people produce only for their own subsistence and maintain a constant population density. Erosion is likely to occur when the cycle of use of the area is shortened either due to increase of the population or to increased commercial export of products to external areas. The shortening of the shifting cultivation cycle (see also Ch. 5) leads to incomplete regeneration of vegetation and soils and therefore to gradual landscape deterioration. Increased use of the more erodible areas may also occur. Both these effects may initiate a dangerous chain of events to result in increasing land degradation (see also Ch. 7).

Human landscape influences may also be of a more constructive nature, often causing the actual construction of artefactial elements such as: dykes, canals, terraces, houses. This human influence may take place in different shapes and dimensions: construction of surface areas (e.g. the Zuyderzee polders of the Netherlands), linear features (dykes, canals, metalled roads) or of small individual features (for example, houses, or a ziggurat, ruin of a temple, in Iraq (Plate 5)). Human activity can also influence the cycling of water and nutrients. The human influences sometimes have particular impact on the visual characteristics of the landscape, but even in such cases the impact on landscape ecological conditions in a wider sense is often considerable.

Plate 5 A 'ziggurat' (old temple) from *c*. 2500 BC near Baghdad, Iraq, partly restored

Remnants of Roman field systems indicate a former human influence on the landscape. These remnants are found throughout the Roman empire from the Netherlands to Tunisia in the form of distinct square fields, now often strongly eroded (Bradford 1957). It was not a general system for the whole Roman empire, but it occurred where army veterans were resettled. Large areas were colonized by farms of a square shape, *villae*, with a fixed side of 709 m. These villae were divided into 100 plots or 'jugae', from which the name 'centuriation' is derived. The systems run continuously over distances of some tens of kilometres across hills and valleys. In Mediterranean countries such as northern Italy, Yugoslavia and Tunisia they are very clearly recognizable on aerial photographs (for good examples see Bradford 1957).

Most present-day field systems originated at a later date. In many parts of western Europe, continuous settlement began in the early Middle Ages. The field systems developed in this period are different and depend on the traditions of the settlers as well as on landscape conditions. Agricultural mechanization began in the USA and was later introduced to many other countries. From the second half of the nineteenth century onwards, a general tendency towards rectangular shaped and large fields developed. As many of these fields are bounded by easily removable fences, they do not constitute a major human influence on the land. Wherever hedges, stone walls or canals constitute field boundaries, the nature of the land as such is modified. Their change or removal is a major effect. Enlargement of fields of ½ ha or less, to large sizes, leads to landscape changes by removal of hedges, fences and canals. Increase in soil erosion may result from these enlargements.

Plaggen soils as mentioned in Chapter 2 provide a typical example of constructional human influence on soils. They occur over large surface areas on the late Pleistocene sands in the Netherlands, Belgium and Western Germany. Figure 9 (page 28) shows their development due to the annual addition of manure together with sods from heather or from lowlands and in certain areas with forest litter. The average annual increase in thickness of the A horizon was approximately 1 mm per year, to produce 1 m thickness, a common depth, in 1000 years.

Some other examples of constructional human influences on soils are found in alluvial areas of the Netherlands where humic material derived from long-inhabited settlements was dug and transported to improve low-lying heavy clay soils. The construction of terraces on many slopes in the hilly and mountainous areas of western and southern Europe also had an improving impact on the soils. The soils of many old vineyards are found to be deeply humic due to the prevention of erosion together with manuring and deep tillage over several centuries.

It is possible that the extraction of materials for industrial purposes may lead to soil improvement. An example is the exploitation of clays for brick production. Sometimes rather heavy clays are used and their removal leads to the possible use of subsoils which are better for arable land cultivation provided that the drainage is adapted to the lower soil surface. In other cases a soil which is suitable for cultivation may be removed and the remaining soils may be less suitable for cultivation or perhaps the whole soil is removed to leave stagnant pools of water. The quarrying of sand, gravel or laterite often leads to complete destruction of soils and landscapes, but in many cases firm planning control may ensure that proper, and sometimes improved, land use is ultimately possible. It is very much the concern of landscape ecology to study these processes, and to propose a suitable rehabilitation programme. In addition, human activities have often specific chemical impacts on soils and landscapes. The most widely occurring of these is salinization of soils in semi-arid and arid countries where irrigation is applied without sufficient drainage (see Ch. 7). Another example is atmospheric pollution of sulphur dioxide (SO_2), which when dissolved in precipitation leads to very acid rain (pH values between 2.5 and 5.0). Industrial fumes may also contain toxic heavy minerals which have serious effects on all plant growth in certain areas.

Heavy minerals and other compounds with toxic properties for plants, animals and human beings are transported by rivers, such as the Rhine, and

Fig. 16 Some influences of man on the biomass production of a soil

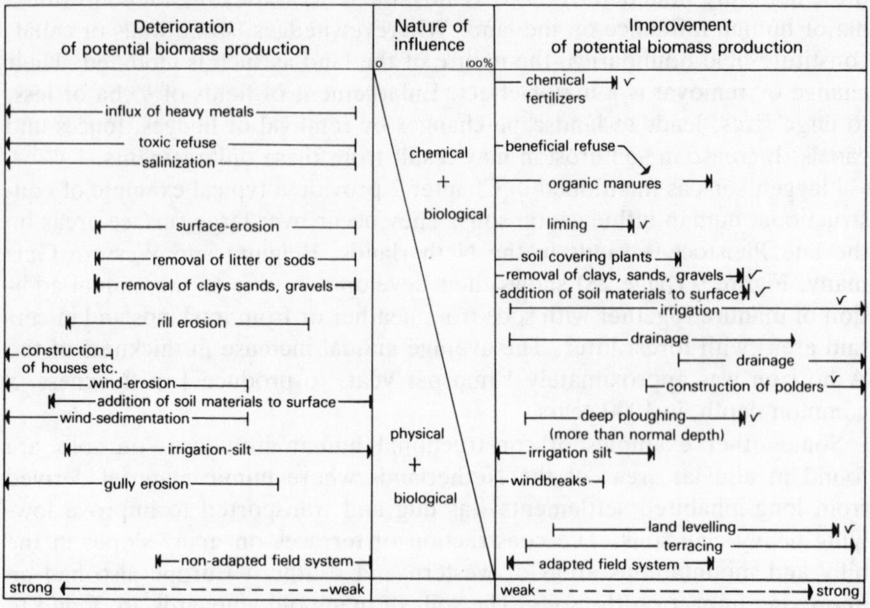

Deterioration of potential biomass production	Nature of influence	Improvement of potential biomass production
influx of heavy metals toxic refuse salinization surface-erosion removal of litter or sods removal of clays sands, gravels rill erosion construction of houses etc. wind-erosion addition of soil materials to surface wind-sedimentation irrigation-silt gully erosion non-adapted field system	0 chemical 100% + biological physical + biological	chemical fertilizers ✓ beneficial refuse organic manures liming ✓ soil covering plants removal of clays, sands, gravels ✓ addition of soil materials to surface ✓ irrigation ✓ drainage drainage construction of polders ✓ deep ploughing (more than normal depth) ✓ irrigation silt windbreaks land levelling ✓ terracing adapted field system
strong ←— — — — — — — — — — – –weak		weak - - - - - - - - - - - - - → strong

*Improvement of potential production of biomass may mean reduction of variability. This is indicated with ✓ where relevant

sedimented on the adjoining forelands at high water levels. Chemical impacts of a more complex nature are caused by organic refuse from industrial, urban and farm sources.

The influence of chemical fertilizers on the eutrophication of water bodies is sometimes exaggerated. This eutrophication, the excessive growth of algae and related organisms due to a strong influx of nitrogen and phosphates, is often due to a large extent to insufficiently purified sewerage and to nitrogen originating from organic manure. Only where soil erosion causes large amounts of fertilizers to be washed off the soil surface, are chemical fertilizers a major source of eutrophication. Properly applied fertilizers with regard to manner and quantity as well as time of application are rapidly taken up by the soil and plants.

An attempt is made in Fig. 16 to give a simple diagram showing the various impacts of human activities on soils and landscapes. To achieve this the influence on potential biomass production on any given soil is selected. This may be either improvement (right-hand side of figure) or deterioration (left-hand side). The soil is specifically viewed as a three-dimensional landscape unit and the selected standpoint has a strong agricultural bias. Those cases where an increasing production of biomass nearly always results in a deterioration of the potential biological variability of species has been indicated with a separate symbol (V). The figure is only intended to present an elementary sketch showing the main influences from a relatively simple standpoint in order to demonstrate the various aspects. The estimates made for the various chemical, physical and biological impacts have only a relative and no absolute meaning. As can be seen, some activities may have an improving as well as deteriorating result, which is then given in both sides of the figure and indicated with an arrow. The nature of the impacts always includes biological aspects, whether it is originally more a chemical or a physical process; therefore the biological component is indicated with both these effects.

4

Landscape ecological surveys

PROCESS STUDIES

Ecological relationships in a landscape are in fact always 'process relationships', i.e. relationships which are established through processes and are maintained by the same or by related processes. These include counterprocesses (feedback mechanisms) which have a tendency to induce steady state. Examples of the first kind of processes are intake of energy, food or water. Examples of feedback processes are the various kinds of competition between organisms, for example for nutrients, and for conditions of shade to cause a decrease of energy intake. These examples all relate to processes in which organisms take the central position and these might be called *direct ecological process relationships* in a landscape. Directly connected with these are a large group of processes due to the effects of organisms in a landscape; for example, the leaching of soils by the influence of vegetation, or the influence of moles and of other burrowing animals on the erosion of slopes. This second group of processes has a clear reverse effect which is often due to impoverishment of the soil; such processes might therefore be called *reciprocal ecological process relationships*. Finally there exist in all landscapes processes which are not specifically caused by organisms, but which often have a very clear influence on the living conditions of many organisms. Examples of these are tidal movements in estuarine areas, sedimentation processes, active processes of slope formation and mass movements. This third group of processes might be termed *indirect ecological process relationships*.

In this classification of process relationships, the human influence was purposely omitted. Indeed, here man differs from all other organisms by his power to enhance processes. This may be done for example by manuring or irrigating whilst eradication of weeds of the cutting of forests may result in processes of degradation. On the other hand the planting of cover crops protects the soil surface. Another example is the planting of beech trees in Mediterranean areas to provide shade for certain crops. In addition, and this is often even more important, man accelerates, consciously or unconsciously, processes such as soil erosion and he retards processes such as tidal movements (by dam construction) in particular localities. This, combined with our philosophy of anthropocentric landscape ecology, is sufficient reason to view man as a separate factor with regard to landscape processes. The relationships which are thus provoked by man might be called *anthropo-ecological process relationships*. This group, even where not explicitly mentioned, has a predominant role in land use as it is treated in Chapters 5 to 8. All processes in a landscape have either direct or indirect ecological significance, as they always have an impact in some way on the environments of organisms including man. Investigation of landscape processes are therefore always relevant to landscape ecology. This relates for example to morphogenetic (genetic–geomorphological) and pedogenetic (genetic–pedological; pedology means soils science) investigations. These and comparable genetic investigations promote a better understanding of the nature, shape and contents of present-day landscape phenomena. They are also essential for comparison and delimitation as in mapping and land evaluation for planning. Even disciplines such as thermodynamics, which are ostensibly of a purely theoretical nature, are often indispensable as they provide the means to understand which processes are really taking place in soils or water bodies. Palaeoecological investigations study the ecological conditions and processes in the past and also contribute to a better understanding of present-day landscape ecology. Examples are the investigation of glacial and interglacial periods, those on pluvial ages and on the development of deserts (see e.g. Flint 1971; Williams 1979). The palaeoecology of landscapes also provides a reference frame against which present-day human influences can be compared.

Of more specific importance to landscape ecology are the investigations on the actual processes which are active in landscapes studied by a separate branch of geomorphology which is sometimes called process geomorphology, 'actuogeomorphology' or 'dynamic geomorphology' (see Ch. 3). Detailed mapping in combination with quantitative analysis of the processes are used to obtain a functional explanation, often based on an approach using systems analysis. In this approach an ecosystem is seen as an integration of geomorphological and biological process-response systems related by various feedback relations.

For these investigations, regular visits to the research area are essential, even when part of the measurements are carried out with automatic recording apparatus. Measurements may be made, for example, of hydrological variables including the quantities of sediment which are transported over soil surfaces and along stream channels. Investigations of this type have been carried out by Imeson and Jungerius (1976) in the Ardennes of the Grand Duchy of Luxembourg. These investigations indicated that even on densely wooded slopes more erosion and colluviation occur than was previously expected. This erosion is partly due to transport of materials brought to the soil surface by burrowing animals. Transportation is in part caused by the surface wash of dead leaves in the beech forests. These and similar measurements can be compared with those under different conditions of land use (see Ch. 7).

Process studies of a different kind are carried out with regard to sedimentation in coastal and estuarine areas and to the 'ripening' of the sediments into soils. Ripening of soils is a process by which an underwater sediment looses its excess water and develops a soil structure with aggregates and pores, the latter having air as well as water under normal conditions. The process of ripening is induced by drying out due to drainage as well as by biological and chemical processes, including the activities of bacteria and other micro-organisms. It has been studied extensively in the Zuyderzee polders of the Netherlands as well as in the coastal areas of the Netherlands and of Surinam (former Dutch Guyana). More recent studies have been carried out in several parts of the world, including Malaysia. The 'unripened' sediment is classed in the US Soil Taxonomy as 'Hydraquent'. Ripening usually includes the settling of heavy claysoils and of peats, including the development of marked microrelief features (see Pons and Zonneveld 1965).

Natural and man-induced processes usually occur together. This has been shown very clearly in recent investigations of the dunes in the coastal areas of the Netherlands. Bakker *et al.* (1979, 1981) have published a map of the changes in this area since 1850. This map, which is based on landscape ecological and historical research, shows positive as well as negative effects with regard to nature conservation. Among the twenty different processes shown are negative ones of coastal erosion, loss by industrial and related activities, dumping of refuse, infiltration of water for the use as drinking water in urban areas, agricultural reclamation; positive processes are the formation of new dunes and coastal accretion, formation of water pools in dune areas and the formation of new natural vegetation in these areas. Some of these processes can be measured by quantitative comparison of the phenomena on maps from consecutive periods. In more recent years, the use of sequential air photography, taken from conventional aircraft or from satellites, is often very helpful. Van Ittersum and Kwakernaak (1977) made estimates of the influence of trespassing on the vegetation of the dunes of the Wadden Islands in the northern Netherlands by comparing aerial photographs taken with a ten-year interval. This permitted estimates of new sand dune formation and wind erosion caused by human influences.

Direct field measurements of erosion, both natural and man induced, are still being made in many countries, a topic discussed in Chapter 7. In many cases, however, only measurements of some aspects are possible. These selected field measurements, when combined with the results of the interpretation of sequential photography and statistical information, often give good results.

In many cases landscape processes are directly related to social processes in human societies. This is, for example, clearly visible in the mountainous areas of Europe today where migration of population to urban centres constitutes a major problem. It is very clear in our investigations in Tuscany, the region of central Italy of which Florence is the capital. Broadly speaking this region consists of three different major landscapes: (1) an area of mountains and hills, part of the Apennines, with medium to steep slopes, mainly shallow soils and extensive processes of mass movement and erosion; (2) an area at a lower altitude of Pleistocene fluviolacustrine terraces with deep and fertile soils, but with serious hazards of erosion and mass movements; (3) the floodplain of the Arno river and its tributaries, with flat fertile soils as well as a rapidly growing urban population. People migrate from the first area to the urban centres in the third, causing neglect of the lands, the loss of younger people from the depopulated zone and the extension of urban areas over highly productive agricultural lands. Agriculture in the second area is being modernized, changing from the traditional, ecologically very stable system of mixed agriculture to large fields with monocultures of vineyards or wheat, often with sprinkler irrigation to cause the activation of latent erosion and instability of the fluviolacustrine terraces. The combination of landscape ecological surveys with field measurements, the study of statistics and of historical documents made it possible to develop computer programs designed to predict the outcomes of various strategies. The probable results in thirty or forty years time have been estimated under different assumptions. The technique of predicting future processes based on these various kinds of research will become steadily more important as techniques are improved (Verbakel *et al*. 1982; Kwakernaak 1981).

All predictions have only a limited probability. They may provide a basis for monitoring processes in coming years by various methods, including sequential aerial photography, pilot experiments and various kinds of surveys and field observations as well as statistical investigations. In an international context UNEP has now established a Global Environmental Monitoring System (GEMS) in order to follow various processes of environmental degration in the Third World. The basis for this has been established by the UN Conference on Desertification (Nairobi, 1977).

LANDSCAPE ECOLOGICAL MAPPING

Various systems and methods of mapping the land have, either implicitly or explicitly, the intention of surveying and representing ecological features. The most generally known of these are soil surveys. Soil surveys are usually carried out as standard surveys covering a large region or a country in rectangular map sheets; for example, the maps published by the Soil Survey of England and Wales, the Soil Survey of Scotland and the Netherlands Soil Survey Institute with the maps at a scale of 1 : 50 000 or 1 : 25 000. In other countries, of which the USA is an example, these systematic soil surveys are published as County Soil Maps, often on scales at between 1 : 20 000 and 1 : 50 000. All standard soil surveys have in common a systematic legend which provides information on all soils encountered in the survey area. Thus soil surveys tend to have a strong taxonomic component. In many countries, including those mentioned above, project soil surveys are also executed; for example, soil surveys for special projects of land consolidation, land reclamation, rural development or town and country planning. The legends of these surveys have often a greater flexibility to facilitate the incorporation of data of direct ecological importance in the mapped region. However, it should be stressed that these are certainly not lacking in standard soils surveys.

Geomorphological surveys have in the past often put emphasis on the genetic aspects of landscapes and their component landforms and materials. During the last few decades various modern geomorphological surveys have been developed which have the expressed purpose of serving social and eco-logical requirements. Examples of these are the surveys carried out by French geomorphologists under the guidance of Jean Tricart (1965) and those developed at the International Institute for Aerial Surveys and Earth Sciences (ITC) (Enschede, the Netherlands) by Verstappen and colleagues (Verstappen and Van Zuidam 1968; Van Zuidam and Van Zuidam-Cancellado 1978). Many of these surveys stress the morphographic (descrip-tive) aspects and the morphometric features in a landscape, i.e. those land-scape characteristics (slope, soil texture, etc.) which can be mapped quanti-tatively and described accurately in the map legends.

The visual and aesthetic aspects of landscapes have always strongly im-pressed the human mind. The systematic mapping of landscape characteris-tics is thus of value to landscape architecture. This may be done for planning of urban areas and new towns as well as for recreation grounds. A system of *physiognomic landscape surveys* has been developed in the Netherlands by Maarleveld and his colleagues at the Netherlands Soil Survey Institute. A large survey has been done for the Veluwe in the central Netherlands, an area where recreation is one of the main land uses. Included landscape char-acteristics are dimensions of open space (with herbaceous vegetation), 'mass' (size and density of forests or buildings), structure and diversity of land use and vegetation, and relief attributes. These physiognomic surveys have many similarities to other landscape ecological surveys as both systems use many visual landscape characteristics. There are, however, essential dif-ferences in the objectives as well as in the nature of the results. Whereas physiognomic landscape surveys have as their objective the portrayal of the visual and aesthetic characteristics of the landscape, landscape ecological surveys in a strict sense collect data on the visual characteristic as well as on others such as soil profiles, component structures, and materials and organ-isms in order to be able to identify complete ecosystems. The latter are therefore sometimes also called holistic landscape surveys (Zonneveld 1979). To some extent physiognomic surveys may be said to be of ecological significance because they indicate those aspects of the landscape which are of psychological importance to man.

Vegetation surveys involve the mapping of plant communities and have for long been carried out in many parts of the world. They can range from very detailed surveys of particular plant communities – for example, on a scale of 1 : 5000 – to the systematic mapping of many square kilometres in semi-arid grazing areas of tropical countries (Rattray 1960). They can be carried out as self-contained projects as well as within other studies such as land systems surveys and other forms of integrated land surveys. In many cases these surveys, which usually have an ecological objective, include data on soils, groundwater and other abiotic aspects of the landscape. Good examples of these are the systematic surveys carried out by French plant ecologists under the auspices of the CNRS (Centre Nationale de Recherches Scientifiques). The institutes of plant ecology of the universities of Montpellier and of Toulouse, under the guidance of such eminent scientists as H. Gaussen and P. Rey, have produced many vegetation maps for a national map of France. In addition they have contributed maps to a world vegetation map. Their vegetation maps of France are not just scientific documents but are also used for providing basic data in land consolidation projects (Rey 1968).

The following main groups of vegetation surveys may be distinguished:
1. Physiognomic surveys, with special attention given to particular dominant species.
2. Surveys of plant associations, their grouping and their components using the system of the French Swiss school of Braun Blanquet and his colleagues and pupils.
3. Detailed vegetation maps in which the represented units are communities of local significance but with reference to the more generally recognized associations, as produced by the German school of the well-known plant ecologist, Tüxen.
4. Maps with a mixed legend which indicate some dominant species as well as the associations of the French Swiss school.
5. Maps of vegetation structures; for example, in the sense of Dansereau (cited by Colinvaux 1973) as already indicated in Chapter 3.

These and similar vegetation surveys are the most common type of ecological surveys. This is because faunal surveys present considerable practical problems, as the systematic mapping of animal communities is very difficult. On the other hand, vegetation is sometimes supposed to be the best and most complete ecological indicator. However, this is only true in particular instances. For example, this approach is valid when concern is with tackling problems of nature conservation or with semi-arid grazing lands. In particular they are relevant in those circumstances where land use objectives are to retain or improve the existing plant communities. Even in these situations it is necessary to map hydrological resources, for example, to aid the planning of grazing. Vegetation surveys on occasion are important for planning the conservation of particular species which are under threat; for example, alpine plants in mountainous areas such as Switzerland and Scotland.

It must always be remembered that in ecological investigations definition is essential of the kind of group of organisms which form the main objective of the research. The following lines of approach to landscape ecological investigations can be identified (Vink 1981a):

1. The phytocentric approach, which studies land and its attributes from the viewpoint of their relevance for plant communities.
2. The zoocentric approach, which studies land and its attributes from the viewpoint of their relevance for animal communities.
3. The anthropocentric approach, which studies land and its attributes from the human viewpoint.

The order in which these three different lines of approach are given is deliberate. A zoocentric approach is only possible if the relevant phytocentric aspects are also considered. For the anthropocentric approach, the relevant phytocentric and zoocentric aspects have to be taken into account. These three different ways of considering landscape ecological mapping are therefore not in any fundamental conflict with each other. They often differ, however, in their practical choices with regard to the relevance of certain phenomena in the landscape and to the hierarchy in classification systems. This sometimes leads to differentiating characteristics being chosen. A purely phytocentric approach may, for example, indicate in arable areas the plant communities consisting of the weeds; a zoocentric approach in the same areas may indicate the soil fauna whilst an anthropocentric approach will primarily map the soils and other land conditions relevant to human land use. The advantage of the anthropocentric approach is the focus on human planning and decisions. Land use, including nature conservation, is always based on human decisions and, as discussed above, these decisions have to include many assessments of plants and animals. Therefore phytocentric and zoocentric aspects may be found in many maps produced for anthropocentric purposes. The crucial point about anthropocentric landscape ecology is its focus towards land evaluation, including land suitability and land capability classifications as well as analyses and predictions of human impact on the landscape. At this point it is useful to discuss the various kinds of landscape ecological mapping which all have strong anthropocentric characteristics and which all have led to land evaluation.

Landscape ecological mapping in the German Democratic Republic is closely related to the work of the geographer E. Neef (Neef 1967), one of the very early followers of the theories put forward by Carl Troll (Leser 1976). The basic system was largely developed by Haase (1968). The methodology was strongly influenced by the planning need for agrarian reforms in that country. Small areas are mapped on detailed scales (1 : 10 000) and emphasis is on relief, soil and water conditions relevant to intensive agriculture. The general approach can be translated as 'agricultural habitat mapping based on landscape ecological investigations'. The goal is 'to produce all data needed for agriculture and for other space using forms of enterprise as a basis for scientifically based planning, modification and execution of all goals of production as well as for all management techniques which seem to be necessary for maximum increase of production'. The results have thus far been used mainly for the socialist types of farming and in village planning.

The approach to ecology used here is called 'agroecology'. A more comprehensive approach is now being developed.

In these East German investigations, three phases are distinguished:
1. Landscape ecological analysis and synthesis, which is the long-term scientific basis for land use, i.e. landscape ecological mapping.
2. Application of the knowledge gained under (1) to specific agronomic considerations in which two phases are distinguished:
(a) assessment of the suitability and of potential yield of the separate types of habitat;
(b) assessment of all natural factors which promote or limit productivity. These phases constitute land evaluation with (a) referring to land suitability and (b) to land qualities (see Ch. 8).
3. Agro-economic analysis and synthesis leading to definite proposals with regard to farm economics. This subject is not treated in the present book, but reference is made to older publications (Vink 1960; 1963a).

In *Britain* the work of the soil survey organizations in the mountainous parts of the island, in particular in the western Highlands of Scotland, has led to a system which is nearer to landscape ecological mapping than to traditional soil mapping. This is clearly the result of the land conditions in these areas where land characteristics other than soils – for example, slope stability, slope regularity and vegetation patterns – are more directly relevant and easier to map. This very interesting development will merit more attention in future years. An organization in Britain which operates in Third World countries is the Land Resources Development Centre (LRDC) of the Ministry of Overseas Development (Surbiton, Surrey). This centre executes large surveys of land areas in many parts of the world for planning and executing development projects. Its methodology is based on the 'land system' concept, originally developed in Australia (Christian and Stewart 1968) though now discontinued for general purposes although it is still carried out for civil engineering purposes in a modified form (Grant *et al.* 1979). The land system concept was developed from the theories of Carl Troll; it is still applied for the integrated mapping of large areas in developing countries. In general it is executed by a team of one geomorphologist, one soil surveyor and one botanist, cooperating in airphoto interpretation and in subsequent field investigations, as well as in the final editing of maps and reports. In addition, other experts may be called in, for example hydrologists and foresters and, in the case of LRDC, agronomists.

The system as now applied by LRDC puts much more emphasis of land evaluation and land use planning than is the case with the Australian approach. As an example, part of a recent report from LRDC will be briefly discussed (Hill 1979). This is a report on the land resources of central Nigeria, but for present purposes consideration is limited to the Benue Valley. The report is selected as a good example of a very comprehensive one, although one aspect is missing, viz. the block diagrams to illustrate the general land conditions of each land system. These diagrams are integral to the Australian work and are sometimes produced in LRDC reports. The maps in the Nigerian study are all on a scale of 1 : 250 000. They consist of: (1) the land systems map as the basic document; (2) a present land use map; (3) a map indicating crop options based on environmental limitations; and (4) a map of agricultural development possibilities indicating which kinds of agriculture (land utilization types, see Ch. 5) can be developed. The land systems map for the Benue Valley only gives over one hundred different land systems. For each of these the following characteristics are shown: generalized landform, geology, relative relief, dominant slope range, drainage, texture and pattern, vegetation, rock outcrops, occurrence of ironpans, soil texture, soil depth and drainage. In addition to this map information, the major limitations for the relevant crops and some additional data, including the surface area of each land system, are given in tables. The latter range from a few square kilometres to some thousands of square kilometres, but in general are of the order of some hundreds of square kilometres. The report includes data on many different subjects. For more information on this very useful system of mapping, the reader has to consult the original reports. Criticism may be made in a few cases; for example, where a proper soil classification is omitted from the legend. Such a limitation makes the transfer of knowledge and experience more difficult on an objective international basis.

In *Canada*, landscape ecological surveys are being carried out within the scope of Environment Canada, a large, perhaps the world's largest, national organization for environmental planning. The Canada Land Inventory produced many maps of the land resources of the lands in agricultural use, and when it was nearly completed a new system was developed for the inventory and evaluation of the only partly developed and in many places very vulnerable northern lands. This system is known as the 'Biophysical Land Classification' and it is in particular developed for the mapping of forest lands and associated wildlands (Rubec 1979: Jurdant *et al.* 1977). It is the first major inventory system which tries to combine within one classification land and water areas of a region. The result is the linkage of the two major kinds of ecosystems with all their interactions and with their combined impact on human activities as well as vulnerability to human action. Land evaluation is carried out for land uses of varying intensity including forestry and various kinds of wildlife. Jurdant *et al.* (1977) demonstrate this system for the Province of Quebec. This system has five classification levels: ecological regions, ecological districts, ecological systems, ecological types and ecological phases. These are mapped respectively at the following scales: 1 : 1 000 000 (regions), 1 : 250 000 (districts), 1 : 125 000 (systems), 1 : 20 000 (types) and 1 : 10 000 (phases). The classification of terrestrial ecosystems gives an integrated view of climate, relief, geology, soils and vegetation. For aquatic ecosystems, the following factors are noted: surface area, depth, geomorphology of the banks, regularity of shorelines and beaches, gradient of banks, and nature of system.

The Canadian system is still under regular review and undergoes amendments whenever more experience is gained. During recent years, special attention has been given to land–water relationships and to large areas of wetlands (Welch 1978). Special guidelines were produced to aid ecological land surveys for environmental impact analysis (Ecological Land Survey Task Force, 1980). The surveys are carried out with extensive and systematic airphoto interpretation supplemented with fieldwork using aeroplanes and helicopters. A very broad but well illustrated ecological land classification of Labrador describes twenty-seven ecological land regions with associated land districts (Loupochine *et al.* 1978). It is only possible to make reference to the rapidly developing literature on these suveys typified by the work of Rubec (1979) and Welch (1978).

In the *United States of America* soil surveys are a well established and extremely useful means of mapping land resources for agricultural and related land uses. The combination in the early 1950s of the US Soil Survey with the US Soil Conservation Service brought about a better use of soil data in land use planning, including the many aspects of soil conservation. In many respects, therefore, the soil surveys in this country include most facts required from landscape ecological surveys. In addition, the former US Bureau of Reclamation, now called the US Water and Power Resources Service, has gradually developed a system of surveys which can be viewed as a special version of landscape ecological surveys, with strong emphasis on comprehensive planning of irrigated land use. A good general outline is given by Maletic and Hutchings (1967), whilst Vink (1975a) summarizes the approach. In recent years, the environmental impact of irrigation schemes has also been comprehensively studied (for example, Dee *et al.* 1973). These surveys, although serving many landscape ecological purposes, have thus far not contributed to the development of clearly expressed ecological principles in their procedures. Understandably the US Forestry Service and its related institutions are better suited to this purpose as demonstrated by Bailey (1981) and McCormack *et al.* (1981): in the latter project the US Soil Survey also took part. In fact, the Soil Conservation Service approach is based on soil survey as the backbone of a woodland site rating system; this system is a very systematic and highly useful kind of land evaluation and will be discussed in Chapter 8.

A special type of landscape ecological survey was developed by the Rocky Mountain Forest and Range Experiment Station (Fort Collins, Colorado). In this technique, which has been used for mapping about 10 million hectares of forest lands, land is classified according to the ecosystems which are present. A complete hierarchical classification has been developed from domains (mapped at a scale of 1 : 3 000 000), via divisions, provinces and sections to districts (mapped at at scale of 1 : 125 000 to 1 : 250 000) and still further via land-type associations, land-types and land-type phases to sites (mapped at a scale of 1 : 2 500 and larger). The criteria for classification include climate, topography, soil and vegetation. The classification is based on the relative dominance in an ecological sense of one factor over other ecological factors: climate dominates most factors, topography dominates many other factors, etc. These systems of surveys have advantages over soil surveys in forest and in range areas where the existing vegetation is truly considered as part of the 'land' as well as of the ecosystems. The existing vegetation, if no plans exist to change it, is a dominant ecological factor. It is also the main land use objective, either for extensive grazing or for forest exploitation and for rejuvenation. In cases where technology is applied to change land use and vegetation, soil surveys are often a better approach; for example, if new forest plantations are being established.

In *France* a new system of environmental mapping has been developed during the 1970s (Journaux 1978). Some map sheets have been published at a scale of 1: 50 000. These maps present a range of human environmental data as well as different processes within this environment. The main groups of basic data are topography, hydrology, atmosphere and the main categories of land use; for example, urban, arable, pasture. The indicated processes are degradation of the soil surface, water pollution and activities undertaken for conservation or improvement of the environment. Although these maps certainly give useful data for environmental planning, they do not indicate a number of essential ecological aspects of the landscape.

In the *Netherlands* landscape ecological surveys are being undertaken by various institutes. The activities of the present author with his colleagues and students are carried out in the Netherlands as well as in western Switzerland and in Tuscany (Italy). The principles which have been developed are thought to have a more general application. These principles are summarized as follows: (1) in order to make a landscape ecological map for practical purposes, it has to be designed with reference to the subsequent land evaluation; (2) this first principle aids the selection of map scale and criteria for establishing the map legends; (3) air-photo interpretation is an essential tool because it facilitates the study of landscapes as a whole; (4) air-photo interpretation is essential for the efficient mapping of large areas with sufficient reliability, and the process aids the choice of traverses and sampling points for field surveys; (5) in any landscape distinctive land units may be recognized which are correlative complexes of several landscape ecological factors including biotic as well as abiotic ones; (6) these complexes may be mapped by using a relatively small set of differentiating characteristics and the boundary lines between these correspond to other ecological factors called 'diagnostic characteristics' and 'intrinsic properties'; (7) each landscape as a main mapping unit is characterized by its own differentiating characteristics. The differentiating characteristics applied within the landscape for distinguishing the land units may be different for each landscape area. Recent investigations have shown that these various points may be determined on a quantitative basis by using a computerized system of calculation. Furthermore, the data thus assembled can be easily used for land evaluation both by manual and by computerized methods. Part of a landscape ecological map of an area in the Netherlands is shown in Fig. 17a., and that of an area in Italy in Fig. 17b.

Our landscape ecological maps have evolved from the system of physiographic soil mapping established by Edelman (1950) and for example also used by FAO and others in many countries (Buringh 1960). Within the soil survey organization, this system evolved towards a more taxonomic approach, although for mapping physiography still provides guidance. Soil maps are always extremely useful and necessary for the planning of agricultural development and for many other applications. When we considered the ecological aspects of various landscapes, we came to the following conclusions:

1. There are many landscape phenomena (e.g. mass-wasting, vegetation, land use and various artefactial landscape elements) which are neglected by soil surveys because of the inherent limitations of their thematic approach.

2. There exist, especially in Western Europe, many areas in which the soils are of ecological importance, but ecologically relevant landscape differences are much better characterized by variations in topography, climate, mass-wasting phenomena, vegetation or man-made attributes.

3. Aquatic areas are neglected by soil surveys, but in many areas they are important landscape ecological elements.

These considerations are of importance for planning at scales ranging from national to local. Soil maps can be considered as special kinds of landscape ecological maps to be used in those regions where the soils provide the best differentiating characteristics for delimiting inter-related landscape complexes. This approach is especially relevant where land development for intensive agriculture is planned. Even then, in areas where land degradation may occur or where irrigation of areas with a varied topography is relevant, additional landscape data are often necessary; these may be mapped using a suitable kind of physiographic soil survey (Fig. 13). Where a decision is made to execute soil surveys, the only proper personnel to carry out such surveys are well-trained soil surveyors with a good knowledge of soil taxonomy and related problems. Where any other kind of landscape ecological survey is planned, the essential classification of soil data has to be done in a national or international system, using, for example, the Legend of the *Soil Map of the World*. This is essential for facilitating the transfer of knowledge and experience from one area to another on the basis of the combination of sufficiently reliable data on climates and soils.

It is useful to make some comments on the use of the various kinds of landscape characteristics.

General landscape characteristics are used for describing and mapping different main landscapes of an area. In Fig. 17a these are (A) old beach ridge landscape, (P) polder landscape, (D) beach and dune landscape, (U)

Fig. 17 Parts of two landscape ecological maps made with the system of the University of Amsterdam
(a) An area in the southwestern delta of the Netherlands, the island of Voorne (Kwakernaak et al. 1979)

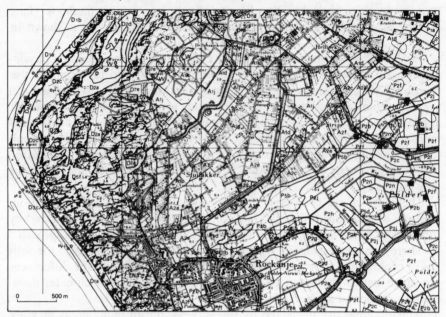

height of dikes in m
above land surface

4	> 5
3	2½ - 5
2	1½ - 2½
1	< 1½
0	excavated areas

w lake

eroded from dike-rupture

■ farm with trees

□ farm without trees

A. Old beach ridge landscape

	Symbols	Humidity	Groundwater Class	Micro-relief (cm)	Land use
A1 sand cover thicker than 40 cm on loam	A1b	moderately humid	III-V	weak < 50	agriculture with hedges
	A1d	dry	V	weak < 50	half open agriculture
	A1e	dry	V	weak < 50	woods
	A1g	humid	II	weak < 50	agriculture with hedges
	A1j	humid	II	weak < 50	half open agriculture with hedges
	A1k	humid	II	weak < 50	woods

	Symbols	Humidity	Groundwater Class	Micro-relief (cm)	Land use
A2 sand cover less than 40 cm on loam	A2a	dry	V-VI	weak < 50	open agriculture
	A2c	moderately humid to moderately dry	III-IV	weak < 50	agriculture with hedges
	A2d	moderately humid to moderately dry	III-IV	weak < 50	orchards
	A2e	moderately humid to moderately dry	III-IV	weak < 50	half open agriculture/ hedges
	A2f	moderately humid to moderately dry	III-IV	weak < 50	open agriculture

P. Polder landscape *g is added for old salt-diggings (irregular surface)

	Symbols	Humidity	Groundwater Class	Micro-relief (cm)	Land use
P1 sand cover less than 40 cm on loam	P1a	moderately dry	IV-VI	> 100	pastures
	P1e	moderately dry	IV-VI	< 50	pastures
	P1h	moderately wet	III	> 100	pastures
	P1n	moderately wet	III	< 50	arable
P2 loamy soils thicker than 80 cm	P2b	moderately dry/ dry	IV-VI	moderate 50-100	pastures
	P2c	moderately dry/ dry	IV-VI	moderate 50-100	arable
	P2d	moderately dry/ dry	IV-VI	weak < 50	farm buildings
	P2e	moderately dry/ dry	IV-VI	weak < 50	pastures
	P2f	moderately dry/ dry	IV-VI	weak < 50	arable
	P2g	moderately dry/ dry	IV-VI	weak < 50	orchards
	P2x	moderately dry/ dry	IV-VI	weak < 50	woods
	P2h	moderately humid	III	strong > 100	pastures
	P2j	moderately humid	III	moderate 50-100	pastures
	P2n	moderately humid	III	weak < 50	arable
	P2m	moderately humid	III	weak < 50	pastures
P5 beds of old creeks with peat on loam or on clay	P5a	wet/humid	I-II	strong > 100	pastures
	P5b	wet/humid	I-II	moderate 50-100	pastures
	P5d	wet/humid	I-II	weak < 50	marshland

D. Beach and dune landscape

Symbols	Relief	Altitude above OD(m)	Geomorphology (height in m)	Stability	Vegetation/land use
D1a	level	0-5	receding beach	n.r.	bare
D1b		0-5	growing beach	n.r.	bare
D2a		0-5	primary valley	n.r.	woods
D2c		0-5	primary valley	n.r.	bushes and herbs
D2d		0-5	primary valley	n.r.	herbs
D3a		0-5	secondary valley	n.r.	woods
D3b		0-5	secondary valley	n.r.	bushes
D3c		0-5	secondary valley	n.r.	bushes and herbs
D3e		0-5	secondary valley	n.r.	recreation area

Symbols	Relief	Altitude above OD(m)	Geomorphology (height in m)		Stability	Vegetation/land use
D4a	strong	5-16	dune complex	tops > 10	unstable	bare
D4b		5-16	dune complex	tops < 10	unstable	bare
D5c		5-16	dune complex	tops > 10	partly unstable	bushes
D5e		5-16	dune complex	tops > 10	partly unstable	bushes and herbs
D5f		5-16	dune complex	tops < 10		bushes and herbs
D6a		5-16	dune complex	tops > 10	stable	woods
D6b		5-16	dune complex	tops < 10	stable	woods
D6d		5-16	dune complex	tops < 10	stable	bushes
D6c		5-16	dune complex	tops > 10	stable	bushes and herbs
D6f		5-16	dune complex	tops < 10	stable	bushes and herbs
D7a	moderate	1-6	solitary dunes		stable	woods
D7b		1-6	solitary dunes		stable	bushes
D7c		1-6	solitary dunes		stable	bushes and herbs
D7d		1-6	solitary dunes		stable	herbs
D7e		1-6	solitary dunes		stable	agriculture
D7f		1-6	solitary dunes		stable	concrete structures

U. Urban landscape: villages and fortifications

Symbols	Kind of built-up area	Building period
U1a	aligned on dike	before 1857
U1b	aligned on dike	after 1857
U2a	village centre	before 1857
U2b	village centre	after 1857

urban areas and fortifications. The differences between these landscapes are expressed in variations in many characteristics though differences also occur within most landscapes. A landscape can range in surface area from 1000 ha to over 10 000 ha. Differences between landscapes ought to be based on the most stable and permanent characteristics. For the map of coastal dune areas in the Netherlands at a scale of 1 : 000 000, a complete classification system based on the differences in importance of the relationships between the various land attributes was developed (Bakker *et al.* 1979, 1981). In most cases, geology provides the best general characterization of a landscape as shown in Fig. 17a. This is true for landscapes formed during the Holocene as well as for areas with older geological formations. In Tuscany a Macigno landscape (Tertiary flysh), a limestone landscape (Jurassic to Cretaceous), a fluviolacustrine landscape (lower Pleistocene) and an alluvial landscape (upper Pleistocene and Holocene) have been distinguished (Fig. 17b). These general geological divisions are reflected in soils, topography, vegetation, hydrology, land use, and various processes such as erosion, mass-wasting and in estuarine areas the differences in impact of tidal movements. Recent investigations by Pedroli (1980) have shown that these complexes can be analysed on a quantitative basis.

Differentiating characteristics within each landscape are crucial to mapping. Their selection largely determines the mapping results and subsequent land evaluation. An example from the Netherlands is given in Fig. 17a; within landscape A, differences in groundwater conditions and land use have been utilized; for landscape P the selected differentiating characteristics are soil texture, groundwater conditions, microrelief and land use. In landscape D, topography, geomorphology, stability and structure of the vegetation are the differentiating characteristics. In Fig. 17b an example from Tuscany (Italy) is given. In many landscapes of Tuscany, topography, slope class stability and water conditions are used, although they are not all relevant in every landscape. In Tuscany, with man-made terraces, the type of land use or vegetation and soils are often useful for differentiating land units. The determination of differentiating characteristics is usually done during the mapping of sample areas, and the first stage of fieldwork after initial air-photo interpretation has been completed.

Additional diagnostic characteristics and intrinsic properties indicate all other ecological phenomena and, where possible, processes which have not been used as differentiating characteristics. These characteristics and properties may be of greater ecological significance than the differentiating characteristics used in the same landscape, but they happen to be less efficient for mapping in a given case. This is, for example, sometimes the case with soil, always an essential ecological factor, but often less efficient for mapping than landforms. The table of diagnostic characteristics and intrinsic properties in a legend to a landscape ecological map is generally much larger than the table of differentiating characteristics. For reasons of space, these are only outlined in Fig. 17. The difference between diagnostic characteristics and intrinsic properties is that the former may be used for differentiation whilst this is not the case with the latter (Vink 1981a).

Finally, a special kind of landscape ecological mapping which is being developed in *Sri Lanka* deserves to be described. This system has not yet been completely published, but a progress report has been written (Somasiri *et al.* 1978). The system has thus far been specially developed for the irrigated rice lands of the country and the result is a classification for rice lands. Its approach will be applicable after some modifications to the dry 'uplands' of the country. The maps and diagrams of the various land systems and subsystems are directly applied to agricultural extension work as well as to obtaining better knowledge of specific ecological problems associated with the growing of rice under certain landscape conditions; for example, iron toxicity.

A separate and comprehensive group of landscape ecological surveys can be labelled *integrated surveys*. These are multidisciplinary surveys in which, from the early stage of preparation through to the final maps and reports, every effort is made to integrate the various kinds of data into a coherent whole. The resultant exercise in land evaluation can then be used for planning and the execution of projects. The initial approach had as its focus integrated surveys of the natural environment. The trend has been towards the integration of natural environmental data with those on the social, economic and institutional conditions of the area. The earliest example of integrated surveys are the land systems of the Australian CSIRO. At a

UNESCO Conference at Toulouse in 1964 an attempt was made to stimulate a more worldwide approach (Rey 1968). This led to the establishment of the ITC–UNESCO Centre for Integrated Surveys at ITC (Enschede, the Netherlands) which has done research on the problems of execution and presentation of the results of integrated surveys (Nossin *et al.* 1977a & b). Many integrated surveys for planning projects are executed by consulting firms, including the British LRDC, as already mentioned. Integrated surveys include various methods of network planning and systems analysis. Latest results show that a computerized approach leading to very detailed and

Fig. 17 (b) A part of a landscape ecological map: the area of Montevarchi in the Valdarno Superiore (Tuscany, Italy), on scale 1 : 50,000 (Van Amstel, 1981)

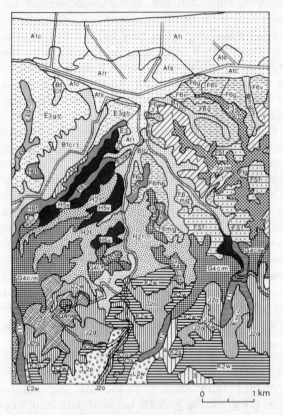

N.B.   the top of the map points towards NE
altitudes in metres above sealevel
soil groups according to FAO/UNESCO, 1974
the town A1t is Montevarchi
n.a. = not applicable
coltura mista (c.m.) = mixture of orchards, arable land and leys
l.s. = large scale

Fig. 17 (b) Legend

Major Landscape: River Terraces and Dissected Fluviolacustrine Areas (below 270 m)

Map Units	Differentiating characteristics					Other diagnostic characteristics		
	Physiography	Altitude	Relief energy	Parent material	Land use + vegetation	Effective soil depth	Drainage	Soil group
Landscape A: River terraces of the Arno river								
A1t	river terraces	135-170 m	0-3 m	alluvium + colluvium	town	deep	well dr.	n.a.
A1s	river terraces	135-170 m	0-3 m	alluvium + colluvium	horticulture	deep	well dr.	cambisols
A1l	river terraces	135-170 m	0-3 m	alluvium + colluvium	large-scale arable	deep	well dr.	cambisols
A1c	river terraces	135-170 m	0-3 m	alluvium + colluvium	coltura mista	deep	well dr.	cambisols
Landscape B: River terraces of tributaries								
B1c	stream terraces	135-180 m	0-50 m	alluvium + colluvium	coltura mista + l.s. arable	deep	well dr.	fluvisols
Landscape E: Very strongly dissected fluviolacustrine area								
E3g/c	lower slopes	171-250 m	26-50 m	pleistocene clay	grassland + c.m.	deep	moderately well dr.	cambisols
E4g/c	divide area	171-250 m	26-50 m	pleistocene loam	grassland + c.m.	deep	moderately well	cambisols
E4v	tops of divides	171-250 m	26-50 m	pleistocene loamy v.f. sand	variable	moderately deep	somewhat excessive	luvisols
Landscape F: Strongly dissected fluviolacustrine areas								
F1g	high terraces	171-250 m	26-75 m	all. + coll. si. clay loam	grassland	moderately deep	moderately well	cambisols
F3g/m	lacustrine terraces	171-250 m	26-75 m	pleistocene clay	grassland + vineyards	moderately deep	moderately well	cambisols

Map Units	Differentiating characteristics					Other diagnostic characteristics		
F5f	steep slopes	171-250 m	26-75m	pleistocene sand	deciduous forest	deep	well	cambisols
F6g	complex slopes	171-250 m	26-75 m	pleistocene clay + sand	grassland	moderately deep	moderately well	cambisols
F6v	complex slopes	171-250 m	26-75 m	pleistocene clay + sand	variable	deep	well	cambisols
F6m/g	complex slopes	171-250 m	26-75 m	pleistocene clay + sand	vineyards	deep	well	cambisols

Landscape G: Moderately dissected fluviolacustrine areas

Map Units	Differentiating characteristics					Other diagnostic characteristics		
G4h/w	lacustrine terraces	251-300 m	0-50 m	pleistocene sand	oak wood	moderately shallow	well	luvisols
G4c/m	lacustrine terraces	251-300 m	0-50 m	pleistocene sand	c.m. + vineyards	deep	well	cambisols

Landscape H: Miscellaneous slopes

Map Units	Differentiating characteristics					Other diagnostic characteristics		
H2f	valleys	171-250 m	26-75 m	weathered sandstone	deciduous forest	deep	well	cambisols
H4r	slopes	171-250 m	26-75 m	pleistocene sand	c.m.	moderately deep	moderately well	cambisols
H5v	rolling divide	171-250 m	26-75 m	pleistocene sand	variable	deep	well	gleysols
H8f	steep slopes	171-250 m	26-75 m	complex pleistocene	deciduous forest	deep	well	cambisols

Major Landscape: Chianti Mountains (above 270 m)

Map Units	Differentiating characteristics			Other diagnostic characteristics		
	Physiography	Parent material	Land use + vegetation	Effective soil depth	drainage	soil group

Landscape I: Valleyfloors and footslopes (0°-7°)

Map Units	Physiography	Parent material	Land use + vegetation	Effective soil depth	drainage	soil group
I1v	valleyfloors	alluvium and colluvium	vineyards + c.m.	deep	well	cambisols
I2o	footslopes	sandstone	olives + c.m.	moderately deep	well/ excess.	cambisols

Landscape J: Moderately gentle slopes (8°–16°)

J2w	footslopes	sandstone	oak woods	shallow	excess.	cambisols
J20	divides	sandstone	olives + c.m.	moderately shallow	well	cambisols

Landscape K: Moderately steep slopes (17°–29°)

K2p	slopes	sandstone	pine forest	moderately shallow	excess.	cambisols
K2s	rocky slopes	sandstone	shrub	shallow	excess.	regosols
K2w	slopes	sandstone	oak wood	shallow	excess.	cambisols
K2o	slopes with man-made terraces	sandstone	olives + c.m.	moderately shallow	well	cambisols
K2c	slopes	sandstone	chestnut woods	moderately shallow	excess.	cambisols

Landscape L: Steeply sloping areas (30°–50°)

L2p	slopes	sandstone	pine forest	shallow	excess.	regosols
L2w	rocky slopes	sandstone	oak woods	shallow	well	cambisols
L2c	slopes	sandstone	chestnut woods	moderately shallow	well	cambisols

quantitative results is sometimes possible (Nossin 1980). The basic philosophy of integrated surveys is directly linked to anthropocentric landscape ecology, even if the surveys are executed for pragmatic planning purposes.

The integration in these surveys does not necessarily mean that all scientists within the survey are in constant cooperation. Differences result because of the timing and the division of labour. In general, natural scientists are heavily involved during the initial phases, whereas social scientists including economists often carry out most of their research during the final phases. It is important that there is collaboration between these natural and social scientists, a process which ought to continue into the execution phases of a project. The various natural scientists should not have to work in continuous cooperation as there are marked differences in their survey methods and measurement techniques. For example, soil surveyors and geomorphologists have to survey more or less fixed and stable conditions, whereas hydrologists have to measure stream discharge and output from testing wells. Both research approaches and many others should be coordinated for optimum integration. The choice of disciplines to participate in a specific integrated survey is only possible after an initial reconnaissance. The participation of too many disciplines and scientists should be avoided. Some points to be taken into account are the nature of the area, the purpose of the project, the map scale of analysis and the scale of the eventual maps, and the available time, money and manpower.

Some special attention has to be given to the use of *remote sensing* in all kinds of landscape ecological surveys. In integrated surveys, the use of aerial photographs is indispensable for coordination as well as for the execution of the surveys in order to distinguish different landscape patterns as well as the details within each pattern. Remote sensing includes the use of stereoscopic images of conventional aerial photographs as well as the use of satellite photography and of special methods such as SLAR (sideways looking airborne radar), of thermophotography and of geophysical methods. In most landscape ecological surveys, the use of systematic interpretation of conventional black and white aerial photographs (scales between 1 : 12 000 to 1 : 70 000) remains by far the most useful tool. However, the interpretation must be done by fully trained specialists in the various disciplines with special training in air-photo interpretation (see for example Vink 1968). Black and white photography may be either panchromatic or include the (near) infrared, depending on local conditions. Colour photography with normal colours and false colour photography, which includes the near-infrared, often have advantages for surveys of vegetation, land use and forests. All the other techniques of remote sensing have their own specialized uses. The rather over-advertised use of satellite photography is useful under special circumstances; for example, where rapid surveys at small scales of large areas are required, or where the need is for sequential photography. The interpretation of subsequent pictures of the same area may outweigh the disadvantages of a small photoscale and lack of stereoscopic images.

NATURAL RESOURCES BUDGETS

In any enterprise of some size, the production of a quarterly or annual budget is the foundation of good management. In land management this methodology is generally neglected, although intensive use and sometimes rapid consumption of natural resources does warrant such an approach. The annual statement of credits and debits as given on a balance sheet has particular application to the use, management and conservation of land resources. In Table 5 (Ch. 3) such a budget is given for water resources in the Netherlands.

Water budgets for crops may be calculated per year, season or per growing period. It is a well-known technique for obtaining a better knowledge of water conditions for ecological and technical purposes. The use of material budgets for road construction and for the displacement of soil materials in land reclamation and soil improvement is also well known in professional circles. In these types of project, calculations have as their objective minimum transport of soil and rock materials. This is done, for example, by using materials of low ridges which have to be levelled, for filling up nearby depressions. Schlichting (1972) has proved that calculating chemical balance sheets gives a much clearer insight into the processes of soil formation within a landscape.

Similar calculations can be done for landscapes and land units for genetic as well as for ecological purposes. In order to be able to do this it is necessary first to make an ecological map of the region; alternatives are a soil or geomorphological map. The scale of map to be used depends on the detail in which the budget calculations are required; the scale could range from 1 : 5 000 to very small scale maps of large areas including the scale of the *Soil Map of the World* at 1 : 5 000 000. The initial calculations can be made directly from the map, including its interpretation for the purposes for which the balances are made. In Table 9 two examples of the result of these are given for the Sudan and for the World Map of Desertification. Both are based on rather small-scale maps – the soil survey of Sudan on scales from 1 : 250 000 to 1 : 4 000 000 and the *World Desertification Map* derived from the *Soil Map of the World* (1 : 5 000 000); the final map was published at a scale of 1 : 25 000 000. Quantitative data of this kind, even if given on very small map scales, are essential for a broad spectrum of economic and ecological planning.

The object of budgetary calculations of land resources, however, goes further than this. The initial calculations should be followed by repeated surveys and calculations in order to establish the trends of the active processes in the landscape. In Table 10 some examples are given from the Netherlands. From this table various trends can be discerned: (a) increase of farm size; (b) increase of reallotment projects; (c) increase in pollution of Rhine up to 1974; (d) general decrease of natural areas but stabilization after 1970 for marshlands and dunelands; (e) decrease of forest areas up to 1973, but

Table 9. Land resources data from the Sudan and on World Desertification

(a) Areas of cultivable land in the Sudan

Cultivable potential (% of surface area of each class) (lands potentially useful for agriculture)	Area in km²	
	total	cultivable
Land development with small capital investment		
90% cultivable within relevant land utilization types	135 000	122 000
50% cultivable within relevant land utilization types	274 500	137 000
20% cultivable within relevant land utilization types	29 000	6 000
Land development requiring large capital investment		
90% cultivable within relevant land utilization types	247 500	223 000
50% cultivable within relevant land utilization types	134 500	67 000
20% cultivable within relevant land utilization types	168 500	34 000
Little or no cultivable land	1 517 000	0
Totals	2 506 000	589 000

(b) Extent of areas likely to be affected by desertification in the world in km²*, by main bioclimatic zones

Climatic zone:	Hyperarid		Arid		Semiarid		Subhumid	
	km²	%	km²	%	km²	%	km²	%
Very high degree of desertification hazards	—		1 110 477	6.4	2 180 546	12.1	158 528	1.2
High	—		13 439 968	77.3	2 440 098	13.6	579 717	4.3
Moderate	—		2 105 167	12.1	12 452 272	69.4	3 172 905	23.3
Extreme desert	7 991 710	100	—					

Sources: (a) Purnell and Venema 1976; (b)* *World Map of Desertification* 1977.

Table 10. Some data on landscape ecology and land use in the Netherlands

(a) Numbers of agricultural enterprises and farmsize classes

Farmsize (ha)	1959	1970	1976
0.1 to 10	210 343	98 652	78 237
10 to 30	69 673	70 436	61 860
30 to 100	10 547	11 807	14 048
more than 100	160	224	351
Total farms	290 723	181 119	2 073 105
Total surface area (ha) in agriculture	2 309 812	2 142 597	

(b) Reallotment projects finished since 1924 (100 ha)

year:	1960	1965	1970	1974	1975	1976
area:	1 341.3	2 264.7	3 684.4	5 589.1	6 129.7	6 765.5

(c) Average transport of some materials by the River Rhine where it enters the Netherlands

Materials	Unit	1960	1970	1974	1975	1976
BOD 20/5	kg/sec	13.5	20.4	17.8	14.8	12.8
Nitrate-N	kg/sec	4.2	8.5	6.8	6.9	5.3
Orthophosphate-P	kg/sec	0.23	0.52	0.61	0.72	0.59
Chloride	kg/sec	270	349	377	337	284
Phenoles	g/sec	50	91	37	34	26
Oil	kg/sec	n.d.	n.d.	1.38	0.64	0.34
Synthetic detergents	kg/sec	n.d.	n.d.	0.72	0.35	0.29
Zinc	g/sec	n.d.	n.d.	486	275	222
Mercury	g/sec	n.d.	n.d.	0.98	0.69	0.84
Cadmium	g/sec	n.d.	n.d.	5.9	4.2	4.7
Lead	g/sec	n.d.	n.d.	88	44	29
Chromium	g/sec	n.d.	n.d.	126	70	67
Arsenic	g/sec	n.d.	n.d.	10.5	9.4	9.9
Waterflow	m³/sec	2155	3150	2118	2114	1321

(d) Natural areas: areas with more or less natural ecosystems (100 ha)

Class	1960	1970	1976
Marshlands	139	57	59
Heathermoors	824	831	789
Inland-dunes, coastal dunes, beaches	517	398	399
Coastal and estuarine mudflats	545	592	226
Reeds and sedges	67	113	175
Totals	2356	1991	1647

(e) Changes in surface areas of forests in the Netherlands (ha)

	1961/1970	1973	1974
Increases by afforestation of:			
agricultural lands	184	228	1541
natural areas c.a.*	886	63	78
other lands	326		
Total increases	1396	291	1619
Decreases for:			
building lands	765	362	239
agricultural lands c.a.	91	147	359
Total decreases	856	509	598
Net increases (+) and decreases (−)	+540	−218	+1021
Net increases of forest lands 1961–1974			1343 ha

* c.a. = cum annexis

Source: From *General Environmental Statistics 1975/76*.

nett increase after that year. The data in Table 10 are only extracts from the full available data and its is clear that these and comparable budgetary calculations are very useful for the realistic planning of land use and nature conservation.

Similar attempts at quantifying data on landscapes, soils and land uses are being made within the United Nations under the aegis of UNEP, in particular for developing countries. This is done in the GEMS project (Global Environmental Monitoring System), which has to be executed by the individual countries who may however obtain assistance through UNEP, FAO or UNESCO. The principal purpose is to monitor 'the desertification, degradation and depletion of soil and living resources such as forests, grasslands, wildlife and aquatic ecosystems'. Monitoring is meant to include various kinds of observations and measurements in a systematic manner in order to arrive at a system of early warning with regard to the various processes of desertification, degradation and depletion and their impacts. Actual observation systems may include various kinds of continuous or repeated observations and measurements of phenomena as well as of the processes themselves. This may be partly done with aerial photography and other kinds of remote sensing, including the use of space photography. As has already been indicated, satellite photography has one advantage – the relatively easy availability of sequential photography over large areas. The impression which sometimes exists, that monitoring is synonymous with satellite imagery, is completely wrong. In addition to any kind of remote sensing, systematic field observations as well selected localities are always indispensable. The latter should be done by repeated observations at regular intervals. The nature of the observations and the necessary apparatus need not be very sophisticated.

Monitoring the whole world or even large parts of it is not possible given limitations of manpower, time and money. It should therefore be concentrated on selected vulnerable areas – those areas of a region, country or a continent in which one or more of the processes is thought to have a serious impact on natural and cultural ecosystems. The selection of vulnerable areas is in general possible by using available maps and data on land resources. The nature of the observations to be made in each vulnerable area may then be decided, depending on the nature of the region and on the processes to be monitored as well as on available human resources. The investigations may furthermore be combined with research already being carried out by existing institutes or within existing programmes or projects; for example, within the MAB (Man and Biosphere) programme of UNESCO.

5
Crop ecology and land management

CROPS: GROUPS, TYPES, BIOMASS

The ecology of heterotrophic organisms is based on the assimilation by plants of carbon dioxide, with the use of energy from the radiation of the sun. The large, and still rapidly increasing, human population of the world is not able to live from the natural vegetation, and therefore man has to take measures to bring those plants which are of particular use to him under specially favourable ecological conditions. For this purpose two aspects are essential: (1) the requirements of the crops with regard to their environment; and (2) the manner in which man can influence certain key variables of this environment, in such a manner that the growing conditions of the crops are brought to as nearly optimal as possible. In Chapters 3 and 4 some mention was made of the ecology of grassland-communities for grazing. The largest contributions to human nutrition and to the fulfilment of other human needs are made by arable agriculture and by horticulture. In addition the production of certain perennial crops, in general grown as tree-crops, plays an important role: fruit trees, cacao, coffee, tea, rubber (*Hevea brasiliensis*) and fibre crops such as sisal (*Agave sisalana*). The following discussion is mainly restricted to arable crops, in general, annual crops having a growth period of less than 12 months. In some cases, for example cassava (tapioca, *Manihot utilissima*) and sugar cane, the length of the growing period may be longer, from 1½ to more than 5 years, often with repeated harvests during that period.

The arable crops may be grouped according to their needs and to their tolerance for sub-optimal conditions, as can be done for all organisms. The temperature factor in this case takes precedence over all other factors. The crops are divided into two main groups:

1. *Cryophilous crops*, needing a certain cold period, such as wheat, barley, oats, rye, peas (*Pisum sp.*), some kinds of beans, flax, mangolds, sugarbeet, clover, lucerne (alfalfa), potatoes, apple, pear, plum, peach, grapes and olives.
2. *Non-cryophilous crops* such as maize, sorghum, various kinds of millets, rice, Phaseolus-beans, soybeans, other bean-like or pea-like leguminous

Table 11. Temperature zones of the world in relation to agriculture, arranged as a determination table

A. Summer insufficiently long and warm for the ripening of the small grains (wheat, rye, oats, barley, etc.)	1. Polar zone
B. Summer sufficiently long and warm for the ripening of the small grains but:	
I. Winter too cold for the growing of winter grains	2. Zone of summer wheat
II. Winter warm enough for winterwheat, but:	
(a) winter too cold for oats	3. Zone of winter wheat
(b) winter warm enough for oats but:	4. Zone of winter oats
1. winter too cold for oranges	
2. winter warm enough for oranges but:	
2.1 two seasons per year (cold/winter and warm/summer)	5. Zone of oranges
2.2 no seasonal fluctuations of temperature*	6. Equatorial zone

Source: After Papadakis 1938.
* But often seasonal fluctuations with regard to the existing precipitation distribution.

crops, tobacco, tomato, sweet potatoes (yam and colocasia), coffee, cacao, many kinds of citrus, oilpalm, coconut-palm, date-palm, rubber (*Hevea*) and sugarcane.

The cryophilous crops need a certain amount of cold weather (below a certain low temperature, which need not always be 0 °C) in order to produce flowers later in their growing period; if they do not undergo this cold, their growth remains vegetative or they only form abortive flowers which do not produce seeds. This low temperatures requirement does not exist with the non-cryophilous crops.

The need for low temperatures is accompanied by the need for a certain length of daylight, which indeed is also necessary for the development of flowers and the production of seeds, which are the parts useful to men. Cryophilous crops are 'long-day' crops, i.e. they need a certain number of days with a length of daylight of more than 12 hours and in general of more than 14 hours. On the other hand, non-cryophilous crops are 'short-day' plants and they flower better with short days of 12 hours. The correlations between cold-long day and warm-short day are of course largely related to the geographical latitudes. The requirement of low temperatures is also accompanied, understandably, by a certain resistance to, or tolerance of, cold weather, and short-day plants in general have a low resistance to cold weather, in particular to frost. Based on these characteristics, Table 11 shows that a broad agroecological zonation of the world may be made. In this table a limited number of crops is used as 'benchmark crops' and for this some of the most characteristic and common crops have been selected. The use of benchmark conditions in general is often a good method for use in agro-ecological investigations.

In Chapter 2 photosynthesis was stressed as being the most important activity of plants. This photosynthesis however starts with different plant species under different conditions of temperature above a certain minimum. Therefore the use of temperature as the first criterion for distinguishing groups of ecologically different plants is supported by theoretical findings. Once photosynthesis is possible, other requirements of plants related to this process have their impact on crop ecology. Some of these are summarized in Table 12. The most important variables in the table are the crop ecological group and the optimum temperature for photosynthesis. In addition, the length of the growing period must be mentioned. The crop ecological group needs additional clarification. There exist in plants two markedly different systems of photosynthesis. Each of these occurs among certain groups of agricultural crops. The first system is noted as C_3 and this requires a rather low temperature, 15–20 °C. It produces as its first product an organic acid with three C-atoms. The second system is noted as C_4, which requires a rather high temperature (30–35 °C) and produces organic acids with four C-atoms. These different systems also show differences in exchange of CO_2 with the atmosphere; rather low with C_3 and rather high with C_4, and the

Table 12. Average photosynthesis of four groups of crops in relation to radiation and temperature

Characteristics	Crop ecological group			
	I	II	III	IV
Type of photosynthesis	C_3	C_3	C_4	C_4
Intensity of photosynthesis at optimal temperature ($mgCO_2$ dm^{-2} h^{-1})	20–30	45–55	70–100	70–100
Optimum temperature for maximal photosynthesis (°C)	15–20	25–30	30–35	15–30
Radiation-intensity at maximum photosynthesis (Cal. cm^{-2} min^{-1})	0.2–0.6	0.3–0.8	1.0–1.4	1.0–1.4
Examples of crops:	Wheat Potato Phaseolus-beans (temperate cultivars)	Phaseolus-beans (tropical cultivars) Soybeans Rice Cotton Cassava Sweet potato	Pennisetum-millet Sorghum (trop. cultivars) Maize (trop. cultivars) Sugarcane	Sorghum (temperate cultivars) Maize (temp. cultivars)

Source: After Kassam *et al*. 1977.

use respectively of lower and higher intensities of radiation. The most typical groups for C_3 and C_4 in Table 12 are the groups I and III respectively. The groups II and IV have come into being by natural or artificial cross-breeding and selection and therefore occupy intermediate positions in many respects, group II being nearer to I and group IV nearer to III. This approach permits a fundamental treatment of the ecological requirements of the agricultural crops. Its combination with the phenological observations mentioned in Chapter 3 provides a possibility to study the nature of the crops by carefully noting their growth, flowering and ripening and their adaptation to given ecological conditions.

A further elaboration permits the differentiation of the biomass of different crops according to their nature and their use for human and animal consumption (stalks, leaves, fruits, tubers). This is done by using the 'harvest index' which indicates the percentage of the total biomass of a crop which is considered to be useful. For most crops this harvest index is between 40 and 60 per cent; for cotton the harvest index is 10 per cent.

ECOLOGICAL REQUIREMENTS OF CROPS

In the preceding section the ecological factors were discussed which together determine the potential biomass. In addition to these, the potential biomass of any given crop is also strongly dependent upon its genetic constitution: high-producing or low-producing varieties or cultivars. It would be exceeding the scope of this book to discuss these topics of genetics and plant breeding. Their essential role in plant production has, however, to be emphasized. The potential production induced by radiation and temperature can only be realized insofar as this is made possible by the genetic composition of the most productive cultivars available at any given time. The importance of plant breeding therefore is found in the first place in the creating of ever more productive cultivars. This is done by cross-breeding to combine genetic factors from various original strains and varieties followed by selection of the most suitable strains from the cross-bred populations. With regard to the ecological requirements of a crop, the higher-producing new cultivars have a need for more favourable conditions in general than have the original primitive breeds. The best known examples are the cultivars produced by the 'Green Revolution', in particular of wheat and paddy-rice, which only give satisfactory results if they are grown under favourable circumstances of climate, water and soils.

In addition to the breeding of productive cultivars, plant breeding also tries to produce in the same manner varieties which not only give high yields, but are also more tolerant to certain less favourable ecological factors. These may have to do with resistance to diseases (phytoparasites: mainly primitive forms of plants including virus and bacteria) and to pests (zooparasites: primitive forms of animals, including insects and protozoa). But also autoecological factors such as drought or salinity can to some extent be tolerated if plant varieties adapted to these conditions are used. Plant breeding can thus to some extent help us to live with less favourable circumstances as well as to profit from very good ecological conditions. This is however also one of the reasons why it is impossible to formulate clearly the growing conditions of crops.

Young (1976) indicates that the aspects of soil–crop relations which influence the selection of crops for given soil conditions are: (1) differences between the optimal soil requirements of crops; (2) the tolerance of crops for suboptimal conditions. The differences between crops with regard to the first kind of requirements are, given certain conditions of radiation and temperature, not very large, although some crops have a preference for somewhat sandy soils; for example, bulrush millet, yams, cassava and groundnuts. Most of the differences between crops are between their tolerances for suboptimal conditions. This is rather well-known for salinity as is shown in Table 24 (Ch. 7). A more general difference is made by Young (1976) between demanding or 'eutrophic' crops and hardy or 'oligotrophic' crops. If for a certain site a choice must be made between two crops, even a marginal advantage of one crop over the other may be decisive.

The ecological requirements of a certain crop with regard to a certain environmental factor – for example, the soil – are never very clearly defined. This is impossible because of the fundamental correlations which exist in ecology. The plant has its relations not with any single factor but always with the ecological complex as a whole, consisting of climate, soil, hydrology, other organisms and human factors of land and crop management. The requirements of a plant with regard to the soil are, for example, less stringent under a favourable climate than under a somewhat less favourable one. On the other hand a plant has less precise requirements with regard to the climate if it is grown in a very good soil, with a high water-retention capacity and with a good supply of nutrients. There are various intercorrelations between environmental factors: intake of nutrients by plants is easier under favourable water conditions and the first effect of oncoming drought is often the appearance of certain nutrient deficiencies of the plants. A good supply of nutrients, with the exception of a too great supply of nitrogen, therefore, is helpful in minimizing the effect of the less serious periods of drought.

With due consideration of the above, some remarks may be made on the requirements of crops with regard to some ecological factors. The most generally applicable topics are:

- water supply,
- nutrient supply,
- supply of oxygen to the roots.

In addition, the following requirements tend to be very critical:

- good conditions for the germination of seeds for annual crops,
- satisfactory room for the development of roots (soil depth and soil structure),

- growth conditions for the crop to be relatively more favourable than those for its possible parasites (for example, root-fungi).

A good biological activity in the soil, in particular in the A horizon, is of course very important for the growth of all crops directly as well as indirectly, for example, by its influence on soil structure. For certain crops such as leguminous crops (clover, alfalfa, 'kudzu' = Pueraria sp., etc.) and for several tree species the presence and favourable growth of the 'symbiotic' plants from which their growth is partly dependent is also of great importance. Meyer *et al.* (1978) give a list of 38 species of trees which are more or less regularly grown in urban areas of Western Europe and these trees depend to some extent on a symbiosis with fungi. Among the tree species are the following: *Abies, Alnus, Betula* (birch), *Castanea* (chestnut), *Fagus* (beech), *Larix* (larch), *Picea* (spruce), *Pinus* (pine) and *Quercus* (oak). The growth conditions for the fungi as far as is known to the present author have not been clearly formulated. Their influence on the growth of tree species is however rather well-known. For many other data on the growth conditions of tree species for urban use, reference is also made to Meyer *et al.* (1978).

As has been stated above, the choice of a crop for the use in certain ecological conditions is more dependent on its tolerance for suboptimal conditions than on its optimum requirements. This is indeed very important as suboptimal conditions are more common in the world than are optimal ones. Very broadly speaking 70 per cent of all soils in the world, as well as in any region are suboptimal or even worse for the crops preferred for social and economic reasons. In addition, for any given region, 5 to 25 per cent of marginal and submarginal soils occur and 5 to 25 per cent soils which more or less approach the optimum requirements may be found. The grouping of crops into 'eutrophic' and 'oligotrophic' ones which was referred to above is of particular importance in the approximately 70 per cent of suboptimal but still useful landscape ecological conditions. Within this range there is in general a sliding scale from fairly good via moderate to rather poor conditions. The less favourable these are, the sooner eutrophic crops suffer diminishing growth and depressed yields, whereas oligotrophic crops may still be growing rather well and giving satisfactory yields under the same conditions. Examples of eutrophic crops are many varieties of maize, various fruit trees and to some extent wheat. Typical examples of oligotrophic crops are rye, various millets and to some extent sorghum and barley. For each crop, or if done precisely for each variety or strain of a crop, two ranges of growth and production may be defined:

1. A range of favourable conditions, within which the yields are not below 50 per cent of the yields which are attainable under optimum conditions.

2. The limits of satisfactory cultivation, between which the yields are still above 25 per cent of the attainable optimum, but are less than 50 per cent.

The growing conditions as indicated here are the result of the combination of the natural circumstances and the human influences such as crop management and land management. The range and limits indicated seem to be very wide, but they are based on actual conditions and differences. For example, wheat yields under optimum conditions may be easily around 7000 kg/ha, but in many parts of the world yields of 2500 kg/ha are already considered to be extremely good.

With regard to the nature of the ecological conditions and human influences, some data on water requirements of crops were given in Chapter 3. Additional information on irrigation is given later on in this chapter and in Chapter 7. Although irrigation is very important in dry areas as well as in less dry parts of the world, most agriculture is carried out under rainfed conditions. In some regions, and in parts of other regions – for example, on not too strongly drained gleysols – the plants benefit from the presence of groundwater. But in general agricultural crops as well as other plants depend for their water requirements on the precipitation which falls during their growing season plus precipitation which can be stored in the soils. The latter is a result of the water-retention capacity of the different soils, ranging from less than 50 mm in shallow or sandy soils to over 200 mm in deep soils in loess and similar silty deposits.

In temperate and cold areas the length of the growing season of plants is mainly dependent on the temperature. In warm-temperature to equatorial areas the length of the growing season is primarily determined by the length of the rainy season. For the continent of Africa, this is outside the mountainous areas. Agroecological zones are therefore mainly distinguished on the basis of the length of the rainy season (FAO 1978). Too much rain however correlates with heavy clouds and thus, while in the equatorial regions the length of the growing period may be said to last 365 days per year, the potential yields in this zone are not always the highest.

In particular, for irrigated agriculture, several methods have been developed in order to calculate the water requirements of the different crops. These depend mainly on the process of evapotranspiration resulting from the physiological activities of the plants and from the working of the stomata in the leaves. The composition of the leaves; for example, the difference between leatherly leaves of citrus species or succulent leaves of various cacti and other 'xerophytic' (dry-climate) species and the manner in which the stomata react to drought are determinants of these processes. These factors, together with the differences between the various growth phases of the plants determine the 'crop-coefficient' of any crop at a given moment. This coefficient indicates the relationship between the evapotranspiration of the crop and the evaporation of a free water surface. The following phases of growth are in general distinguished: (1) germination, (2) vegetative development resulting in full coverage of the soil surface; (3) the rest of the growing season from the end of (2) to ripening of the fruits or seeds; (4) final period of ripening and harvest. The water requirements are calculated per phase or, more precisely, per 10-day period within each of these phases. This results in rather exact calculations of the irrigation water needs.

ROTATIONS AND MIXED CROPS

There is often a tendency to indicate the more common kinds of arable farming as 'monocultures'. This is in general true for a given parcel of land in a given year, but except in some rather exceptional cases (extensive wheat growing in semi-arid parts of the USA and the USSR) this picture is much too simplified. Arable land farming is in general carried out with rotations in which a sequence of different crops are cultivated in subsequent seasons or years. Within any given farm, as a farmer needs several kinds of products and wants to spread his risks, this results in various different crops being grown on adjoining fields. These rotations are a common phenomenon in most old-established systems of agriculture and are still found whether the present kind of land use is more 'industrial' (using various industrial products such as pesticides and chemical fertilizers) or more 'traditional'. In 1811 Albrecht Thaer, one of the fathers of modern agronomy, described in a systematic manner the rotations then prevalent in Germany. At that time, the choice of rotations was also strongly related to the ecological conditions. Even today, using all modern techniques, this is still largely true, although in most industrial countries the rotations have become more flexible. In Table 13 an example is given of the normal rotation which was still practised on many sandy soils of the Netherlands around 1960 and of the resulting differentiation in any given year.

Rotations are practised by farmers for one or more of the following reasons: (1) the maintenance of some kind of biological equilibrium including the availability of nutrients; (2) to combat weeds; (3) to decrease the incidence of both soil-borne and other pests and diseases; (4) to produce the various products needed within the enterprise (for example, for human and for animal nutrition); (5) to spread the hazards of the market, or to produce for the market (money) as well as for home-consumption (for example, groundnuts for the market and millet or sorghum for home consumption).

In those countries where the climate permits the growing of more than one crop per year, the rotation is adapted to the season. For example, in Pakistan a difference is made between kharif crops and rabi crops, the former being grown during the dry hot summer and the latter during the some-

Table 13. Example of a crop rotation on sandy soils in the Netherlands around 1960

| Years | Parcels | | | |
	(a)	(b)	(c)	(d)
1	Rye	Oats	Potatoes	Mangolds
2	Oats	Potatoes	Mangolds	Rye
3	Potatoes	Mangolds	Rye	Oats
4	Mangolds	Rye	Oats	Potatoes

what cooler winter. In Indonesia, in particular in the provinces of Central Java and East Java where there is a marked difference between the wet and dry monsoons, paddy (irrigated rice) is mainly grown during the wet monsoon season and various 'second crops' ('polowidjo') such as maize, soybeans and others, are grown during the dry monsoon. On the other hand, in the province of West Java it has been possible, for many centuries, to grow two or three consecutive crops of paddy each year, due to the beneficial effects of irrigation with rather fertile surface water.

Mixed crops, the cultivation at the same time and on the same parcel of a number of different crops together in irregular or more of less regular patterns, is found in various parts of the world in various forms. This is excepting the various grasses found in most pastures, which are treated separately in Chapter 3 as grassland vegetation. 'Leys', temporary grasslands where various kinds of grasses are sown together and maintained for a number of years, in general less than 7 years, may be said to be a mixed crop in our sense. In forestry many mixed stands are also planted and maintained and these may include mixed coniferous stands as well as mixed hardwood stands and mixed stands of both coniferous and hardwood species. In normal arable farming, the growing of mixed crops is less common, although the combined growing of maize ('corn') and soybeans is a rather old practice in some parts of the USA. In various temperate countries, the practice of sowing clover together with wheat is not uncommon. The clover is partly suppressed during the growing and ripening of the wheat, and it starts to grow properly after the wheat is harvested, thus producing a certain amount of fodder and contributing to the nitrogen content of the soil. In some regions the growing of a mixed crop of oats and barley is often found; for example, in Tuscany (Italy). The advantage of this is that the oats grow better in rather wet summers, and in rather dry summers the barley produces satisfactorily, thus ensuring a satisfactory crop for fodder purposes every year.

In many subtropical and tropical countries mixed crops including one or more perennial as well as annual crops are fairly common. In Italy and Greece the growing of a wheat crop between often very old, olive stands is still very common although this practice seems to be decreasing. In Tuscany the 'coltura mista' or 'coltura promiscua' was the main type of agricultural land use until some decades ago; it is still flourishing in some areas. In this system, olives and/or grapevines, the latter as climbers on *Acer* sp. stems, are planted in rows and between these rows annual arable crops (wheat, oats, beans, alfalfa) and three-year leys are sown. In arid and semi-arid regions the growing of mixed crops is less common. In an irrigated area near Baghdad (Iraq) the author, however, found a mixed crop of date-palms and tomatoes, as shown in *Plate* 6. The tomato plants are still small and are protected against the dry winds by plucked palm leaves. This system of land use contributes to the needs of the city of Baghdad in a substantial manner.

In the humid tropics mixed crops are perhaps more common than in other parts of the world. The interplanting of various perennial crops such as cof-

Plate 6 Mixed crop of date-palms and tomatoes near Baghdad (Iraq)

fee, tea and cocoa with – generally leguminous – shadow trees is still a
rather common practice where it can be done without increasing the incidence of plant diseases ('blister blight', *Exobasidium vexans*, in tea). Capoc
trees are often interplanted in sisal crops (*Agave sisalana*) and sometimes in
cacao plantations. Interplanting of other crops such as Hevea-rubber and
cacao or nutmeg and rubber, is occasionally found, but these combinations
often result in less satisfactory yields for both crops. In tropical plantations
of perennial crops (Hevea-rubber, tea, coffee, cacao), not only interplanting
with leguminous tree-crops but also with annual or biennial leguminous
bushes and creepers, as ground-covers, is practised. In general this has very
useful results with regard to the biological activity and the nitrogen-level as
well as to the protection of the soils against erosion. An example is *Pueraria
javanica*, sometimes known as 'tropical kudzu' to distinguish it from
Pueraria triloba, the Japanese kudzu, which, at least in Java, grows less
satisfactorily.

By far the most important kinds of mixed crops are found in the 'homesteads' of Southeast Asia, for example in Sri Lanka and in Indonesia, and in
the original shifting cultivation fields in primary forest areas such as the
author found in some parts of Cameroun. In *Plate* 7 an impression is given of
the latter; the enormous variety of different crops is but poorly demonstrated
here. At the various levels, from creepers to trees, many different species,
producing fruits as well as other useful products, are found. These mixed

Plate 7 Impression of an original shifting cultivation field in a primary forest area

crops may later be followed by less variegated mixed arable crops or by cacao plantations.

The homesteads of Southeast Asia are of a more permanent nature. An example is shown in *Plate* 8, although no true impression of the variety of crops can be shown. Some additional information for Indonesia is given in Table 14. In Sri Lanka the composition of the homestead gardens is strongly dependent on climatic conditions of the different agroecological zones (Somasiri 1980). In the wet zone, for example near Kandy, the variety of crops is much greater than in the intermediate rainfall zone. In the dry zone the homestead gardens show only a few crops, but even so these are essential for understanding land use and living conditions in the area.

Generally speaking, many traditional farms in large areas of Southeast Asia consist of approximately ½ to 1 ha irrigated paddy, ¼ to ½ ha upland (dryland) arable land and ⅛ to ½ ha homestead garden. The latter is the land immediately around the house, which is very intensively cultivated,

Plate 8 Homestead garden in West Java (Indonesia)

mainly by women and small children and where many different crops are cultivated in small quantities, only some of which have been indicated in Table 14. The products of this part of the farm play an essential role in the nutrition of the population, in particular with regard to proteins, sugar, vitamins and minerals. In some cases the area of the homestead garden may be more than 40 per cent of the total farm area and this is made productive with only 7 per cent of the total labour and 8 per cent of the invested money. In particular the incidental, but more or less continuous, labour of women and children is usefully invested here.

CROP MANAGEMENT AND LAND MANAGEMENT

Agricultural land use may be seen as cultural ecosystems in which man is the controlling factor by using his influence on certain key variables. Basically this includes the following activities: (1) the creating of growth conditions for the selected crop which are as favourable as possible; (2) the prevention

Table 14. Some crops of homestead gardens in Indonesia and their nutritive values compared with some nutritional deficiencies

(a) Some crops and their nutritive values (per 100 g)

Crop	Latin name	Calories	Proteins (g)	Fats (g)	Carbohydrates (g)	Vitamins A	B1
						(Int. Units)	
Avocado	*Persea americana* Mill.	192–203	2	20	1–5	200	20
Pineapple	*Ananas comosus* Merr.	47	0.4	0.1	11	60–150	25
Djambu bidji	*Psidium quajava* L.	24	0.7	0.6	4	200	10
Djeruk besar	*Citrus maxima* Merr.	45	1	0.1	10	200–250	—
Djeruk manis	*Citrus aurantium* L.	45	1	0.1	10	350	40
Durian	*Durio zibethinus* Murr.	80–160	3	3	10–30	—	—
Coconut (hulled)	*Cocos nucifera* L.	423	4	43	5	—	10–20
Mango (ripe)	*Mangifera indica* L.	55	1	0.3	12	1000–5000	20
Manggistan	*Garcinia mangostana* L.	7	0.4	0.1	1	—	—
Markiza	*Passiflora quadrangularis* L.	96	3	0.4	20	—	—
Pawpaw (ripe)	*Carica papaya* L.	41	2	0.1	8	700–2600	8
Banana	*Musa paradisiaca* L.	110	1	0.6	25	0–2500	15–150
Zuurzak	*Annona muricata* L.	31	1	0.3	6	0	15

(b) Some nutritional deficiencies in Indonesia

Nutritive matter	Preventive	Deficiency (generally complicated) Name	symptoms	Occurrence in Indonesia
Vitamin A	Lettuce, young cassava-leaf, celery-leaf, tomato, carrots, banana, mango, pawpaw, red palmoil, sweet potato (Ipomaea)	Xerophthalmia	Nightblindness	In certain regions
Vitamin B	Lightly hulled rice other cereals, beans, vegetables	Beri-beri	Heart disturbances	In particular in isolated communities
Vitamin C	Lettuce, sweet potato, beets, curries, citrus, mango, paw-paw, celery leaf, tomato, other fruits and vegetables	Scurvy	Mucous bleedings	Of historical importance (old sea voyages)

Source: Minderhoud *et al*. 1956.

of unwanted competition by other plants, which from this viewpoint are called 'weeds'; (3) the prevention of damage to the crop by parasites, which may be animals ('pests') or plants (including viruses; 'diseases'); (4) the harvest of the products, including their transport; (5) the storage of the harvested crop and its protection during storage against pests and diseases as well as other kinds of corruption.

The scope of this book does not permit a discussion of any extent of the latter two points. Their importance must however be stressed. The methods for harvesting a crop are often closely tied to various land qualities; for example, the nature of slopes with regard to the use of complicated machinery such as used for cereal crops. The harvest indeed is the most essential part of agriculture as this finally provides the required products. Also, the losses of product which may occur during harvest may be of such a magnitude that they obliterate any differences in yields due to ecological conditions occurring during previous stages. Storage, protection and further processing of the product are often of even greater importance within the context of agricultural land use. In a quantitative sense this may be demonstrated by the fact that in developing countries often more than 30 per cent of the harvest is lost during storage due to beetles, fungi and other agents. The quality of the product is also in some cases strongly influenced by the methods and the duration of storage; for example, for cereals to be used in bread production and for barley to be used in breweries. The further processing of the harvested product is indeed highly important for crops such as flax, sisal, oil seeds, fruit of the oil-palm, tea, cacao, coffee which demand a special biochemical treatment to make them suitable for further use. The methods used during the first processing after harvest, and the care applied to the use of these methods, largely determine the ultimate quality of the product and thus are responsible for the final financial results. In many cases therefore the apparatus for the initial phases of processing are closely tied to the agricultural enterprises. Examples of these are the flax retting, which is often done by farmers' cooperatives in the regions where flax is produced, and the factories which are essential parts of many kinds of tropical plantations, for palm-oil, tea, rubber, coffee and sisal. In many cases this is also true for saw mills and pulp factories in or near forests.

Returning to the discussion of the growth conditions of crops, the following human activities are the most generally relevant: tillage, manuring and fertilizing, and water management. Eradication of weeds is mainly done by tillage and to some extent by the use of fertilizers, the result of the latter being better crop growth which prevents the growth of weeds by its shadow effect: less radiation for the weeds growing below the crop. Sometimes water management, in particular basin irrigation, also provides a means for controlling weeds. In the following we shall therefore make some remarks consecutively on: tillage; manuring and fertilizing; water management. Reference is also made to the latter in Chapter 7. The combation of pests and diseases is separately treated in the next section.

Tillage has as its primary purpose the production of favourable conditions for seed germination; for example, of annual crops and of new leys, and for the development of the roots of young plants such as tree crops. During the preparation of the seedbed, the remnants of previous crops such as roots and stalks and organic manure are mixed into the soil. In addition, the weeds are turned over and partly annihilated. The intensity with which this is done depends on the kind of tillage and on the nature of the weeds. Tillage contains one or more of the following activities:

- turning the topsoil with spade or hoe, the latter in particular in primitive systems of agriculture,
- ploughing with wooden or iron ploughs, using the traction of cattle, buffalos, horses or tractors,
- puddling the topsoil under wet (irrigated) conditions in paddy growing (wet rice),
- harrowing,
- hoeing with Dutch hoes, horse hoes or mechanical hoes,
- milling with rotary cultivators driven by tractors or with power-driven rotary cultivators,
- digging of planting holes for trees.

The first three of these methods are in particular used for the preparation of the seedbed in the sense described above. Harrowing is done for seedbed-preparation as well as for the covering of seeds and for the combation of weeds in young crops, such as cereals. Hoeing with horse-hoes or machine-hoes is carried out in growing crops for weed combation. Milling with rotary cultivators is mainly applied in horticulture and sometimes for the preparation of the seedbed for grasslands, including sports-fields. The digging of planting holes is essential in all kinds of land use where trees are the main crop. In extreme cases, for example for trees in urban areas, the trees even have to live exclusively within the circumference of the originally dug hole (see Ch. 6). Plate 9 shows an example of the puddling of paddy fields in irrigated rice-growing in Indonesia, with buffalos for traction.

The eradication of weeds may also be done with chemicals or with fire, the latter with the use of portable flame-throwers. These systems however are, within the context of world agriculture, relatively unimportant. Their less favourable ecological side-effects furthermore cause these rather expensive systems to remain exceptions.

Separate mention has to be made of 'minimum-tillage' or 'zero-tillage' systems of agriculture in which tillage is reduced to a minimum or even completely abolished. Investigations on these have been induced by the objections which exist against very intensive, and often too deep, tillage in mechanized agriculture. These might lead to unnecessary disturbance of the biological processes in the soil by too much ploughing and harrowing and also to a strong compaction of the soils by the use of heavy machinery. It has to be noted however that the pressure per surface unit (cm^2) of these machines is in general less than that of horses or men. The way in which this

Plate 9 Puddling with water buffaloes in paddy culture in Indonesia

pressure, with high velocities and on humid soils, is applied may, however, lead to unfavourable compaction of the soil. In areas with erosion hazards, too much tillage may also lead to an unwarranted increase of soil erosion. Field experiments on zero-tillage in the Netherlands however have led to unfavourable results. Zero-tillage seems to enhance stagnation of water in the topsoil and to lead to less favourable soil–air conditions, causing earthworms to die because of lack of air (Boone *et al.* 1976). Perhaps more than in other aspects of agricultural ecology, tillage needs to be done carefully and certainly not more than is strictly required for the purposes of seedbed preparation, weed eradication and essential maintenance of the crop and the land. The latter sometimes also comprises the use of special ploughs; for example, 'listers' for use in relatively dry conditions to enhance water retention. Special tillage for the construction of bunds or terraces is not treated here.

Manuring both with the use of organic manures and with chemical fertilizers means the adding by man of those substances which contain nutrients for plants to the 'system plant-soil'. This system consists of various parts as indicated in Fig. 18. Reference is also made to the nutrient cycli which were discussed in Chapter 2. Manuring is mainly done with the following substances:

- stable manure and liquid manure (faeces and urine of cattle and horses, often with addition of straw),
- domestic garbage, sometimes including human faeces,

Fig. 18 Model of the system 'Plant-Soil' (after Hudig, Wageningen 1937)

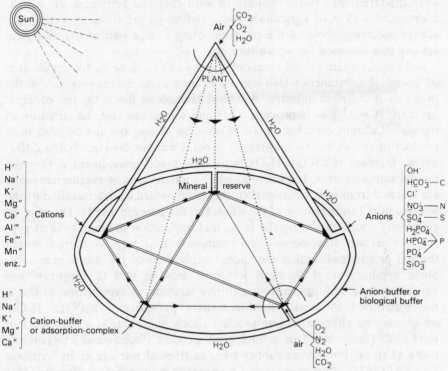

- green manure, often by turning remnants of leguminous or other crops into the topsoil.
- mineral fertilizers, generally called 'chemical fertilizers', although these encompass natural mining products and bonemeal as well as the products of chemical industry.

In addition, several substances are used less for the introduction of nutrients into the system and more for the improvement of the soil with regard to its water-retaining capacity or its capacity to buffer, to regulate the cycling, of anions and cations. This includes for example the application, incidentally or regularly (e.g. every 5 or 10 years) of compost. This compost may be made locally from household garbage or at an industrial scale from town refuse. Industrial refuse, some agricultural or biochemical industries excepted, in general is not suitable for application to soils due to its contents of heavy metals and other toxic substances. The fundamental distinction between nutrient supply and soil improvement is clear, but the two processes often coincide, in particular in old-established systems of agriculture. Continued manuring with stable manure may induce a certain soil improvement, although the effects of this are often exaggerated. Increase of the organic matter content of soils occurs also from the decay of roots of annual crops and this amount may be of the same order of magnitude whether the crops were manured with stable manure or with chemical fertilizers. In a well-maintained system of agriculture the activities of the roots as well as the always occurring decay of the old roots carry a large part of the biological activity in a soil used for agriculture.

Soil improvement or soil amendment may also be done by the application of 'chemical' substances which may be either natural mining products or the products of chemical industry. A typical example of this is the use of 'lime' or 'marl' ($CaCO_3$) to improve the pH and sometimes also the structure of the soil. Calcium carbonate may be won by mining but it may also be a product of the chemical industry, in general without distinguishable differences. Gypsum ($CaSO_4.x\ H_2O$) is used as a soil amendment during the desalinization of soils. In particular when sodium–salts or magnesium–salts are leached from soils by irrigation, there is a hazard of deterioration of the soil structure (arrangement of the solids and the pores in a soil). This may be effectively counteracted by the incidental application of some tons of gypsum per hectare. In some soils, for example in Iraq, a gypsic horizon within the soil profile itself makes the special application of gypsum unnecessary. Some applications of chemical fertilizers may be said to constitute soil amendments in addition to their nutritive function. A typical case of this is the application of poorly soluble tertiary phosphate ($Ca_3PO_4.x\ H_2O$), which may be either a mining product ('rock phosphate'), a byproduct of steel mills ('basic slag') or a 'biological' product ('bone-meal') to planting holes of trees. For Hevea-rubber trees in tropical nitosols or in ferralsols (see FAO 1974) often as much as 1 kg per hole is given before planting. This suffices for the whole life of the tree (some decades, up to approx. 50 years) and even then leaves a remnant after the rubber garden is felled. In other cases typical soil amendments are given in planting holes; for example, sulphur-powder in planting holes for teabushes in order to lower locally the pH of the soils, thus preventing rootrot in soils rich in cations (andosols in Indonesia). In forestry, manuring, if applied, is nearly always given once during the lifetime of a forest plantation as a capital investment.

Most manuring is however done in yearly applications for the nutrition of a crop, although the following crop may to some extent also profit from the same gift. Plants mostly need applications of nitrogen (as NO_3^- or NH_4^+), phosphate (PO_4^{3-} or HPO_4^{2-}) and potassium (K^+). Other essential nutrient elements are often provided in sufficient quantities by the soil itself (in many fertile soils this is also true for phosphate and potassium), or the nutrients are given in combination with the above-mentioned ones, as is the case for calcium (Ca^{2+}), magnesium (Mg^{2+}) and sulphur (S), the first two as cations with nitrates or phosphates, the latter as SO_4^{2-} ions in potassium sulphates and as admixtures in superphosphates. Magnesium is essential for the composition of chlorophyll and therefore for carbon dioxide assimilation, and sulphur is an essential component of most proteins. Other nutrients are only needed in much smaller quantities (Fe, Mn, Cu, Co, Bo) and these 'micro-nutrients' have only to be given in fertilizers in exceptional cases.

Nitrogen is, in general, applied in fertilizers in one of the following basic formulas: $Ca(NO_3)_2$, $(NH_4)_2SO_4$ and CH_4N_2O (urea), sometimes also as $NaNO_3$ or NH_4NO_3. Phosphate is either given as tertiary phosphate (natural 'rock-phosphate', basic slag or bonemeal), $Ca_3(PO_4)_2$ or as superphosphate $Ca(H_2PO_4)_2.CaSO_4$ and sometimes as ammoniumphosphate, $(NH_4)_3PO_4$, the latter being an efficient combination with nitrogen. Potassium is given as KCl, or K_2SO_4 or as $K_2SO_4.MgSO_4.6H_2O$. The latter is often necessary to prevent an imbalance of the three-cornered equilibrium of K–Ca–Mg in the soil, which may lead to deficiency-diseases.

There is today some discussion on the advisability of the use of chemical fertilizers in agriculture. The most basic consideration in this discussion is the fact that it is already impossible to feed the population of the world without the extensive application of chemical fertilizers and this will become more essential in the decades to come because of the rapid population growth. The influence of chemical fertilizers on the eutrophication of surface waters is in general very small, except in those cases where the topsoil together with the applied nutrients is eroded and deposited in surface waters. The loss of expensive fertilizers from the agricultural system is prevented as far as possible by all good farmers and is almost negligible in well-established agricultural land use. An additional danger might be the leaching of nitrogen through the soil into the drainage system. Several experiments in the Netherlands have proved, however, that the effect of nitrogen fertilizers in this respect is in general less than the effect of the leaching of nitrogen from stable manure applied to the fields at regular times. Eutrophication of rural surface waters is in most cases primarily due to the effect of local disposal of domestic sewerage into the surface waters. The latter is also nearly the only way in which phosphates are brought into the surface waters; phosphates applied to the soil are taken into a strongly buffered ecosystem and are only rarely leached through the soils, cases of surface erosion excepted.

It is possible, and sometimes extremely useful, to calculate the turnover of nutrients in agricultural ecosystems and to develop this into nutrient balance-sheets. This leads to a better understanding and wherever necessary a better control of the nutrients applied to agricultural ecosystems (Frissel 1977).

Irrigation, next to tillage and manuring, is one of the important complexes of management activities applied to cultural ecosystems. Special application of water for plant growth is not everywhere necessary, but this is still often applied even in humid areas as a supplement to precipitation. Irrigation is often discussed within the framework of land improvement and this is understandable as many kinds of irrigation need major changes in the land itself by construction of terraces, irrigation canals, drainage systems, weirs and

dams. These aspects will be indicated in Chapter 7. But the essential goal of irrigation is to provide water to the plants and this may also be done without major land improvements. There exist four main systems for irrigation:
1. gravity irrigation or irrigation by flooding;
2. subsoil irrigation;
3. sprinkler irrigation;
4. trickle irrigation or drip irrigation.

Gravity irrigation or irrigation by flooding is the most common, and is the traditional system for the old-irrigated areas of the world. In the old agricultural areas along the Nile in Egypt, along the Euphrates and Tigris in Iraq and along the Indus River in India and Pakistan, irrigation developed naturally as a consequence of the annual flooding of the lands by the rivers. Gradually people learned to regulate these annual events into local, and later into large regional irrigation systems, such as those of the Babylonian Empire, the Egyptian dynasties and the Harappa and Mohenjo Daro cultures. Irrigation in this form is over 4000 years old. Somewhat younger but still very old are the irrigated paddy cultures (irrigated rice, *Oryza sativa*) in India, Ceylon and Indonesia, of which those in Indonesia were brought there by Indian immigrants some 1000 years ago. Gravity irrigation is also the irrigation system with the largest surface area. The total surface area of irrigated lands in the world was 223 million hectares in 1975, of which 92 million ha were in developing countries. The latter consist nearly wholly of gravity irrigation, and also in the other countries by far the largest surface is irrigated with some kind of gravity irrigation.

Gravity irrigation may be carried out as 'basin irrigation' in which the fields are completely flooded for a shorter or longer period, for example for cereal crops, including rice. It may also be done by 'furrow irrigation' where the fields are ploughed into ridges and furrows, the crop being planted in the ridges and the water applied to the furrows, as done is for example in row crops and tree crops such as citrus. Plate 10 gives a view of irrigated 'sawahs' (terraces for paddy-rice) on the Isle of Java (Indonesia).

Rice irrigation requires some additional remarks, due to the special methods which are related to the nature of the crop. The rice-cultivars which are used for irrigated cultivation, by far the most important group of cultivars (strains, varieties, clones) for this crop, are by nature marsh plants. The system of cultivation therefore is aimed at recreating marshy conditions which last from the period of seeding until just before the harvest. During this period, which lasts approximately 3 months, the land is kept continuously covered by a shallow layer of water, with a thickness from 5 to 10 cm. At the beginning of the period the land is ploughed in a special manner – 'puddling' – which produces a very dense topsoil with a maximum content of water. The topsoil contains virtually no air and air, which is essential for root growth, is transported to the roots by internal channels within the plant, thus transporting air from the leaves to the roots. By this process the essential oxygen for the functioning of the roots is provided.

Plate 10 Terraces with irrigated rice ('paddy') in West Java (Indonesia)

The water brought onto an irrigated rice-field contains the following components: (a) water used for the evapotranspiration of the crop; (b) water lost by infiltration to the subsoil; (c) water needed for the saturation of the topsoil; (d) water required to cover the surface with a water layer of 5 to 10 cm thickness. An average figure for the order of magnitude of a+b+c+d is 11 ha^{-1}.sec^{-1}. For these various aspects much information is available, but detailed examination of this topic is beyond the scope of this book. As a general indication in nearly all systems of gravity irrigation, for rice in humid tropical areas as well as for wheat and other crops in arid regions, it is also assumed that one third of the water provided at the source (river, dam, main canal, well) is lost before the field to be irrigated is reached. This means that of the water required at the field, 50 per cent must be added in order to estimate the amount needed from the main source.

Subirrigation, or subsurface irrigation, sometimes called infiltration, is a system which provides water directly to the subsoil at a depth of a approximately 50 cm by means of drainage tubes to which the water is led by ditches. This system was originally used in the sandy areas of the older Zuyderzee polders for the Netherlands; today it is extensively used for irrigating sports fields in flat areas with sandy, non-gravelly, soils.

Sprinkler irrigation is an efficient technique of providing additional water to crops at the most appropriate times and in the quantities needed. The system requires a rather complicated apparatus with pumps, metal tubes, sprinklers and often also partly flexible tubes. It may be installed as a permanent system, or it may be only used for the required periods. In the former case metal tubes are often mounted above the ground at a fixed height of some 1½ to 2 m, whereas in the latter rotating sprinklers are used. The rather complicated technical nature of the apparatus makes the system more vulnerable to misuse and poor maintenance and this is a disadvantage in many less developed regions. It is particularly effective as a means of additional irrigation to prevent drought hazards (for example, 200 mm in a month), or to lengthen the growing season. An additional disadvantage is sometimes that sprinkler irrigation with saline water produces damage to the leaves of the crop. The system is extensively used in intensive agriculture and in horticulture in western and southern Europe. It is used in an adapted form in hothouses. Irrigation of sports fields is often done with sprinkler irrigation.

Trickle irrigation is a relatively new method which was developed in citrus orchards in Israel some 10 years ago. The system consists of plastic or metal tubes with valves at regular distances corresponding with the width between plants or trees planted in rows. In these tubes the water is kept at a certain pressure which causes the valves to give water to the crop at certain conditions of drying out. This means that the essential water is available at the appropriate times with very little loss and with little risk of damage caused by water salinity. It is also a very efficient means of applying chemical fertilizers in solution. The system is now also extensively used in modern vineyards in Italy, for example on the island of Sardinia. It may be applied on soils with a rather impermeable subsoil.

Maintenance and management of irrigation systems and associated drainage systems is too often neglected in the planning and execution of projects in many parts of the world. Exceptions are found in the old-established irrigation areas with rice ('paddy') in Southern and Southeastern Asia, where the maintenance of tanks and weirs as well as of the irrigation and drainage canals has for more than ten centuries been a well-established part of the local agriculture and of the related social systems. But even in these areas modern developments have sometimes led to disrupted channel systems. It is relevant to describe the system of management and maintenance of the drainage systems in the Netherlands in more detail, considering the fact that a large part of this country would not exist without these and that, in the remaining half of the country, agriculture and land use in general would not have attained the present-day high level of productivity. This does not exclude the fact that also in present-day Netherlands new problems in this respect have to be solved, in particular with regard to the ecological impacts of drainage works.

The systematic management and maintenance of *drainage works* in the Netherlands is well-documented from the eleventh century onwards, when regional and local authorities started to register ordinances for its organization. The local unit for the organization was always, and still is, the polder, a land area with a surface of between some hectares for some of the oldest polders to approximately 50 000 ha for the largest polder in the Zuyderzee area, which was reclaimed between 1957 and today. A polder may either be an inland area, consisting of peat, river clay or reclaimed lake bottom, or a coastal area reclaimed from the sea. The polders consisting of peat or of reclaimed lake bottom are always situated below the local water level and therefore from their establishment have always had to be pumped dry and maintained by pumping, originally with windmills, now mainly with diesel or electrical pumps. An intermediate stage of pumps driven by coal-burning steam engines was necessary from around 1850 to 1950. This was essential for the reclamation of some of the larger lakes, for example the Haarlemmermeer Polder, at present the site of Schiphol International Airport, a total surface area of some 10 000 ha at 4 to 5 m below sea level. Polders in the river clay and in the coastal areas in general had drainage through sluices though this was not always effective. These are now nearly always drained with engine-driven pumps.

By the twelfth century adjoining groups of polders were combined into larger units, the 'waterschappen' ('water-scapes') and 'hoogheemraadschappen' ('high-home-scapes'), the latter covering some tens of thousands of hectares and having extensive authority with regard to land- and water-use. Examples are the hoogheemraadschap of Delfland, in which the towns of The Hague and Delft are situated, Schieland with Rotterdam and Amstelland with Amsterdam. The establishment and later growth of the towns would have been impossible without the establishment of proper water management. The whole organization of polders and higher authorities was, from the beginning, based on a democratic system including all landowners, under the supervision of what today are the provincial governments.

Management and maintenance for each of these units depends on the nature, the size and the impact of the various parts of the system. The following parts may be distinguished:

- ditches and small canals which are not the concern of the local authority and which are maintained by the landowner or his tenant because of well-considered self-interest;
- canals which come under the jurisdiction of the local authority and have to be cleared and maintained at least twice per year by the landowner or his tenant, the maintenance results to be shown before a certain date to the polder authorities;
- main canals which are managed and maintained by the polder or waterscape itself, which levies its annual due from the landowners (also from urban dwellers);

- sluices, pumps and other installations for general use, which are managed and maintained by the technical personnel of the polder or waterscape.

Not all drainage and irrigation has to be carried out in large organized projects. In many countries farmers have their own small installations, including small windmills for additional drainage as well as sprinkler irrigation apparatus and other systems for irrigation of their own fields. Such individual systems are common in the Netherlands. Along the Tigris and Euphrates rivers of Iraq, the system for some thousands of years of bringing the water from the river onto the land was the use of various kinds of dippers and water-wheels. In general these have now been replaced by small petrol-driven pumps. The Persian wheel, driven by animals and constructed over a well, is still in use in date gardens in Iraq as well as in various kinds of agriculture in other semi-arid and arid countries. A modernized version of the Persian wheel might as an alternative technology be very applicable to many present day small irrigation projects, given the problems of rising oil prices and difficulties of maintenance of sophisticated machinery. Locally, the scarcity of water resources rather than of land resources leads to a water rent being paid to the farmers who live on lands adjoining the river – for example, the River Nile in Sudan – and provide water to their neighbours on less favoured sites.

In developing countries, in general, there is a tendency to put too much emphasis on the establishment of large new projects. In many cases it would be better to encourage the development of small irrigation systems, adapted to local variations of the landscape and to the dimensions of the farming systems. This may be clearly seen in some areas of Italy where the smaller valleys have small local tanks used by one or two farmers, whereas in the large valleys and plains irrigation projects of large dimensions are found. A similar development is seen in Sri Lanka where on the one hand the large Mahavelli Ganga irrigation system is developed, and on the other in many areas the reconstruction of local village tank systems is advocated. In both cases however management and maintenance of the irrigation and drainage systems are of primary importance. According to a recent estimate by FAO, approximately 50 per cent of the surface area of 92 million hectares of irrigated lands in the Third World have to be rehabilitated for future use. With a view to the needs for food for the populations of the world in the coming decades, this is much more important than the development of new projects.

In the preceding discussion nothing has been said about some of the most essential parts of land management; the sowing and planting of crops. It is not possible to give a comprehensive discussion of these activities within the context of this book and a brief review would neglect too many of the special properties of the many different crops and land utilization types. For most crops, sowing is the normal method of bringing the crop to the field. Irrigated 'paddy' rice is an exception as this crop is often, for example in Indonesia, first sown on small irrigated nursery beds and later transplanted to the large rice fields ('paddys' or 'sawahs'); this method saves water and inhibits weed growth. Many horticultural crops, in particular vegetables, are also first sown and then transplanted, although here the vegetative parts often constitute the main product. Arable land crops of which the tubers are harvested, such as potatoes and cassava (manioc, *Manihot utilissima*), are planted as tubers, but turnips, mangolds and sugarbeet are sown. In general, tree crops are sown on nurseries and left to grow there for two or three years, sometimes with irrigation. During this period often a clone (cultivar which is reproduced by vegetative methods) is grafted onto the sown plants with better rooting qualities to produce a crop with higher quality and bigger production. Various different methods of grafting are used depending on the nature of each crop. As has been indicated above, the planting of tree crops in general requires the digging of planting holes, the size and quality of which may partly compensate for the less favourable soil conditions.

CONTROL OF DISEASES; INTEGRATED PEST CONTROL

Control of crop diseases and pests (parasites of many different kinds which can sometimes do considerable damage) has many different aspects. In general the damage caused by vegetable parasites, such as fungi and bacteria, as well as that caused by virus infections, is indicated with the term 'diseases'. This term may also include the damage done by toxicity or by lack of certain mineral ions in the nutrition of the plants, but these have already been indicated in our section on plant nutrition. The term 'pests', in general, indicate damage caused by animal parasites, of which insects are by far the most important kind. Animal pests and diseases are only briefly mentioned here, although these are in some regions the most serious limitation to the prevailing land use; for example the 'tsetse' (*Glossina sp.*) or Tripanosomissis as being the dominent pest of cattle in many parts of Africa (Vink 1975a; Traill *et al.* 1979).

Plant protection is a national concern in most countries. It starts at the frontiers, where the importation of plants is strongly regulated to exclude the introduction of new pests and diseases by the complete prohibition for some species and quarantine systems for others. However, plant diseases are not only transported on plants, but spores of fungi may also be brought over by many other ways; for example, on human clothes or on the soles of shoes. This danger has strongly increased in the last decades with the burgeoning use of air transport.

Plant protection in a more direct sense, including the control of both pests and diseases, may be carried out in several ways and often some of these are combined. The most important methods used are:
1. The cultivation of crops in as favourable conditions as possible with regard to climate, soil and crop management, as a well-growing crop is, in general, less liable to damage by pests and diseases.
2. The breeding of cultivars (strains, varieties, clones) which have a certain

natural resistance to known parasites, by cross-breeding and subsequent selection of the more promising types.

3. The promotion of natural predators of the parasites, where necessary and applicable by introducing these predators or fungi as 'parasites of the parasites' into an area.

4. The establishment of ecological conditions in which the crop is still able to grow well but which are less favourable for its parasites.

5. The rotation of a crop with other crops in order to diminish the incidence of parasites.

6. The destruction of a heavily infested crop by burning, sometimes applied to tree crops such as orchards and cacao plantations.

7. The spraying or dusting of a crop with special products (pesticides, fungicides).

In some countries and in some cases the removal of insects by hand, often done by young children, is practised, but as a rule this has only a very limited effect.

The first point mentioned does not need a special explanation. Mention has to be made only of the fact that excessive nutrition with nitrogen, due to natural causes or to organic manure or chemical fertilizers, often increases the susceptibility of a crop to pests and diseases, whereas it may have a favourable influence on the growth of young plants with regard to the damage done by nematodes and other soil-borne diseases.

Plant breeding is not only a means for producing cultivars with a higher resistance against parasites. It is also used for breeding drought-tolerant varieties and other kinds of tolerances against less favourable ecological conditions, in addition to the production of cultivars and clones with a higher potential productivity. The subject is too comprehensive to be treated here in any detail. The basic process is the cross-breeding of two varieties which each have some characteristics which have to be combined for optimal plant production. The cross-breeding produces a large variety of offspring, among which favourable as well as less favourable types are found. The types which are considered favourable are selected from the first population and the breeding process is continued with these, sometimes with inclusion of one or more extra stages of crossing, and always with the testing of their characteristics, and finally their multiplication and promotion for practical use. The breeding of varieties resistant to pests or diseases may be based on several different reactions of the plant to the parasite: mechanical resistance resulting from thick cutanic tissues, chemical resistance caused by a higher or a lower pH (acidity) of the plant juices, rapid growth of tissue around the original damage (and thus localizing it), changing the growth periodicity causing the evading by the plant of the impact of parasites in its critical growth phases.

The promotion or introduction of natural predators or parasites living on the plant parasites, especially applied to insect pests, may sometimes be very effective; it was already applied before 1940 in several countries; for example, in the former Netherlands East Indies (now Indonesia) with relatively good results. This method during the past decade has started to draw more, very justified, attention.

The establishment of favourable crop ecological conditions which are less suitable for certain parasites may sometimes have good results for insect pests but more often for diseases caused by fungi. This is sometimes done by the planting of shadow trees in tropical or subtropical regions, producing less favourable conditions for insects, or by the opening of the leaf cover which causes drier, and therefore less favourable, conditions for the growth of fungi on leaves and stems. The two conflicting approaches indicate that a choice is often necessary between the prevention of insects and the prevention of fungus diseases. This is exemplified by the experiences in tea-growing in Sri Lanka and Indonesia. In Indonesia until 1950 the main damage was caused by insects (*Helopeltis* sp.) and their damage was partly prevented by the regular planting of leguminous shade trees (*Albizzia* spp., *Acacia* spp., *Leucaena* spp.). The increased air traffic caused the fungus disease 'blister blight' (*Exobasidium Vexans*) to be transported from its endemic area in north-western India to Indonesia. This is a very destructive disease and caused most of the shade trees to be eradicated, resulting in the need for the chemical eradication of the insects and the application of more nitrogen fertilizers (Vink 1975a). Another example of changing ecological conditions, again from tea-growing areas in Indonesia, is the application of 250 g sulphur dust in planting holes in volcanic soils, thus lowering the local pH to a level at which the tea bushes grow well and the rootrot fungus (*Rosellinia arcuata*) has rather unfavourable growth conditions.

Crop rotation is a very common means of preventing a high incidence of pests and diseases. In addition, rotation helps to prevent excessive growth of weeds. With regard to plant protection, a rotation is particularly effective against soil-borne diseases such as nematodes. Originally in the Netherlands, there was a legal obligation for farmers to rotate their potato crop with at least two years of other crops before a new potato crop was allowed to be planted. This system has now been abandoned because of the availability of chemical products to combat this pest, as was already done in intensive horticulture, but some negative environmental impacts have occurred during the last years. In horticulture, nematodes are often combated with steam fumigation which has no negative side-effects.

The destruction of a heavily infested crop by cutting and subsequent burning is an extreme measure, which is only necessary in those cases where no other means are effective and where the spreading of the disease over a large area has to be prevented. This is in general done to gain time for the development of less destructive means of plant protection. It was applied on a large scale in western Africa around 1950 in order to prevent the total destruction of the cacao-plantations by a virus disease.

The spraying or dusting of a crop with special products, which may be either pesticides or fungicides ('chemical plant protection') is often considered to be the only real means for combating pests and diseases. In some cases the product used is of natural origin, such as Derris-powder, the ground or extracted roots of *Derris elliptica*, a tropical plant containing rotenon as its active agent. In other cases rather simple mineral products such as copper-sulphate ('Bordeaux-mixture') have been used for more than a century on, for example, vineyards and orchards. Only since the Second World War have more sophisticated chemical products been produced on a large scale. The use of chemical products for plant protection is often unavoidable for a good agricultural production and this does not always produce negative effects on other parts of the environment or on human beings. With regard to the direct transference of pesticides into human food, by 1950 and subsequent years most countries had established a means of control. The indirect and sometimes cumulative impact of the application of pesticides was clearly demonstrated in the case of DDT, a very effective insecticide. This was found to accumulate in the subsequent stages of animal foodchains, and this led to the very necessary critical analysis of other cases. The results of these investigations are found in data on the unwarranted side-effects of pesticides, on their persistence in the soil and in other parts of the ecosystems and on the development of what is now called 'Integrated Pest Control' (IPC). The latter has been developed in particular with regard to cotton growing and this is very relevant since agriculture uses approximately 80 per cent of all pesticides in the world and cotton requires approximately 80 per cent of all pesticides used in agriculture (Falcon and Smith 1973).

Integrated Pest Control may be used against pests as well as against diseases and tries, by means of ecological integration of the various measures applied, to arrive at an effective plant protection with a minimum of side-effects. One of its basic principles is that it is neither possible nor necessary to completely eradicate any parasites. A damage to any crop of, for example, 2 per cent is negligible to all concerned with regard to yield as well as to quality of the product. The system pays special attention to the conservation, and where possible promotion, of natural predators and parasites of the pests and diseases, and of pathogens of the plant parasites. Chemical products are only applied in a selective manner – insofar as their use is warranted from an economic as well as an ecological viewpoint.

The main approaches of IPC are: (a) agriculture is carried out in 'agro-ecosystems', which are ecological complexes of the organisms in agriculture in a given area with its climates, landscape and soil and with the various human activities; (b) each group, such as cotton, has its special characteristics. Cotton is a bushlike plant of warm climates which flowers at any moment when the meteorological conditions are favourable and which is a perennial crop normally cultivated as an annual crop; its growing period may be divided into different growth phases in each of which the crop has varying sensitivities to different parasites; (c) the various cotton parasites (mainly insects but also some fungi and virus-diseases) each have their particular ecological requirements and tolerances; (d) several different mechanical and chemical plant protection methods are available.

The plant protection programme for cotton is divided over three periods: (1) before planting, (2) from planting to harvest, (3) after harvest. During the first period, the basis for the parasites is reduced as much as possible by means of soil preparation and the rotation with other crops. Each year the date of planting is determined by meteorological conditions and this varies according to climatic zone; it has been found in this context that there is a certain influence of the phases of the moon on the development of certain parasitic butterflies. In this first period, there is usually no or very little need for the application of chemical pesticides. In the second period, decisions on their application are taken in a very selective manner and chemicals are actually applied only where really necessary. In the third period, the decisions on whether at all and in what quantities chemicals have to be applied is based on observation of initial damage to flowers and fruits.

The *persistence of pesticides* in relation to their environmental impacts has been an object of study since 1950. Many of these investigations have not been published as they belong to the prescribed documentation required by phytosanitary services before giving the licence for application in a country. Since around 1970 more public attention has been paid to these effects, as the growing use of more effective pesticides, such as organochloric prescriptions, has been found to be damaging to many ecosystems. Often, especially in developing countries, extreme pesticides such as DDT cannot yet be abolished because of their effectiveness against extreme attacks of insects. Research on the replacement of such prescriptions by other pesticides is being carried out. The resulting types should combine the same effectiveness with a lower persistence in foodchains and ecosystems. This persistence may be seen in the transport and resulting accumulation of the pesticide from an insect to its predators up to the large birds or other animals which are at the end of a particular foodchain. Persistence in other cases, in particular for fungicides, may mean the stability of the prescription in soil ecosystems, with the effect of damaging the soil organisms and thus the biological activities in a soil. Modern pesticides are not always aimed at the death of individual certain pests; they may also lead to the sterility of pests and thus prevent their reproduction and the spreading of certain pests to unacceptable dimensions.

GRASSLAND: PASTURES AND RANGES

In this context grassland is defined as all lands systematically used for domesticated animals to graze on, with special emphasis on cattle of various kinds. Leys and other forms of temporary pastures are not considered to be grassland. True grasslands carry a vegetation in the sense as described in Chapter 2, with various plant species which have a structural relationship with each other and with the natural and cultural ecological conditions in which they are grown. Such grassland usually consists not only of grasses in the botanical sense, *Gramineae*, but also of various dicotyledonous herbs;

the latter may even form the largest part of the vegetation. The heather moors of Scotland, England and Ireland are typical examples of pastures in which rarely occur grasses. A complete treatment of the various kinds of land use involved would also comprise discussion of the cattle grazed on the pastures: choice and breeding of different kinds of cattle, their value for meat and/or milk, their diseases and other aspects. The scope of our text does not allow this. For examples, reference is made to a report on Trypanotolerant livestock in West and Central Africa (Traill *et al.* 1979) and to the Jubilee Book of the British Hill Farming Research Association (1979).

Grazing land use may be carried out at many different levels of intensity. This is often expressed in the number of grown cattle, or their equivalents, per hectare. In intensive grazing systems, such as found in certain areas of Switzerland and the Netherlands, this may be more than 2 grown cows per hectare. Extensive grazing in semi-arid regions often carries only 1 cow per 100 hectares.

The differences in grazing density are partly a result of the conditions of climate and soil, but the kind of land management and the availability of suitable drinking water for the cattle also have a large effect. Under extensive grazing, management often consists only of the guarding of the cattle and the movement of the herds to other pastures. Sometimes the first addition is the maintenance of wells for drinking water. In many regions a seasonal change of pasturegrounds is a regular feature; this is indicated by the French term 'transhumance'. The most typical examples of this are found in Africa where in many regions the cattle are grazed on the rather dry steppes during the rainy season and on the floodplains of the rivers in the dry season. A next step may be the use of barbed wire fences which caused many social and other changes in the USA during the nineteenth century as demonstrated in many cowboy films. The regular maintenance and repair of the fences is one of the most exacting management features. (Plate 11). A further addition is the regular disinfection of the cattle with cattle dips.

In some countries, for example in New Zealand, grasslands are fertilized with phosphate fertilizers from airplanes; this has a very good effect on their grazing capacity as phosphates are taken up by the cattle and stored in their bones, whereas nitrogen and potash are largely recycled through the excrements.

Extensive grazing, often called range land use, may lead to overgrazing due to an uncontrolled increase of the cattle density. Overgrazing, in particular in semi-arid and arid regions, leads to some of the most serious kinds of erosion, partly due to the general ecological conditions and partly because the land use itself has few possibilities to control erosion once this has started. In this respect it is essential to maintain an equilibrium between the carrying capacity of the land and the quantity of drinking water which is made available to the cattle. This equilibrium is often endangered due to social reasons, including the prestige which nomadic peoples attribute to the ownership of cattle but increasingly now the population increases of the last

Plate 11 Barbed wire for improved pastures in the Great Plains Region of the USA; in the background are the Rocky Mountains

decades tend to create a need for more food which is even more dangerous. Investigations on means of conservation and improvement are now being carried out by FAO and by several national and international research institutes such as ILCA (International Livestock Centre for Africa, Addis Ababa) (FAO 1974; CGIAR 1974; Triall *et al*. 1979). Many of these projects are carried out with the assistance of UNEP. The MAB-project no. 3 of UNESCO on 'Impact of human activities and land use practices on grazing lands: savanna, grassland (from temperate to arid areas), tundra' has also been established for this purpose.

In intensive grazing systems on pastures, the following management practices are usually carried out:

- fencing with natural hedges, stonewalls, wooden or barbed wire fences or, in wet areas, with water-containing ditches and canals;
- maintenance of the grasscover by various light kinds of harrowing;
- manuring with organic manures and/or with chemical fertilizers;
- mowing for hay, for silage or for daily feeding;
- sprinkler irrigation either as a regular practice in dry summers or as additional irrigation in dry periods, wherever this is found to be feasible;
- shifting of the cattle from one pasture to another in order to have a

regular harvest of the grass without overgrazing, and to produce a regular regrowth of the grasses after grazing, depending often on the natural growth conditions of the grasses: early growth on dry lands and late growth on the wetter lands (see also Vink and Van Zuilen 1974).

The shifting of cattle may in some cases, such as the mountainous areas of Switzerland, have a seasonal character and be accompanied by a seasonal movement of at least some of the people, in which cases it is rather similar to the transhumance of the semi-arid regions. The movement in Switzerland is however more conditioned by temperature than by rainfall as the growth of the grass in the higher-situated Alpine meadows only starts in early summer: cattle are brought to these meadows from the pastures in the valleys in June and brought down again in early autumn. In many areas today, the milk-cows are not brought to the Alpine meadows and only the young cattle are taken there.

In addition to the land management activities mentioned above, many regular activities with regard to the cattle, such as the daily milking, are essential in many cases.

NATURE CONSERVATION, GENETIC RESOURCES

Some kinds of nature conservation have for long been practised in forestry areas and in hunting preserves (see Buchwald and Engelhardt 1968/9; Laban 1981). A more general approach, with practical as well as idealistic tendencies, has only started to develop since the last decades of the nineteenth century. Only very recently a World Conservation Strategy has been formulated (IUCN 1980). This is a programme for 'living resource conservation for sustainable development' and aims in particular at the following objectives:

- 'to maintain essential ecological processes and life-support systems (such as soil regeneration and protection, the recycling of nutrients, and the cleansing of waters), on which human survival and development depend';
- 'to preserve genetic diversity (the range of genetic material found in the world's organisms), on which depend the functioning of many of the above processes and life-support systems, the breeding programmes necessary for the protection and improvement of cultivated plants, domesticated animals and micro-organisms, as well as much scientific and medical advance, technical innovation, and the security of the many industries that use living resources';
- 'to ensure sustainable utilization of species and ecosystems (notably fish and other wildlife, forests and grazing lands), which support millions of rural communities as well as major industries'.

These matters are much more urgent than is often thought, both in developing and in industrialized countries. Living resource conservation is not a limited sector. It is, rather, a process which must be considered by all sectors of human activity in rural areas. This needs emphasis, particularly with regard to long-term planning with a view to the destructibility of natural ecosystems and the irreversibility of their destruction. The World Conservation Strategy defines this conservation as 'the management of the human use of the biosphere so that it may yield the greatest sustainable benefit to present generations while maintaining its potential to meet the needs and aspirations of future generations'. 'Conservation, like development, is for people; while development aims to achieve human goals largely through the use of the biosphere, conservation aims to achieve them by ensuring that such use can continue'. It is therefore an anthropocentric approach to the biosphere, including man's needs as well as his responsibilities to future human generations and, with this, to the other organisms of the biosphere (see also Vink 1981a). It embraces therefore more than just nature conservation and may be said to include a general ecological approach to land use, of which nature conservation forms a part.

Nature conservation is a form of human land use. It is decided on by men and carried out for several different purposes. In general it tries to conserve certain natural ecosystems and natural components of cultural ecosystems, such as the grazing of migratory birds in agricultural areas. It is often combined with various kinds of recreation, but this is not necessarily the case. The various kinds of very detailed nature conservation practised in industrialized countries are often looked at askance by people from developing countries, but this is a difference in degree and not in the essential nature of the activities. Most industrialized countries, in particular in Western Europe, have had the advantage that their early development took place gradually over a period of more than 1000 years with relatively simple technical means. It took place furthermore in a mild temperature climate where new equilibria have often been established before too much damage was done. The present-day technology of land reclamation, as well as the enormous increase of population in many regions, have a much more destructive tendency in particular climates such as those with one or more arid seasons. Part of the solution to these problems will have to be found by establishing highly productive cultural ecosystems on suitable lands, but on other lands nature conservation will have to be practised in a more systematic manner than is often done today.

Nature conservation includes both nature protection and nature conservation in a more restricted sense, the latter may also be called 'nature management'. Nature protection is an activity of a social nature, aimed at finding support in human society for the protection of natural or semi-natural ecosystems in general or in specific areas. It is done by societies collecting money, including various kinds of subsidies, for the buying of endangered areas; it is also achieved by national, regional and local governments and by international organizations, and finally by lobbies and action groups trying to find government support and money for the protection of specific areas or species.

Nature-management is the actual management of nature-reserves consisting of natural or semi-natural ecosystems or, wholly or partly, of cultural ecosystems which have been found to be of special value. To the latter belong several kinds of forests as well as some of the more traditional kinds of grazing and arable land agriculture.

Nature management has two major aspects – external management and internal management. The former is aimed at the prevention of the deleterious impacts of processes and activities which take place outside the nature reserve. The latter encompasses all the various activities which are needed to gain and maintain the objectives of the particular nature reserve. External management may, for example, try to prevent the impact of erosion, of drying-out, of salinity, or of forest-fires to influence the ecosystems within the nature reserve. Internal management depends very much on the kind of ecosystems to be maintained as well as on the overall objectives and functions. With regard to ecosystem conservation, the basic difference is whether the natural development of a vegetation succession is to be guarded or if a certain stage of the succession must be maintained because of its special values for science or for recreation. An example is given by many heather moors which have been originally maintained by the regular grazing of sheep and are being colonized by natural forest unless special measures are taken. Two decisions are possible: (1) to let the natural rejuvenation of the forest proceed, leading perhaps from pine-forest to deciduous forests and finally, at the end of the succession cycle, back to heather moor; (2) to conserve the heather moor either by subsidized grazing of sheep or by cutting and burning at regular intervals. The former seems to be the more 'natural' decision, but for various reasons, in which recreation-uses play a considerable role, often the latter decision is taken. A similar example is found in the clearing or non-clearing of windfalls in forests. Originally in most nature reserves the windfalls were cleared as this has always been the normal forestry practice. In natural forests, however, the windfalls contribute to the recycling processes within the ecosystem and therefore it might be advised to let these processes also take place in nature reserves. A further complication is sometimes caused by the animal communities in nature reserves. Basically the objective is to maintain as much as possible the natural animal communities and, where necessary, to prevent poaching by the local population and by commercial hunters, both often very difficult to control; the need for proteins of the local population may even be so great that matters of morality may intervene. On the other hand many nature reserves have become overstocked with certain kinds of animals, e.g. ungulates, because of emotional resistance to regulating the populations by regular shooting. This may even lead to animal densities which attain the order of magnitude of rather densely stocked agricultural grazing lands. The introduction of the natural predators of the ungulates, such as wolves, however poses severe problems. The reintroduction of animal species which have already disappeared in early history is a problem which has yet to be solved.

Internal management of nature reserves also depends very much on the needs for regulating and controlling recreation and of repairing the often unavoidable damages caused by this secondary land use. Recreation in nature areas is in general a very normal secondary function; it is even the primary function of many recreation areas which may have many natural or seminatural components. Many people see nature reserves even primarily as recreation areas and this is understandable as some of their own money, either through taxes or as subscriptions to nature conservation societies, is used for their establishment and maintenance. A certain balance has to be found which differs for each area as a function of the nature of the ecosystems as well as of the degree of urbanization in the surrounding parts of the country. The costs of nature management have also to be paid. This may be partly done through subsidies and subscriptions, but in many cases each nature reserve also has to find some of its own money, from agricultural or forestry land use, from hunting or shooting licences or from admission fees of tourists. All these considerations lead to the conclusion that in nature management land utilization types with many similarities to those in agriculture (as discussed in the final section of this chapter) may be distinguished. Reference is also made to Vink (1975a) and Beek (1978). Nature management is, in fact, much more complicated than is realized by the average urban dweller taking his leisure in a nearby nature reserve.

Within the MAB-project no. 8 of UNESCO; 'Conservation of natural areas and of the genetic material they contain', a number of different aspects of nature conservation are created. Here special attention is paid to the need for creating buffer zones around nature reserves to prevent the impact of external influences. In addition, the scientific importance of nature reserves and the need for more systematic scientific research in their ecosystems is stressed. Some special investigations on the nature of the soils in tropical nature reserves, as compared with soils of a similar origin which are used for agriculture, are now being carried out by UNESCO in cooperation with the International Soils Museum at Wageningen (the Netherlands). Scientific investigations in nature reserves have their special requirements but may also have considerable ecological impact on the ecosystems in which they are carried out. This may be a reason for separating in certain nature reserves central areas in which no human activities are carried out, surrounded by parts where scientific investigations are allowed but no other human activities are permitted.

National parks in most countries have a multiple function. They are partly established for nature conservation, but they often have as secondary objectives the maintenance of resting areas for wild animals in order to keep a certain level of 'game-cropping' for the population in the surrounding areas. Game as a source of proteins for the local populations is often superior to, and, if proper hunting methods are used, more reliable than the meat production from cattle. The latter is often very vulnerable to endemic diseases, although this may be reduced by crossbreeding of imported cattle with local cattle. A transition between national parks and agricultural land may perhaps be found by establishing special game reserves which have game cropping as their major objective, but here again the overcropping by commercial poaching has to be prevented. National parks often also serve a useful purpose by attracting two different kinds of tourists: (1) urban dwellers from the country itself who thus obtain an impression of the importance of nature conservation; (2) foreign tourists who provide the country with not inconsiderable amounts of foreign currency. In both cases the danger of souvenir hunting for trophies shot for commercial purposes has to be prevented as much as possible.

Genetic resources are specifically mentioned in the World Conservation Strategy as well as in the related MAB-project. It is highly necessary for future human generations as well as for the populations of today that a sufficient variety of species, subspecies and cultivars of the various organisms living now is maintained. This is partly possible by the conservation of natural ecosystems as well as of traditional cultural ecosystems, which have a large natural variability. The conservation of a large range of species as well as of a large variability within each biological species is necessary for the retention of the genetic variations which are contained in each. These variations may at any time be used for the breeding of new varieties and cultivars or for the production of new clones for improving the various kinds of land uses. Genetic properties of wild subspecies or varieties may be bred into existing high-producing agricultural cultivars in order to produce such characteristics as: tolerance of cold, of drought, resistance against pests and diseases, quality (for example, protein-content), resistance to lodging of grain crops (thus allowing for higher nutrient levels producing higher yields). These breeding activities are essential for a healthy development of world agriculture, in particular with a view to the strongly increasing world population and for the retention of ecological equilibria.

The largest variability within the various species of cultivated plants are concentrated in certain regions of the world, the 'centres of genetic diversity' which were discovered by the Russian phytogeneticist N. I. Vavilov, mainly in the years between 1935 and 1945 (Vavilov 1951). In the different centres different groups of plants have special importance. Originally it was thought that these centres represented the regions of origin of the related species of cultivated plants, but this was found to be inaccurate. The centres are mountainous areas; for example, the Alps, the Himalayas, the Andes, the mountains of Ethiopia, all of which provide a large variety of isolated areas with different ecological conditions. These areas provide the means for the natural differentiation and conservation of many different genetic types and their combinations. In large agricultural areas, in particular where agriculture is practised with modern and often rather uniform methods, a tendency exists that all genetic types which do not sufficiently contribute to the production are exterminated; this causes a lack of diversity within the cultivated species. This growing tendency to modernization and its resulting danger of uniformity means that it has become very urgent to take the necessary measures for conservation of genetic variability.

The following are some examples of centres of genetic diversity for some of the agricultural crops (Frankel 1973):

1. The Mediterranean centre (Italy, Greece, Cyprus, parts of southern France, eastern Spain and northern Africa): wheat.

2. Southwest Asia (Turkey, Georgia, Syria, Iraq, Iran): wheat, barley, rye, oats, several legumes (for example, chickpea = 'greengram' = *Cicer arietinum*), many fruit trees (apple, pear, apricot, almond, etc.).

3. Pakistan/Afghanistan: wheat, pear, plum, grape.

4. African centres (Ethiopia, western Africa): sorghum, African rice (*Oryza barthii*, as compared with *Oryza sativa* the Asian rice), millets (*Pennisetum* sp., *Eleusine sp.*), barley, wheat, various legumes, sweet potato (*Dioscorea sp.*), coffee.

5. South America: potato, tomato, maize, rubber (*Hevea brasiliensis*).

The conservation of genetic variability may be done in various different ways. In some cases nature conservation in large nature reserves is satisfactory. In many cases however it is necessary to ensure the regular cultivation of the species or varieties to be preserved in special institutes with experimental farms. The regular cultivation is essential because seeds have only a limited period of capability for germination, which may be only one or two years after harvesting for some species.

SPECIAL PROBLEMS OF TROPICAL COUNTRIES, SHIFTING CULTIVATION

In the preceding sections, special mention was made of some of the characteristics of tropical soils. The particular problems of land use in tropical regions are partly caused by the nature of the various soils and by the kinds of climates which prevail in these areas. In addition, the nature of some tropical crops requires special methods of cultivation. The cultivation of irrigated rice is not limited to the tropical zone of the world, but only in this zone can this crop, if sufficient quantities of irrigation water are available, be planted throughout the year; two and sometimes three consecutive crops of 'paddy' per year are possible. As an irrigated summercrop, rice is also planted in Mediterranean climates and warm-temperate climates in such localities as southern Portugal, and the Po valley of northern Italy.

Many different kinds of soils are found over large surface areas in the tropics. These include young alluvial soils, soils in volcanic parent materials of various ages and stages of development, as well as various kinds of soils with textural B horizons which are also found in temperate climates: luvisols, nitosols and acrisols, in order of degree of leaching. The ferralsols, which are strongly leached soils with kaolinite as their main clay mineral, and are very poor but often have very good physical properties, are certainly the most typical soils with regard to their soil formation processes, although they occupy perhaps less than 30 per cent of the tropics. These soils, sometimes red, but often brown or yellow in colour, merit some special attention because they rarely occur outside the tropics and have some special characteristics. They are also called oxisols or ferralitic soils and formerly were called latosols. Their properties with regard to land use include the following (Van Wambeke 1974):

1. Tillage: after reclamation from primary forest intensive tillage is impossible because of the many remnants of roots, but in all other cases tillage for the preparation of the seedbed does enhance the yields of the crops; it is uncertain whether this is due to improvement of soil structure and pore-volume or to other factors, such as improved availability of nitrogen caused by the oxidation of organic matter. In general, however, the methods and timing of tillage on ferralsols should be carefully considered as the heavy rainstorms in the tropics are liable to induce erosion; ferralsols are particularly vulnerable to erosion of the A horizon as this horizon contains most of the chemical soil fertility.

2. Fallow: the periodic fallow period in the rotation is a practical way of land use in those areas where the intake of new land is cheaper than the investment in additional materials to maintain the chemical fertility. The fallow used on these soils, which is in general an untilled fallow with spontaneous growth of weeds, has the following effects: (a) increase of organic matter, leading to higher nitrogen content and increased adsorption of cations; (b) the roots of the fallow weeds bring Ca, Mg, K and other nutrients from lower horizons and concentrate these in the topsoil for the benefit of the next crop; (c) soil structure is improved; (d) soil moisture is conserved for the next crop. The efficiency of this kind of fallow is enhanced by the special sowing or planting of leguminous crops.

3. Chemical fertilizers: lack of phosphates is a major constraint and concentrated applications of phosphates near to the roots of the crop (in seed rows, in planting holes) is in general the best method of application. These soils also show a lack of potash and the hazard of leaching of potash is great, due to the low adsorption capacity of the dominant claymineral (kaolinite); potassium fertilizers should therefore preferably be applied regularly in small quantities. Application of calcium-carbonate ($CaCo_3$) for the improvement of pH may also have beneficial influence on phosphate availability.

4. Irrigation: most ferralsols are situated in undulating or rolling topography and are therefore often little suited for gravity irrigation. In general, however, irrigation may be useful, provided that the possibilities of Fe toxicity and deficiencies of mainly bivalent cations (Ca, Mg) are taken into account. These are often due to local reduction of the topsoil leading to a change in the redox potentials (see also Moormann and Van Breemen 1978).

The application of chemical fertilizers on ferralsols and on other tropical soils will have to be strongly increased in the near future in order to feed the growing populations. This is very well possible on most tropical soils within the context of general agricultural development. Despite being strongly weathered without mineral reserve and with a low adsorption capacity ferralsols have the potential for those increases due to their good structure.

It is often suggested that the tropical regions have a less favourable ecological situation than many other regions of the world with regard to agricultural production, and that shifting cultivation, semi-nomadic primitive arable land cultivation organized in a modernized manner, is the best kind of land use in the tropics. This is certainly not true in a general sense. Suggestions of this kind are mostly based on conditions in large areas of Africa, but even in this rather poorly favoured continent, many good soils and favourable landscape conditions are found. In Africa as well as elsewhere in the tropics, many areas with rather young and fertile soils in volcanic parent materials are found, which do not suffer from the limitations of the ferralsols or of the acrisols, another soil group with rather unfavourable properties for land use. But apart from that, many tropical soils are not as strongly weathered as the ferralsols or the acrisols. The formation of these poor soils takes a long time, in any case much more 10 000 years (the duration of the Holocene Period) and therefore, on all younger, or rejuvenated, land surfaces less weathered soils are found. Furthermore, active volcanic areas, although often of limited surface areas themselves, contribute by their volcanic ash often considerably to the mineral reserve of surrounding areas. In addition, the possibilities of improving agricultural methods, even without adopting fully industrialized agriculture in the Western sense, are often underestimated. If, for example, a very general comparison is made between certain agricultural systems in Eastern and Central Africa with those in certain parts of western Africa, the differences between the methods used is very remarkable. In the equatorial parts of Western Africa, the agricultural populations are still only barely sedentary: during the German colonial period in Cameroun, which ended in 1918, still very large migrations occurred and these continued in part after 1945. In Rwanda, on the other hand, a long-settled population of traditional arable land farmers, the Bahutus, have a much better developed system of agriculture, which according to some authors goes back to the old Egyptian systems of agriculture. The present author found, in comparing these systems, that important differences occurred in the use of household refuse for manuring, a very common practice in Rwanda but, at least in 1963, still nearly absent in Central Cameroun. Considering these and other experiences, the possibilities for improving primitive agriculture in the tropics are decidedly greater than is sometimes suggested, provided a prudent approach, adapted to local conditions, is adopted.

On the other hand, well-managed perennial crops (rubber, tea, cocao, coffee, etc.) and shifting cultivation do have certain advantages in some areas of the tropics. These are contingent on the high temperatures, causing rapid oxidation of organic matter, and on the rather rapid leaching of some soils, but probably mostly on the erosion hazards of bare soils due to the heavy tropical rainstorms (sometimes more than 100 mm within one hour). In other aspects as well, including the great vulnerability of this kind of agriculture under modern conditions, some special attention to shifting cultivation is warranted.

Shifting cultivation. In Southeast Asian languages this is often called 'ladang', which may be either a rotation of forest/arable land or grassland/arable land, and has been for thousands of years, not only in tropical regions but also in other parts of the world, the only system for agricultural food production (see for example FAO 1974). Many different kinds of shifting cultivation exist, which all are, or have originally been, adapted to the nature and the possibilities of a certain type of landscape, a certain kind and density of the population and various influential external conditions. In Table 15 some data are given on the farm budget of a comparable system in the Andes of Venezuela. It may be concluded that to some extent, on productive soils, the sale of a part of the product may be possible. Shifting cultivation today is very often not just 'subsistence agriculture' and this is very often necessary because of the external needs and obligations of the farmers.

Over the last few decades several attempts have been and are being made to maintain shifting cultivation as the basic system in some tropical areas, but also to increase its productivity. This may for example, be done by adding small quantities of chemical fertilizers, by the limited use of pesticides, by better weed eradication, or by the introduction of 'agrisylviculture' or 'agroforestry'. The latter is a group of systems, adapted to local conditions, in which not only the arable land is more or less carefully tended, but also the woods grown between two periods of arable cultivation

Table 15. Income and expenses on a typical farm of 3 hectares in the Andes of Venezuela* in Bolivars

Income (including partial sale of products)		Expenses (partially paid to external sources)	
Maize (2 ha) sale 2/3 of product (1070 kg at B 0.30)	320	Labour 50 mandays/ha on 3 ha at B 8.00/day	1200
Black beans (1 ha) 3½ cargas at B 80	280	Implements (incl. depreciation	50
Other income (paid labour at other farms)	300	Seed	120
Value of product used for own nutrition: 1/3 of maize 530 kg at B 0.30	160		
other food crops	350		
Total	1410	Total	1370
		Saldo	40

Source: *After FAO 1974.

are systematically cultivated and planted with selected species of leguminous or other useful crops. This is of high importance both for the useful application of the wood products and for creating favourable soil conditions for the subsequent arable land period. The wood products are of great importance as firewood, often a very scarce commodity, as well as for various on-farm uses such as houses, barns and fences. One of the oldest attempts to systematically improve shifting cultivation is the 'corridor system' or 'couloir system' which was initiated in the period from 1950 to 1960 in Zaire (then the Belgian Congo). In this system the rather haphazard cutting and burning of parts of the forests was replaced by the systematic cutting of 'corridors', in which agriculture was practised, at regular distances. The relation between the width of the corridor and the width of the forest area separating it from the next corridor indicated the duration of the rotation between arable land and forest.

ALTERNATIVE METHODS OF AGRICULTURE

In some cases the excessive application of technology to agriculture since 1945 has led to the development of alternative strategies. One of these is biodynamic agriculture; this approach has existed since early in this century. Various other systems are also trying in different ways to increase ecological awareness in agriculture. In particular, during the 'environmental boom' of 1970 and subsequent years, attention to these methods has grown. A common characteristic of these systems is that they advocate a more holistic approach, i.e. they want to see the cultural ecosystems as living wholes. This is a reaction against the often rather analytical and schematic approach used in the usual technology-focussed methodologies. The latter do have a hazard of deteriorating into a one-sided approach in which those aspects of land use which may be directly influenced by human action, such as tillage, application of fertilizers and pesticides, are over-emphasised and lead to neglect of other aspects. An example of this was found in the approach to soil biology in the years between 1940 and 1950. During that period official science was nearly fully restricted to soil bacteriology, probably partly due to the availability of suitable laboratory techniques. The advocates of more 'biological' methods of agriculture emphasized the importance of earthworms and of other soil animals; the activities of earthworms were described in detail by Charles Darwin. Gradually observations convinced some 'official' scientists of their validity, in particular when it was found that earthworms, termites and other animals play an essential role in 'soil homogenization' and thus in the formation of A horizons and of biological soil activity in general.

The 'biological' approaches present some difficulties in their comparison with conventional methods. Some of their reported phenomena are difficult to measure with conventional standards. They also have a tendency to underestimate the economic aspects of agriculture, which are essential for individual farms as well as for national economies. Furthermore, the very serious problems of the world food situation seem to be rather outside the viewpoint of the people advocating these methods.

This does not mean, however, that the 'biological' methods are of negligible significance as long as it is clearly understood that all agriculture uses biological methods, although sometimes of different kinds. The term 'alternative methods of agriculture' is therefore often preferred. Some of these alternative methods are often applied on farms which yield products of a better than average quality due to a very careful treatment of plants and animals; as a result of this they are often, as long as they are a minority of the farms in a country, able to contain better prices for their products. This is justified, not only because of the special care taken, but also because these farms are to some extent of an experimental nature and may be said to have a pioneer role to fulfil. It should be realized, however, that these prices would not be obtainable if the majority of farms in a region applied their methods with the same care. For certain groups of people, other aspects of life and matters of a religious nature are part of their adherence to these methods; these must of course be respected as long as their believers do not force their beliefs upon other people. The experience which these various groups of people obtain with the application of their methods may, perhaps with suitable modifications, have a certain importance for developments within the normally prevailing kinds of agriculture and horticulture. This is one of the reasons for us to indicate some aspects.

The best known alternative methods of agriculture are: (1) the biodynamic; (2) the organic, (3) the organic-biological; (4) the macrobiotic. The first are based on the anthroposophic tenets of Dr Rudolf Steiner, which consider processes in nature not observable with the normal sense-organs, and which are thought to be based on forces from outside the earth which have influenced on nature. The second originated from the composting techniques developed by Sir Albert Howard, which are aimed at providing all plant nutrients in organic compounds. The third has mainly a bacteriological background, which is used in the approach to plant nutrition. The fourth is based on the law of polarity in life of radiation and contraction (the Chinese philosophy of Yin and Yang), from which is derived the production of a bioconcentrate, sometimes resorbed on ground lava, and made from a well-balanced composition of 80 trace and micro-trace elements. In addition, minute prescriptions on tillage, manuring, crop rotation and other aspects of crop and land management are given. The bio-dynamic agriculture has a complex of well-developed methods which are being applied on many different agricultural and horticultural enterprises, for example in the Netherlands and Switzerland. The importance of earthworms is one of the many facets of their methodology.

The Netherlands Ministry of Agriculture established in 1971 a commission to investigate these various methods. The commission consisted of members from the Ministry and from official research institutes as well as from the various societies representing the alternative methodologies. The final report of this commission was published in 1977 (Commissie 1977). Some conclusions of this report will be given.

Alternative agriculture in the sense of this report are 'those kinds of agriculture which differ from the current agriculture and, which the supporters find that they are "better" or "more biological"'. The following kinds of alternative agriculture were taken into consideration: (1) ANOG-agriculture (of German origin); (2) bio-dynamic agriculture, (3) macrobiotic agriculture; (4) organic-biological agriculture; (5) Howard-Balfour agriculture; (6) mazdanan agriculture; (7) veganistic agriculture; (8) individual methods developed by some growers. Parallels with the medical sciences were also considered. The following aspects are briefly discussed here:

- diseases, pests and weeds,
- yields in kilograms per hectare,
- quality of the products grown with alternative methods,
- economic aspects,
- change-over to alternative agriculture,
- environmental impacts,
- technical means available for the expansion of alternative agriculture.

For the control of pests and diseases alternative agriculture uses the following as much as possible: a varied crop rotation, resistant or tolerant cultivars, non-cultivation of crops in areas where pest-hazards are high, biological plant protection (predators and pathogens), planting of hedges to harbour birds and other predators, placing of nesting-boxes, application of special preparations based on ash and on liquid manure (bio-dynamic), growing of combined crops and of cover crops below trees, crops which catch nematodes, pesticides of vegetable origin but sometimes also other pesticides such as copper (ANOG, Howard-Balfour) and sulphur and comparable herbicides. In the current as well as in the alternative agriculture, the prevention of pests and diseases is preferrèd to combating them. The difference lies mainly in the emphasis on economic criteria in current agriculture which often prefers chemical means as being cheaper, as least as a short-term solution; by this it may too much neglect the long-term problems of an ecological nature.

The *yields in kilograms per hectare* of many arable land crops grown in the Netherlands using alternative agriculture, with the exception of potatoes, are equal to those in the current systems of agriculture. For potatoes and for open-air horticulture, the yields of alternative agriculture have been found to be considerably lower (10 to 30%). The nutritive value of the products of alternative agriculture is said to be higher. The good yields from alternative agriculture are, however, partly made possible by the use of large quantities of organic manure which is obtained from normal farms. The use of the excess quantities of manure from what is sometimes called 'bio-industry' (pig-raising, calf-fattening) could be said however to be an advantage to society as the disposal of these is a major environmental problem in some areas of the Netherlands.

The *quality* of the products grown with alternative methods may be investigated with regard to the external properties (shape, colour, freshness, solidity, etc.) and to the internal quality. The former is in general not lower than that of current agriculture except for hard fruit (apple, pear) which in general is lower in alternative systems (less consumption quality, more industrial quality). There exist differences of opinion with regard to the internal quality as the norms applied by adherents of alternative agriculture cannot be verified with the normal approaches of nutrition science. In some cases which could be checked, such as the nitrate-contents of lettuce, often but not always the results were in favour of the alternative systems: lower, i.e. better, nitrate content during the summer months.

With regard to the *economic aspects*, thus far no well-founded judgement has been possible. The growers with alternative systems often are prepared to accept a lower income for their labour than those in current agriculture and consider that their feasibility is sufficient reward. A considerable part of the labour on alternative farms is provided by volunteers of several kinds, which is not possible under normal conditions. In general, it cannot be said that the costs in alternative agriculture are higher than those in the normal systems, but in cases of lower yields in kilograms per hectare the costs per unity of product might be higher. At present, the exclusiveness of the products of alternative agriculture obtains higher prices with consumers. This advantage would disappear with expansion over large surface areas. A different kind of economic system would then be needed to keep this kind of agriculture feasible.

The *change-over* from normal agriculture to any kind of alternative systems depends on the original situation and on the kind of alternative system which is chosen. The duration of the change-over period may in general vary from at least one year (to ANOG) to five or six years (to macrobiotic systems).

The *environmental impact* of alternative systems of agriculture is in some cases definitely less (for example, the soil is not disinfected with chemicals) than in current agriculture, but in other cases (nitrogen manuring) approximately equal. Neither alternative agriculture nor current agriculture produces any environmental impact with regard to phosphates. The use in some systems of alternative agriculture of composted urban refuse may lead to increases in the contents of heavy metals in the soils. The use of manure from pig-fattening, which often contains excess copper, is completely rejected in some kinds of alternative agriculture, whereas this is allowed, below certain maximum limits, in current agriculture. The application of some of the pesticides and herbicides used in alternative agriculture may be just as deleterious as that of the chemicals normally used in current agriculture. This is also true for their side-effects and their persistence. In alternative agriculture the degree and manner of application are more precisely controlled, which still results in a less unfavourable environmental impact. The popular idea that alternative agriculture is, per definition, more propitious for the environment is however based on an insufficient knowledge of the data.

The *technical applicability* of a large extension of alternative agriculture must be regarded from two different points:

1. The very small surface area currently used in alternative agriculture (in the Netherlands 0.3 per cent of the total agricultural area).

2. The total production of calories by a country with regard, to the needs of the world population; in the Netherlands this is at present more than required by its own population and in the future has to be at least large enough to cover the country's requirements.

Regarding the first, it has to be pointed out that alternative agriculture often has to obtain its seeds and other planting materials from normal agriculture. The latter has very strict regulations with regard to the freedom from diseases and pests of these planting materials. Alternative agriculture, which today operates as small islands within large areas of current agriculture, profits to some extent from the effective plant protection applied in its surrounding areas; it obtains from normal agriculture a large amount of indirect plant protection. The nutrient equilibrium of minerals in alternative agriculture shows large deficiencies in phosphates and potassium, which would lead in the case of a nationwide expansion of the alternative systems to a rapid decrease of production of considerable size; the total food production of the Netherlands would in that case be only 20 per cent or less of the actual production (a decrease of 80%). The phosphate deficiencies could be improved by enhancing the consumption of fish of various kinds and by applying the refuse resulting from this completely to agriculture; but this raises the problem of the intensity of fisheries allowed in the adjoining seas, already today a serious problem. The deficiency of potassium would be incurable, even if the most efficient systems for compost production would be applied; and if the application of potash-containing manures is done as efficiently as possible, for example by liquid applications at regular periods. A possible solution might be found by recovering as much as possible the potassium from the sewage plants, but this would require very specialized technical methods. Even then, for the Netherlands, a need for the application of mineral fertilizers would remain. Only a systematic adaptation of the human pattern of food consumption might eventually lead to a permanent solution. This would lead to serious problems in society but in this manner the national food requirements of the country might be met.

LAND UTILIZATION TYPES AND FARMING SYSTEMS

A land utilization type provides a specific manner of classifying, and where necessary modifying, land use. Land utilization types in planning are also called 'land use alternatives' (Beek 1978). The land use to which this concept is applied may be one of many different major kinds of land use; for example, agriculture, forestry, recreation and nature management (the internal management of nature reserves). A land utilization type may be described in greater or lesser detail and this may be useful in clarifying certain technical and ecological management problems as well as for land evaluation (see Ch. 8), in particular with regard to land suitability or land (use) capability. In detailed studies for agriculture, the following data are used for characterizing land utilization types: crop or crop rotation, nature of the source of power (man, animals, machines), the amount of labour applied per unit surface area (acre, hectare), the application of capital investments (irrigation, drainage, machines, chemicals, etc.), the level of knowledge, both general and technical, of the farmers, and the surface area of the basic unit (field, parcel) of the land utilization type. In forestry, some of the determinants for specific land use objectives or forestry land utilization types are related to: : (1) government (development situation, policies, status of services etc.); (2) location (critical distances, urban influence, infrastructure, means of transportation); (3) produce; (4) labour; (5) capital; (6) technology; (7) management; (8) socio-economic parameters; (Laban 1981).

The human activities for production and management are the focal point of a land utilization type. They are the means of converting natural ecosystems to production-directed ecosystems as well as to protect, and where necessary manage, natural ecosystems, either for production or for nature conservation. The following definition of a land utilization type is used here:

Definition.'A land utilization type is a coherent complex of human activities which are applied over a long period by one or more men, organized in some coherent system on any given tract of land for the satisfying of one or more, material and or spiritual, human needs.'

A land utilization system is the combination of a given land utilization type (LUT) with a given land unit (L) (see also Beek 1978).

A coherent complex of human activities encompasses activities which are applied only once as well as activities which are repeated with a certain regularity, either seasonal or annual or otherwise. In general, in any LUT, both kinds are applied, but in different proportions for each LUT. The activities may be the building of a house, a factory or a theatre as well as the planting or management of a forest or the growing of crops within any kind of agriculture, horticulture or pastoral system. This also includes the establishment and management of parks, sports fields, and other recreational facilities, all of which are typical examples of the satisfying of body as well as spiritual needs. The coherent system in which men are organized may be a natural unit, such as is found on family-farms, a commercial enterprise such as a large commercial, co-operative or state farm, or a public institution (state forestry service, nature conservancy organization, municipal sports-grounds). Some of these systems have a clear economic purpose, for example in agricultural enterprises or factories, others have ecological goals (nature conservation) or goals which are related to the psychological needs of people (recreation). The various kinds of industrial land utilization types have, as such, only a limited ecological meaning, but their impacts on their environment, i.e. surrounding ecosystems, may be considerable both as users of land resources (mining, including such activities as gravel pits, clay extraction, etc.) and with regard to various kinds of physical and chemical impacts (pollution, noise).

The term 'land utilization type' has been originally introduced for use in the methodology of land evaluation, where it has been found to provide a means for combining the ecological and technical aspects of land use with the economic and social circumstances (see Beek 1978; FAO 1976). Figure 19 is a diagram of land utilization types within their context of land utilization systems and farming systems. A certain LUT, with a particular crop rotation (e.g. of cereals and row crops), with a defined set of human activities, is applied on a certain tract of land L, with its own climate, topography, soil etc. Together these form a land utilization system, LUS. Even with a relatively small number of different units of LUT and L, a rather large number of their combinations (different LUS) is possible. LUS are technological and ecological entities. One or more LUS form together a farming system, FS, which is an economic unit containing one or more technological – ecological LUS as the means of obtaining its economic (and/or sociologic, or conservational etc.) goals. An example of a simple FS is found in wine-growing in various parts of Italy, where farms of approximately 10 ha surface area consist of farm buildings plus one LUS: a vineyard on flat to undulating well-drained chromic luvisols in sandy clayloam. More complicated farming systems are, for example, found in Sri Lanka and in various parts of Indonesia, where a normal farm has at least three different LUS: (a) paddy on irrigated fields; (b) a homestead garden on the lower slopes of the hills; and (c) dryland arable land (chena, tegallan) on the upper slopes and on the tops of the hills.

Definition: 'A farming system is a complex of relationships between land, labour, capital goods and influences of the social, economic and political environment, directed by an entrepreneur or a group of entrepreneurs, who try to produce products on the basis of his/their knowledge, preferences and goals, with certain methods.' A farming system may cover the area of one, or part of one, land (evaluation) unit or of a combination of such units, including the land utilization types present or projected on these areas, therefore of one or more land utilization systems.

A still larger unit than the farming system is the village system. In many rural areas this is a very applicable quantity, as the village, with its village green, village pond and central goods and services and artisan activities, is a combination of ecological, social and other aspects which functions as a complex system. An example of this is given by Soemarwoto (1977) and similar systems occur in many Asian and African areas and have existed in most parts of Europe until the early years of the present century. The basic

Fig. 19 Diagram of land utilization types within their context of land utilization systems and farming systems

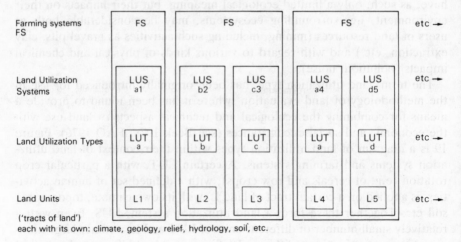

Farming systems FS — FS — FS — etc →

Land Utilization Systems — LUS a1, LUS b2, LUS c3, LUS a4, LUS d5 — etc →

Land Utilization Types — LUT a, LUT b, LUT c, LUT a, LUT d — etc →

Land Units — L 1, L 2, L 3, L 4, L 5 — etc →

('tracts of land')
each with its own: climate, geology, relief, hydrology, soil, etc.

unit in all these cases is, however, the land utilization system as a technological and ecological system.

Most land utilization systems, including rural as well as urban kinds, may be considered to be special kinds of ecosystems. They contain certain structured communities of organisms in combination with biotic and abiotic factors, including their material as well as their psychological aspects. All these ecosystems are however systematically managed by man and therefore, following several Russian authors, they are to be called '*cultural ecosystems*'. Some aspects of urban ecosystems will be discussed in the next chapter. In a previous section the land utilization types of nature conservation were mentioned. Some indications on land utilization types in forestry and in recreation are given in Table 16. In the following some factors determining other rural land utilization types, in particular in agriculture, will be discussed.

Land utilization types are mainly characterized by the following sets of characteristics: (1) social and institutional characteristics; (2) infrastructural characteristics; (3) nature, kind; and (in broad dimensions) quantity of products; (4) basic (long-term) investments; (5) annual costs, (6) labour intensity; (7) sources of power (nature, type and use intensity).

Examples of social, institutional and infrastructural characteristics are the nature of land tenure (full ownership, various kinds of tenant right, primitive communal rights, etc.), surface area of the farm and of a land utilization type within a farm, and level of knowledge of the farmer (general schooling, technical schooling). The latter may for example be expressed as levels of management. The American Soil Survey Manual (Soil Survey Staff 1951) distinguishes between three different levels of management: (1) the average level of all farmers in a region; (2) the average of the best 10 per

Table 16. Some illustrations of land utilization types in recreation and in forestry

(a) Recreational land uses in the Netherlands

Environment	Facility	Density (pers./ha)	Surface area (ha)
A	Crowded beach	3000	2–5
	Sport stadium	over 3000	5
B	Beach	1000	5–10
	Open-air pool	1000	5–10
	Zoo	500	20
	Sports field with tribune	1000	5
	Racecourse	500	30
C	Camping	120	10–25
	Quiet beach	100	10
	Playgrounds in park	100–200	various
	Beaches, lakes forest-fringes	100	various
	Sports fields	100	20–30
D	Small sailing lake	20	50–100
	Golf course	20	50
	Forest-park	10–20	50–100
E	Productive forest (easily penetrable)	3–10	over 250
	Heather (easily penetrable)	3–10	over 100
	Agric. area in recr. zone	5	over 200
	Large lakes	10	over 200

* Different types, not specified here

(b) Recreational features from the Canada Land Inventory

Angling	Upland wildlife
Beach	Cultural landscape
Canoe tripping	Topographic patterns
Deep inshore water	Rock formations
Vegetation	Skiing area
Waterfalls and rapids	Thermal springs
Glacier	Deep water boat tripping
Historic site	Viewing
Gathering and collecting	Wetland wildlife
Organized camps	Family boating
Landforms	Man-made features
Small surface waters	Miscellaneous
Lodging	

(c) Land-use objectives in forestry and major kinds of forest use

Specific land-use objectives	Major kind of forest use	Other specifications
Storage of genes and/or development of knowledge	1. Nature conservation forest	No other use

Specific land-use objectives	Major kind of forest use	Other specifications
Environmental protection	2. Watershed protection forest	To limit undesirable effects on air/water/soil
	3. Arrest of desertification	As 2
	4. Sand dune fixation forest	As 2
Foraging	5. Foraging forest	For foraging of wood and minor products by local population
Recreation and tourism	6. Recreation forest	Other uses limited
Wood production	7. (Semi)-natural forest for timber	For concession exploitation with or without enrichment with indigenous or exotic species
	8. Conversion forest	As reserve prior to conversion to man-made forest or non-forest use
	9. Production forest for fuel-wood	On permanent or temporary basis
	10. Production forest for industrial wood (pulp, etc.)	
	11. Production forest for timber	Plantations in long-cycle rotations
Production of other forest products	12. Production forest for resin, game harvesting, etc.	On a commercial basis
Agro-forestry production	13. Shifting cultivation forest	Mostly combined with foraging
	14. Agroforest for wood and food crops	Forestry and agriculture combined on a permanent basis
	15. Agroforest for wood and fodder crops	As 14
	16. Range forest	Forestry and grazing combined on a permanent basis

Source: (a) Maas 1971, cited by Vink 1975; (b) Department of Regional Economic Expansion 1969, cited by Vink 1975a; (c) Laban 1981.

cent farmers of the region; (3) the best which is to be found on experimental farms. In general, these levels have less correlations with the nature and quantity, or the cost, of the land management and more with the careful and well-timed application of the various measures. These depend largely on the weather conditions, the soil conditions at a given moment, the stages of growth of the crops or the condition of the cattle. Regarding infrastructural characteristics, special attention has to be paid to the transport and marketing situation, in particular with regard to easily perishable horticultural products. In regions with polders and with similar needs for systematic land drainage, as well as in regions with irrigation and in those with a need for soil conservation, the institutional and infrastructural requirements for drainage districts, irrigation districts or soil conservation districts are of particular importance.

The nature, the kind and, to some extent, the quantity of products are characteristic indications of land utilization types. These refer in the first place to the crops grown (monocultures, rotations, improved grasslands, forests). It is also necessary to note the manner in which the products are either directly sold (cereals), or fed to cattle on the same farm (some cereals, various forages). In some cases products are further treated within the same farm (tea, coffee, cacao) to half-products or fully treated end-products. The quantity of a product within a land utilization type may only within major dimensions be seen as a characteristic of the land utilization type as it is rather a result of the interaction between land utilization type and land unit, and therefore of the land utilization system as a whole.

The basic long-term investments are those which are made within the farm or within a particular land utilization type of the farm, in land improvement, in land conservation or in farm buildings. With regard to the former, terracing, permanent drainage systems and irrigation systems are within this category. Some of these will be indicated in Chapter 7. Other, partly comparable, investments are those in large agricultural machinery, but their discussion is outside the scope of this book. Regarding landscape ecology, the permanent investments in the land, sometimes called 'major land improvements', are more relevant as these lead in general to the formation of artefactial attributes of the land itself. In particular, the annual costs are related to seed, planting materials, fertilizers, pesticides, herbicides and other regularly recurring costs of crop- and land management as well as to harvest and further treatment of the products. Labour intensity, also mainly one of the annually recurrent costs, is in general considered separately; it is often very characteristic for a particular land utilization type. It is often very much related to the power sources which are used, the most elementary power source being human labour and in primitive land utilization types all energy applied is directly derived from this. Human labour as an exclusive source of energy is generally applied with the use of simple implements such as spades, hoes and, for irrigation, with simple levers with a water scoop such as the Assyrian 'Dalia', which was already used in some arid countries some 4000 years ago and still is a useful instrument in some areas (Vink 1975). The next step in developing power sources is found in the use of animals (horses, cattle, donkeys, camels) and this is still the most important source in most traditional agricultural land utilization types. Water and wind power, such as windmills for drainage, are locally next in the line of development and may become more important again in the near future, as the present development stage, the use of fossil fuels, may tend to decrease in importance due to its rapidly rising cost. Water power for use in irrigation may even be combined with the use of the same water for irrigation, as is shown in the Flumendosa project of southern Sardinia. In this large irrigation project, which will eventually cover approximately 200 000 ha, the original energy of the water eventually used for irrigation is partly converted into electricity which is then applied for the pumping systems and for sprinkler irrigation in the same area. Energy flow is important for cultural as well as for natural ecosystems. The most typical aspect of cultural ecosystems may even be said to be the addition of human energy (see Odum 1975 and H. P. Odum cited by Vink 1975a). The present trend to give more attention to energy flow may have been partly induced by the predicted scarcity of fossil fuels, but it has a more fundamental character. Various kinds of energy balances are possible within different land utilization types. Even in modern industrialized agriculture, various proportions of human labour and fossil energy may be used to produce the same results (De Wit 1975). Some examples of the application of energy in different kinds of land use are given in Table 17.

Some comments have to be made in regard to Table 17(b). Traditional Mexican maize-growing produces an energy output which is 128 times its energy input, whereas the fully mechanized type from the USA gives an output which is only somewhat over two times the energy input. This does not mean at all that by these figures the industrialized systems of agriculture have to be condemned. This becomes clear when the differences are compared, rather than the ratios. In this comparison the North American industrialized type produces a nett gain of 10 104 210 kcal (over 42 million kJ) and the Mexican type a nett gain of 6 712 120 kcal (some 28 million kJ). The difference means a considerable advantage for the industrialized type, in particular if the possible means of a more stable production in industrialized agriculture (due to plant protection, irrigation and other cultural techniques) are also considered. This calculation does indicate, however, that the design of new land utilization types has to take these aspects into account. An old, generally unspoken, axiom that industrialized agriculture would always be better than the traditional systems will have to be replaced by a careful comparison of needs and results. It may be found that in various circumstances, even without taking socio-economic constraints into account, the traditional land utilization types, possibly with some adaptations, will be more useful than the introduction of modern industrialized agriculture. Decisions on these aspects have also to take into account the relative performances of the different land use alternatives in the different landscapes and on different soils. Conventional solutions for land use development will have to be replaced by carefully considered options in which potential degradation as well as energy efficiency and other ecological aspects of land and land use have to be balanced against human requirements. Some attention will be paid to land degradation in Chapter 7. Finally, in Chapter 8, some indications will be given for the comparison and combination of the various aspects by means of land classification and land evaluation.

Table 17. Some data on energy in agricultural ecosystems

(a) Total energy investments in irrigated rice production in Kcal/ha

Process	Traditional	Transitional	Green revolution	Experimental
Seeding	27 000	27 000	31 770	5 580
Land preparation	109 650	373 900	496 340	283 650
Fertilization	9 360	111 390	1 954 627	1 146 467
Insect control	—	108 000	65 365	45 117
Weed control	—	72 000	435 395	156 027
Irrigation	3 600	36 000	1 183 980	609 990
Harvesting	131 500	180 300	167 847	104 990
Threshing	46 800	135 900	139 430	77 840
Other (cost of energy, seed*, drying†, and transportation)	—	419 740	1 020 000	1 020 000
Totals	327 910	1 464 230	5 494 754	3 449 661

* Cost of seed production based on estimates calculated by Pimentel *et al.* (1973).
† Energy estimates of drying and transportation based on an assessment done by the Food and Agricultural Organization reported in 1976.

(b) Comparison of energy inputs and outputs in a traditional farming system for maize production in Mexico and in an industrialized farming system for maize production in the USA, all data per hectare

(A) Mexico: farm exclusively with human labour, maize production

Input		
Labour	1 144 manhours	16 570 kcal
Axe and hoe	0.8 kg	
Seeds	10.4 kg	36 192 kcal
Total	(a)	52 762 kcal
Output		
Gross production	(b)	6 765 120 kcal
Ratio output/input		128.2 kcal
Nett production	(b) – (a)	6 712 358 kcal

(B) USA: completely mechanized farm, maize production, irrigated

Input (year 1975)		
Labour	17 manhours	
Machines	—	1 420 250 kcal
Fuel	210 litres	2 100 000 kcal
Fertilizers	315 kg	3 003 500 kcal
Seeds	21 kg	146 160 kcal
Irrigation	—	780 000 kcal
Insecticides	1 kg	101 000 kcal
Herbicides	2 kg	181 000 kcal
Drying of product	—	375 000 kcal
Electricity	—	380 000 kcal
Transport	—	180 000 kcal
Total	(a)	8 666 910 kcal

Table 17(b) cont

Output	
Maize production (5 394 kg) (b)	18 771 120 kcal
Ratio output/input	2 16
Nett production (b) – (a)	10 104 210 kcal

Conversion factor: 1 kcal = 4.2 kJ
Sources: (a) Freedman 1980; (b) After Pimentel and Pimentel 1977.

In these and in other aspects of land development for agriculture, the research institutes of the Consultative Group on International Agricultural Research (CGIAR) will have to play a considerable role, together with other national and international institutions. The following list of the institutes of the abovementioned group is given for the information of the reader:

International Rice Research Institute (IRRI), Los Banos, Philippines.
International Maize and Wheat Improvement Center (CIMMYT), El Batan, Mexico.
International Institute of Tropical Agriculture (IITA), Ibadan, Nigeria.
International Centre of Tropical Agriculture (CIAT), Palmira, Colombia.
International Crops Research Institute for the Semi-Arid Tropics (ICRI-SAT), Hyderabad, India
International Potato Center (CIP), Lima, Peru.
International Laboratory for Research on Animal Diseases (ILRAD), Nairobi, Kenya.
International Livestock Centre for Africa (ILCA), Addis Ababa, Ethiopia.

6
Urban ecology

GENERAL

During the last few years there has been a growing insight that towns, and in general urbanized areas, have to be considered as cultural ecosystems. Towns are structured communities of various kinds of organisms (men, animals, plants) which have a certain structured set of relationships with the abiotic environmental factors: climate, soil, water and topography. Various processes are active within these structures and these influence the phenomena in a manner which is basically not so very different from that in rural cultural ecosystems.

Urban areas are landscapes in the sense of Chapter 1. They consist of certain patterns of tracts of land and these fulfil the basic definitions of land and landscape. The fact that the influence of man strongly dominates with regard to the nature of the artefactial attributes of the land (houses, streets) as well as of the processes, does not make a fundamental difference with rural landscapes. This strong human dominance does explain, however, that urban landscapes have long escaped the attention of physical geographers, although human geographers have often investigated various social aspects. Investigations on urban environments have also been carried out by medical as well as technical research groups and by sociologists. Urban architects as well as landscape planners have paid attention to the visual aspects of towns, the latter in particular with regard to urban parks. In the Netherlands and in Belgium soil surveyors have during the last three decades made special surveys for town and country planning and for urban extension. The development of the environmental sciences after 1970 has increased attention to the urban areas as human environments in a more general sense. This included in the first place the study of environmental hygiene, especially the pollution of air, water and soils. Concurrently, however, more insight was obtained on the urban structures and processes as a whole. This included phenomena and processes in the geosphere (see Ch. 1) which have always been studied for rural landscapes by physical geographers. It is understandable that urban climatology was one of the first subjects to attract more attention (Duvigneaud 1974; Van Zuylen 1971, 1973). Drainage problems in towns have also gained more attention at a rather early stage.

In an international context these developments were stimulated by the start of the MAB project no. 11: Ecological effects of energy utilization in urban and industrial systems, which in fact was enlarged to include the urban environment as a whole (UNESCO 1973; Boyden 1980). An expert panel for the establishment of this project gave the following conclusions:

1. The term 'urban system' is used for all human settlements with 20 000 or more inhabitants who live close together and where the system shows a considerable degree of social, economic and political organization.

2. Various ways of approaching the problems are needed; for example, large-scale model investigations, research on budgets of energy and materials and investigations on indicators of the quality of the urban environment; with regard to the latter, biological and medical indicators of human well-being are taken into consideration.

3. Regarding the execution of investigations, the following points merit special attention: (a) integration of urban systems and analysis of urban ecosystems, including the zones of contact between urban and rural systems; (c) investigations on human well-being in urban areas.

4. Investigations will have to take into account the existing differences in cultural, economic, physical and biological characteristics of the various urban ecosystems (see Fig. 20 and Table 18).

An American workshop on urban ecosystems (Stearns and Montag 1974) attempted an holistic approach to the various aspects of urban ecology. This was done in an interdisciplinary context in which understandably the social aspects predominated. From the 26 recommendations of this project, the following are of particular importance for our subject:

- more investigations are needed on the relationships between land units and social variables in order to arrive at a better spatial planning;

Fig. 20 The dynamic feedback structures of natural and cultural ecosystems within the context of MAB-project no. 11 (after UNESCO 1973)

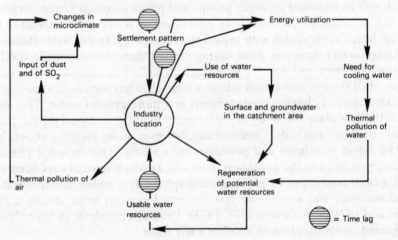

Table 18. Suggested categories and subcategories for the collection of information in urban ecosystems

Ecology of urban–industrial systems

(1) General environmental conditions for man	(2) Structural units (urban subsystems)	(3) Human activities
1. Availability and quality of space	1. Industry	1. Production, consumption and investment
2. Climate	2. Central business district	2. Exports and imports
3. Air quality	3. Housing areas	3. Transportation and communication activities
4. Water supply and quality	4. Public utilities	4. Residuals management
5. Material supply	5. Transportation and communication lines	5. Migration
6. Solid waste	6. Green space	6. Education activities
7. Energy supply	7. Suburban rural and wooded area	7. Social activities
8. Noise level and quality		8. Political activities
9. Organisms (other than man)		9. Recreation and cultural activities

Sources: UNESCO 1973 (see also Boyden 1980)

- more investigations are needed on the functioning of plants and animals in urban ecosystems and on their significance for man;
- more investigations are needed on the role and significance of urban parks, marshy areas, abandoned lands and other (semi)natural areas for urban ecology;
- the use of energy in towns has to be investigated with special attention to the internal structure of the different towns (e.g. topography in relation to traffic);
- thorough investigations are needed on the comparison between urban and natural ecosystems in order to study the laws and processes which may, or may not, be applicable.

In the following text, attention is as much as possible concentrated on those aspects of urban ecology which have clear relationships with landscape ecology. It is hoped that the available, often rather fragmentary or local, data will lead to more systematic investigations in the near future. The aspects to be discussed are:

- the urban system,
- the situation of a town in the landscape (climate, water, geology, soils)
- biological structures and processes in the urban environment,
- some references to energy, to visual aspects and to bio-indicators.

In urban ecology, perhaps more than anywhere else, the boundaries between natural sciences, medical sciences and social sciences become vague.

In the following, the natural science aspects will dominate as these belong more properly to physical geography.

THE URBAN SYSTEM

It has been found useful to investigate and discuss a town as a system in a manner comparable to that used for other ecosystems. This has been done in a very clear manner by the Belgian ecologist Duvigneaud (1974), who writes of the 'System Urbs' (Urbs: Latin = town). An outline of this is given in Fig. 21.

A town, like any other ecosystem, is an open system which exchanges energy and materials with its environment. The incoming energy consists of the radiation of the sun as well as of various imports: electricity, fuels, food, the latter in particular as carbohydrates for human nutrition. On the other hand, energy is exported from the system and a part of this consists of heat as will be indicated below with regard to urban climates. To the imported materials belong the rainwater and the water imported by pipelines for public utilities; in urban areas with a sloping topography also water from surface flow and from subsurface flow is imported as well as exported. Figure 21 furthermore indicates several other materials such as clothes, building materials and commercial materials. Export of materials consists, for example, of water through sewerage systems, of industrial products, of commercial materials and of solid refuse. Traffic and migrating birds also take part in import

Fig. 21 Diagram of the system 'Urbs' (after Duvigneaud et al. 1975)

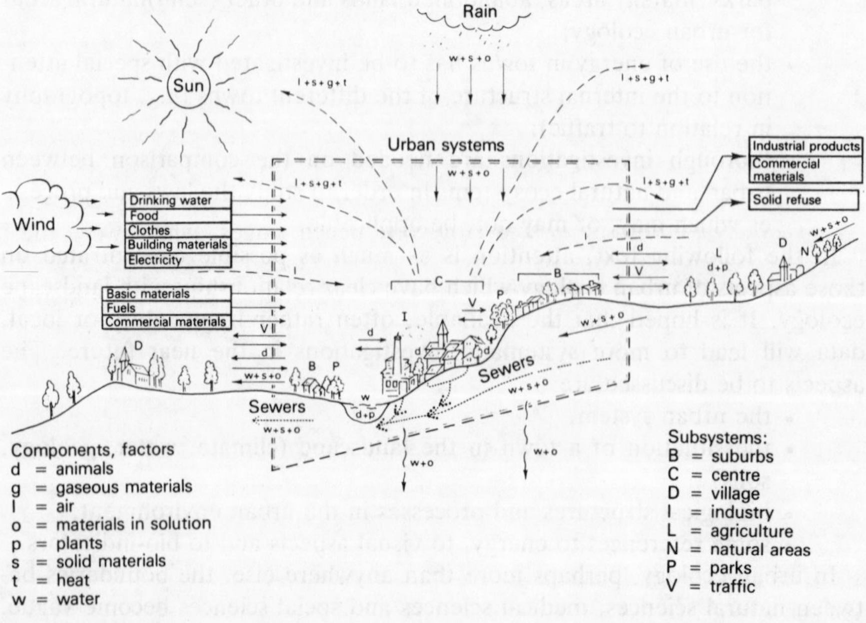

into and export from the system. For Brussels various quantitative data are given by Duvigneaud (1974, 1975).

The urban system consists of various subsystems. Some of these have been indicated, for example: centre, industry, suburbs, parks and traffic. To indicate some relationships with other systems, some of these have been indicated: D = village, L = agriculture, N = nature areas. Some of the characteristics of urban subsystems are described in the following sections. Various phenomena and processes of rural systems have been discussed in Chapter 5.

The base of urban systems consists of the abiotic landscape, which has been indicated in the figure with relief and water. These, together with geology and soils, will be discussed in a separate section. Although the human interference is much greater here than in most rural landscapes, the abiotic aspects of the landscape have much more influence than is often thought. The case of Brussels makes this clear. Three different major landscapes may be distinguished: (1) the low-lying area which is a part of the Humid Loam Region of Belgium and in which a number of small rivers are found (e.g. the Zenne) as well as a marshy area (le Marais, the Marsh) after which Brussels was in fact called (Brussels in Flemish = Broek-zele, a settlement in or near a marsh) and where the old town centre is still situated; (2) a cuesta (steep escarpment) of Tertiary formations (viz.Eocene, the Bruxellien) with related dissected slopes; (3) the higher situated area where the Tertiary surface is covered by loess deposits and which slopes gradually towards the south at Waterloo. These three major landscapes are easy to find even for the non-trained observer and are indicated by the main relief features themselves as well as by the nature of the urban land use. With some knowledge of geomorphology, similar distinctions may be made in other towns; for example the glacial relief features to be found in Glasgow and the late Pleistocene and Holocene eolian relief features which are found in large parts of Berlin. Even in the flat country of the Netherlands comparable landscape differences may be distinguished, such as the Pleistocene ridges of Arnhem and Nijmegen. Many of the towns in the polder areas of the western Netherlands have originally been built on old-Holocene beach ridges, which were the only relatively high and dry parts to be found for human settlement. This is still clear in the town centre of The Hague as well as in Haarlem and Alkmaar. The significance of this with regard to the planting of trees in these towns will be discussed below. In other towns, for example in Amsterdam, which was mainly built on peat marshes adjoining the Amstel river, social settlement processes have always dominated the urban land use. In general social processes are a dominating factor in urban settlement and development, but these are outside the scope of this book.

The way in which human beings undergo the positive and negative effects of their urban environment is a crucial factor in urban ecology. Investigations on this are lately beginning to influence urban planning. A very comprehensive research project on this was carried out under the auspices of the

Table 19. Data on nuisance to the population caused by air pollution and noise respectively in: the Amsterdam area, the Rotterdam area ('Rijnmond Administrative Region') and the other parts of the Netherlands combined, according to a systematic enquiry initiated by the Rijnmond Administrative Region around 1973

(a) Degree in which personal nuisance is experienced from *noise* (in % per area)

Frequency	Amsterdam area* (%)	Rotterdam area (%)	Netherlands (%)
Never	58	66	71
Occasionally	18	15	14
Regularly	11	9	7
Often	12	9	7

* This area is near to Schiphol International Airport

(b) The nature of nuisance experienced from *air pollution* (% of total contacted persons indicating the nuisance)

Nature of the nuisance	Amsterdam area (%)	Rotterdam area (%)	Netherlands (%)
Stench	71	82	63
Dirtying of washed linen	25	12	11
Dirt enters houses	23	11	8
Soot layer on cars	19	14	8
Soot is precipitated	14	7	9
Coughing, throat complaints	8	12	12
Headache	7	10	12
Irritated, watering eyes	3	9	5
Vomiting tendencies	4	5	5

(c) The nature of the nuisance experienced due to noise (% of total contacted persons)

Nature of the nuisance	Amsterdam area (%)	Rotterdam area (%)	Netherlands (%)
Disturbance of sleep	35	52	40
Disturbance of radio and reception	29	18	14
Disturbance of thought concentration	24	17	19
Disturbance of conversation	24	15	16
Lack of privacy	2	4	4
Causes fright	10	9	16
Causes irritation	7	8	13
Causes restlessness in children	5	4	6
Causes terror	2	1	3
Numbers of respondents: (a)	1971	2000	477
(b)	725	1052	118
(c)	820	640	134

Source: Van Rijn *et al*. 1976.

Rijnmond Administrative Region, a sub-province administering the Port of Rotterdam and its surrounding area, including Rotterdam itself as well as some smaller towns. The project included sociological enquiries in various quarters of the towns situated in this region as well as similar investigations in the Amsterdam area whilst comparative investigations were carried out by sampling in the remaining parts of the Netherlands (Van Rijn *et al.* 1976). Some data from this project are given as an example in Table 19.

Boyden (1980) mentions several research projects on urban ecology which have been established according to the guidelines of MAB project no. 11. These include investigations in Papua New Guinea, Venezuela, Egypt, Italy (Rome), Thailand and in Poland. Many of these projects have been established in order to provide data for planning and many of their data and conclusions are being used for this purpose.

URBAN CLIMATES

As has been discussed in Chapter 3, climate is the most dominating factor in landscape ecology. This is also true for towns, which are considered to be a special group of landscapes. The following elements of the urban climate show marked differences with the climates of rural ecosystems (see also Duvigneaud 1974):

1. A town has predominantly stone surfaces which conduct heat approximately three times as well as does a normal humid soil; in addition the absorbed heat is stored in buildings and warms the air inside these buildings.

2. The town itself produces a large amount of heat, in particular in winter, but also in summer and in warm climates due to industry and traffic.

3. The distribution in space of the precipitation is in towns very different from that in natural ecosystems; the water runs rapidly towards runnels, drains and sewers. This also increases the nett availability of heat as it is less used for evapotranspiration of plants.

4. The composition of the air in towns is different from that in rural ecosystems with respect to solids, liquids and gases. Approximately 80 per cent of solids and liquids consists of very small particles which, as aerosols, remain in suspension in the air for a duration of several days. This suspension causes the formation of a cloud-like mass, which on the one hand reflects radiation from the sun, and on the other hand causes the heat of the earth surface to be retained in the near layers of air.

The properties of the land surface in towns differ from those in natural areas in two respects, namely the physical properties and the surface structures. Building stone or concrete has a different 'albedo' (reflection of radiation) from that of a natural soil surface and it has also a different specific heat and a different coefficient of heat conductivity. With regard to the surface structure, many surfaces in a town are in such a manner that the radiation of the sun has, at certain times, a vertical incidence. The rapid drainage of precipitation furthermore causes the relative humidity in towns to be lower by some percents than in rural areas (in American towns 8% in summer and 2% in winter (Van Zuylen 1971)). Observations in Amsterdam (Van Zuylen 1971) indicated that the monthly average daylight temperatures are 0.3 to 0.5 °C higher than in the surrounding areas; the maximum temperatures in Amsterdam are 0.1 to 0.3 °C higher and the minimum temperatures 0.8 to 1.5 °C higher than in the rural areas.

A town, therefore, is a heat island due to the above-mentioned factors which include the presence of a dome of dust which, especially during the night, impedes the radiation of heat from the town outwards. Amsterdam has more summer-days, less frost days and less ice-days, according to the definitions of the Royal Meteorological Institute, than have the surrounding rural areas. In Table 20 some data are given on the heat production by man in Amsterdam for the year 1970.

The heat production of a town causes the development of a low-pressure area and this leads to the flow of a more or less continuous wind from the rural areas towards the town. This is a different phenomenon from the alternating sea-winds and land-winds which is also caused by a heating phenomenon. The higher temperatures in towns have a special influence on the vegetation as the vegetative growth period is longer and there is less hazard of night frost. Some species which cannot be grown in the normal climate of the area may therefore be found in the towns (Duvigneaud 1974).

Air pollution in towns, and in other areas strongly influenced by human activities such as major motorways, has its own impacts. One aspect which has been investigated is the impact of lead from the petrol used by motor traffic. In Switzerland around the year 1970 about 600 metric tonnes of lead was ejected over the country by motor traffic (Zuber *et al.* 1970). This amounts to approx. 100 to 300 kg lead per kilometre of motorway. The quantities of lead which are found in the vegetation depend strongly on the distance to the motorway. A large part of it is found as dust on the leaves (30 to 65%). The amount of dust caught on the leaves varies for different species and depends on various morphological characteristics; for example, shape and size of the leaves, position of the leaves, roughness and hairyness of the leaf surfaces. A part of the lead found had been taken up by the plants via their roots but this depended also on the nature of the plant spe-

Table 20. Heat production by man in Amsterdam during the year 1970

Total heat production per year 15 to 16 000 $\times$ 10^{12} calories = approx. 65 $\times$ 10^{15} kj in 1970, distributed as follows:

Electricity works	4824 $\times$ 10^{12} cal.	= 20 $\times$ 10^{15} kJ
Natural gas heating	4158 $\times$ 10^{12} cal.	= 17 $\times$ 10^{15} kJ
Burning refuse	673 $\times$ 10^{12} cal.	= 2.8 $\times$ 10^{15} kJ
Car-traffic	2040 $\times$ 10^{12} cal.	= 8.5 $\times$ 10^{15} kJ
Motorcycles	170 $\times$ 10^{12} cal.	= 0.7 $\times$ 10^{15} kJ
Heating with oil and coal	3500 $\times$ 10^{12} cal.	= 14.7 $\times$ 10^{15} kJ

Source: Van Zuylen 1971.

cies. In agricultural crops an increased concentration of lead was still found in the tissues up to a distance of 100 m from the motorway. The increased quantity of lead in the soils had no special impact on the growth of the plants. Animals who were fed these plants rich in lead had little or no trouble as the lead was almost totally ejected via the faeces.

WATER, GEOLOGY, SOILS

The need for water resources of urban areas is very great as human beings require a large amount of water for their drinking and household uses as well as for industrial purposes. Even for a humid country in a rather humid temperate climate urban water supply is a problem, as not only a sufficient quantity but also a good quality must be continuously guaranteed. Water resources are therefore a major problem for most urban areas. Some data on the water resources management of Bandung (West Java, Indonesia) were published by Riemer and Rozestraten (1978). Greater Bandung (altitude approximately 500 m above sealevel) which includes not only the city itself but also the adjoining regencies of Cianjur, Garut and Sumedang, is expected to reach a population of 8.5 million in 1985 and to grow to more than 11 million around the year 2000. Its water resources are mainly found in the river basins of the Cimanuk and the Citarum rivers. In these basins some dams have been built and the development project includes several more structures to regulate the water flow for the needs of the urban area. These dams are multifunctional as they provide not only water but also hydroelectric power to the city and irrigation water for the adjoining rural areas. Even with an annual precipitation of over 2000 mm and a relatively cool tropical climate (mean annual temperature approximately 24 °C), the water resources are becoming scarce. At present urban water supply in the area takes second place after use for irrigation, with 2 m^3/sec for the city of Bandung which however serves only 30 per cent of the population as most people are still dependent on water from shallow wells. However, most sources are also in danger of water pollution. Most industrial consumers use water from various kinds of wells. The total industrial water demand is estimated at present at 125 1/sec for the city and 250 1/sec for the suburban industries. In order to flush the drains and sewers, approximately 200 1/sec are needed. The total urban and industrial needs in this area are of the same order of magnitude as those of irrigated rice growing if the urban areas are not too densely populated, but a more even distribution over the year is needed for the urban areas. Deforestation in the surrounding mountains, uncontrolled groundwater development and pollution tend to decrease the availability of good quality water for the growing town. A careful survey of the water resources is now being undertaken to fulfil the needs of the next decades.

Drainage of urban areas, a particular problem in the polder areas of the Netherlands, has to take the following into account:

1. Drainage needs of urban and industrial areas are higher than those in agriculture. The total quantity of water to be drained away is lower (approximately 70% of that in agriculture), but there is less tolerance for groundwater fluctuations, in particular with regard to foundations and cellars.
2. The use of open water areas, for example as ponds in parks, is advisable as these can buffer some of the fluctuations.
3. Hygienic requirements may require additional drainage.
4. Artificially raised areas, such as are needed in low lying regions and polders (Amsterdam, Rotterdam), have special drainage problems, which are partly caused by the poor structure of the soils brought on by pipelines.
5. Drainage plans have to be adapted to the patterns of the buildings; this is in general not very difficult for residential areas but it does give problems in industrial areas.
6. Drainage plans for urban extensions have to be carefully developed by a team in which architects, hydrologists and economists have to participate; they have to consider the groundwater fluctuations tolerated.

Data on *the geology and the soils* of existing towns are in general found in the archives of the public works departments. Very little has thus far been systematically compiled and published. Geological maps and soil maps often leave the urban areas blank, but their interpolation, together with field observations in the towns wherever possible, is useful for obtaining a better knowledge and understanding. Recently some special soil surveys in urban areas of the Netherlands have been made, of which that of Haarlem will be briefly discussed below (Van Dam and Wopereis 1978).

A more general outline of the importance of geology, geomorphology and soil science for urban ecology may be given as follows (Vink 1975c):
1. Deeper subsoil: geological investigations of the deeper subsoil are indispensable for the construction of large buildings and for that of tunnels, subways and related projects.
2. Geohydrology: the construction of large buildings and other works in a town, as well as various activities at or near the surface, may have a large impact on groundwater flow, both with regard to its nature and quality and to its quantity and fluctuations; special danger exists for groundwater pollution of the deeper subsoil which only becomes apparent at a rather great distance.
3. Geomorphology: the topography of a town is firstly of importance for its visual aspects, but it has often also considerable interest with regard to the hydrology and to the circulation of traffic, in particular in towns with large differences in altitude between various town quarters, such as Brussels, Neuchatel (Switzerland), Edinburgh and, to some extent, Glasgow. In relatively flat areas, the well-considered adaptation of towns to the existing microrelief has for long been a normal practice and is still advisable today (see also below: soil maps).
4. Soil mechanics: investigations on the physical nature of the soils are not

only essential for high buildings and other heavy constructions but also generally advisable for all urban building and road construction. In some regions, special investigations are needed for the selection of suitable sites for cemeteries. In more rural areas, where septic tanks are used instead of a central sewerage system, the suitability of soils for the proper functioning of the installations is often highly necessary (Bouma 1971; Bouma *et al.* 1972).

5. The soil as substratum for the growth of plants has to be specifically considered with regard to gardens, parks and the planting of trees along roads. The choice and, where necessary, improvement of areas for sports grounds and playing fields needs special research (see also below: urban greenery).

The production of soil maps for urban extension schemes has become normal practice in many countries, even in areas where standard soil maps are already available, as some special requirements, already partly indicated above, have to be met both in the production of the soil map itself and of the soil survey interpretations. The general needs for the production of soil maps for this purpose have been formulated by Van Mourik *et al.* (1970):

1. The building of residential areas on specially levelled or raised surfaces may have some advantages in a technical sense, but it also has some serious disadvantages: high cost of land preparation, loss of identity and poor soils for establishing any plantations or greenery.

2. In particular the need for establishing green areas in a town, a general requirement for today, is better met on soils which are left as natural as possible. This also produces greater diversity for the kinds and patterns of buildings, and a better living environment for the future residents.

3. A better integration with the hydrological situation is promoted and the soil map points toward specially vulnerable transitional situations ('gradients' such as high-low, dry-wet, see Ch. 2).

4. Soil suitability maps derived from the soil map can indicate the possibilities and limitations of the various parts of the planning area as well as suggest means for improvement (see also Ch. 8). The following maps are often useful: (a) soil map or landscape ecological map; (b) map of landscape elements; (c) map of the groundwater hydrology (see also Ch. 3); (d) map indicating the bearing-capacity of the soils for human beings and machines; (e) soil suitability map for construction of buildings; (f) soil suitability maps for the establishment of trees and other urban greenery.

5. In some cases a separate map of the geomorphology including the microrelief of the area is useful for various purposes of planning, both visual and other.

In Table 21 information is given on the relationships between soil characteristics in low-lying areas and the soil qualities which are relevant for urban planning.

In their excellent book on human adjustment to floods, Smith and Tobin (1979) give various examples of the flood hazards of urban areas. For more general information reference is also made to Capper *et al.* (1971) and to

Table 21. Examples for low-lying areas such as found in the Netherlands, between soil characteristics and soil qualities with regard to urban planning.

Soil characteristics	Soil qualities
Soil profile and groundwater phase	Suitability for growth of plant roots
Soil profile and groundwater phase	Excess water and drought incidence
Soil texture and content of organic matter and groundwater	Vulnerability to wind erosion
Soil texture and content of organic matter and groundwater	Bearing power for walking and riding
Soil texture and content of organic matter and groundwater	Vulnerability to frost damage to roads
Texture, nature and quantity of organic matter of the topsoil	Dirtying of people and clothes during recreation
Geological formation and deeper hydrology	Bearing power for foundations

Source: Van Mourik *et al.* 1970.

Flawn (1970). Several County Soil Survey Reports of the US Soil Conservation Service also provide useful information (Calhoun and Wood 1969; Grice *et al.* 1971; Rasmussen 1971).

URBAN GREENERY, PLANTATIONS AND ANIMALS

Until one or two decades ago, attention for trees, parks, recreation grounds and gardens in urban areas was in general considered to be a minor technical matter and delegated as a routine function to the relevant municipal department. Many cities encompassed remnants of the old green zones originally encircling the old town. In some cases, in particular during the nineteenth and twentieth centuries, more attention was paid to the parks and trees as an attraction to residential quarters for the well-to-do. Some urban parks and plantations were incorporated in the urban extension plans and occasionally special garden towns were developed. Attention to animals in towns lacked any systematic approach. The essential ecological functions of the plants and animals in urban areas are still only being explored, but, often due to the activities of action groups from the local population, a greater awareness of the importance of these is developing. The attention to the presence of various bird species in towns led in some cases to the establishment of small woods to provide a better habitat. In order to provide a more varied vegetation, more attention is also being paid to 'ruderal' vegetations, i.e. the semi-natural vegetations in left-over fields and patches between built-over areas. Some special studies have been made of the age and species of the trees standing in the older well-to-do residential areas, where neglect of these trees due to changes in the ways and means of the residents tends to lead to deterioration.

Gradually more specific investigations are being carried out on the function of the urban vegetation and plantations for human ecology. For example, some data have been obtained on the influence of hedges and woods on the impact of the specially strong winds which sometimes blow around high-rise buildings (Feis 1970). These led to several suggestions about the disadvantages and advantages as well as the best way to use various kinds of plantations. Some other data were collected on the influence of trees on the impact of street noise (Janse 1970). In this respect, there are great differences between the various species: *Salix* sp. and *Cotoneaster* sp. have for example a low absorption capacity for noise, whereas *Acer pseudoplatanus* and *Tilia* sp. were found to have a high absorption capacity. In general, trees grown under good water conditions with a large water intake and luxuriant foliage have a higher noise absorption than trees with water deficiency. The noise absorption increases strongly with the width of the plantation. The noise absorption of trees is, however, of little use for high-rise buildings:

Some results of investigations in the town of Haarlem (the Netherlands) on relationships between soils and urban greenery may be summarized (Van Dam and Wopereis 1978). This pilot study should be seen within the context of the large surface area of urban greenery which is found in most countries of Western Europe. In the Netherlands (total surface area approximately 3 million ha) the total surface area of urban parks and plantations officially owned and run by municipalities is 50 000 ha, to which should be added an unknown but at least equal surface area of privately owned gardens. This excludes the trees in streets and along roads but includes sports grounds. The total surface area of public greenery within the urban sphere is approximately 125 000 ha, which also includes over 30 000 ha of verges of motorways. In the City of Amsterdam alone there are approximately 200 000 trees along streets and roads. The annual amount spent for urban and related greenery on the public budgets is of the order of f 750 million ($300 million). The annual increase of the surface area of urban greenery in the Netherlands is of the order of 2000 ha, an investment of f 150 million ($60 million) per annum.

The pilot study carried out in Haarlem by the Netherlands Soil Survey Institute started with the production of a semi-detailed soil map, in itself a rather unique experiment. The town of Haarlem was originally built on a prehistoric beach ridge of the North Sea, originating from the time around 3000 BC. This beach ridge still carries the old town centre, a not unusual phenomenon which is for example also seen in towns such as Alkmaar and The Hague. The old beach ridges were, and to some extent still are, the relatively highest and driest part of a very flat and wet polder country. They consist of deeply decalcified sandy soils with local inclusions of peat.

The surface of the beach ridge of Haarlem lies at 1.50 to 2.50 m above OD and has a groundwater level of approximately 60 cm below OD. To both sides of the approximately SW–NE running ridge are former sandflats overgrown in later ages by peat; on top of this peat a clay cover of 30 to 50 cm thickness is locally found. For the purpose of later extensions of the town, these soils have been artificially raised by bringing on a sand layer. Before 1950, this was done with lorries and the sand was largely spread by hand. During the last decades, the sand was mixed with water and spread over large areas by pipeline. The three kinds of sandy soils resulting from the different formation led to varying ecological results. This is largely due to the great differences in soil structure, the natural beach ridge sand having the best porosity and the sand brought on by pipeline having the worst, and indeed a very low, porosity. The differences in porosity have a very strong influence on the rooting and hence on the growth of trees. Soil suitability for the trees to be planted in the urban areas can therefore here be indicated in three classes: (1) beach ridge soils, well drained with good porosity, easily penetrable for roots with good growth of trees such as beeches; (2) soils made by lorries and hand labour, heterogeneous and locally great differences between the best and the poorest soils; (3) soils made by pipeline, which have a specially brought on humic top layer of 25 cm thickness but are otherwise often completely impenetrable by roots; these soils also exhibit great sensitivity to drought, apart from those localities where some clay lenses have been sedimented between the sand.

Related investigations in three Dutch towns, Haarlem, Amsterdam and Eindhoven, led to some interesting results on the growth of trees in urban areas. The vitality of these trees under the prevailing climate may be best seen from the end of August to the beginning of September as the poorly growing trees by then show autumnal colouring, whilst trees with better growth conditions only show this in October. This low vitality occurs, for example, in trees which are closely surrounded by a cobbled or metalled street cover, in particular if these trees grow in poor soils and are fully dependent on the original planting holes for their roots. The better the rooting conditions for the trees, due either to the original soil conditions (beach ridge soils), or to their position in even small grassed verges, or to the vicinity of gardens in front of the houses (which may be reached by some roots), the higher is the vitality of the trees. Compaction of the soils around the trees by traffic and by parking of cars is very deleterious to tree growth. Specially valuable trees may sometimes be restored by individual care which may include tree surgery by experts.

A systematic treatment of many aspects of the growing of trees in urban areas is given by Meyer *et al.* (1978). This includes the discussion of the ecological requirements of relevant tree species as well as their problems due to pollution and other urban influences.

An enquiry was held in the Federal Republic of Germany some years ago on the occurrence and growth conditions of trees in the streets of some towns. The number of trees was found to be lower with a higher density of occupation of residents. In many cases great care was taken to protect and restore the trees standing in the streets and this sometimes included tree

Table 22 Quantities of urban dust which were adsorbed by urban greenery in Frankfurt*

	Particles per unit of volume
Central station	100
Town centre	88.5
Street without trees	66.5
Avenues with trees	20.3
Town parks	14.4

Source: Bernatzky 1975.

* The figures given indicate the amount of dust still found in the air; they provide a relative measure for the amount adsorbed by the plants.

surgery (Bernatzky 1975; Duvigneaud *et al*. 1975). Growing attention is being given to the function of urban greenery and norms have been developed for minimal surface areas for the various kinds of recreation within the towns. The functions of the trees have been schematically represented by Bernatzky (1973) and this includes the importance of concentric zones of trees around and inside a town for the purification of the circulating air. In these German investigations it was found that *Ginkgo biloba*, a tree originating in Japan, was the most tolerant species with regard to various urban influences. In Table 22 some data are given on the amount of dust which is adsorbed in the different parts of a town by the trees and by other urban greenery.

Relatively few investigations have been carried out on the *animals* in urban areas, but in fact many different kinds of animals are living under these conditions: mammals, birds, fishes, reptiles and insects. In the Greater Brussels agglomeration some years ago, 85 different species of nesting birds were counted (Duvigneaud *et al*. 1975), of which 25 species did occur more or less regularly. Domestic animals are, of course, very frequent and they cause some rather well known problems. Of all American families 46 per cent have a dog or comparable animal and 20 per cent have at least one cat (Stearns and Montag 1974). In addition, large numbers of roving cats are living in many cities; the large groups of cats in the ruins of Rome are an example. The faeces of dogs are one of the problems: an average dog produces 227 g solid faeces and 720 ml urine per day. For New York City this amounts to 125 tons of faeces per day (Stearns and Montag 1974). In those parts of an urban area where enough parks and avenues are found, a large amount of the faeces serves as manure for the plants, which causes at least a partial recycling.

In addition to the number of bird species of Brussels cited above, some further comments on bird life in towns may be given. Approximately 200 bird species are found in American towns (Stearns and Montag 1974). Systematic investigations on bird life have been carried out by Kühnelt (in Duvigneaud *et al*. 1975) for Vienna (Austria). The migration routes of certain migratory birds such as geese did not change as a result of an extension of the town. For most birds, however, several different zones may be distinguished:

1. The outer residential quarters with gardens, which contain the richest relict-fauna and which also have possibilities for exchange with the surrounding rural areas.

2. The residential islands inside the town with parks and avenues, which are much more strongly disturbed by man, but where avenues with trees often still provide possibilities for migration of animals to and from other areas.

3. The enclosed islands between treeless streets, which show a very much impoverished fauna.

4. The almost completely desert-like areas in those parts of the town which are all covered by stone, brick and concrete.

Some investigations in a residential island in the centre of Amsterdam, between tree-lined canals and a street, showed that there is still a considerable range of different species of large trees, bushes and herbs. Life on and in the soil was found to be still rich in slugs, snails, beetles and very other small animals. Frequently occurring bird species were: sparrow, starling, blackbird, great tit, wood pigeon, Turkish turtle-dove, blue tit and carrion crow. The following species are also more or less regularly seen: magpie, robin, finch, chiff-chaff, cap-gull, herring-gull, swift, kestrel, buzzard and dark-breasted barn-owl. Furthermore, some 14 different species of sporadic

Plate 12 View of an enclosed island in a nineteen century quarter of Amsterdam

visitors are indicated among which are: icterine warbler, great warbler, merlin, fly-catcher, greenfinch, jay, wood-pie, cuckoo, golden oriole, willow-warbler, crane, heron, and tree-creeper (Ruting 1977). It is clear from these lists that the study of animals in urban areas is very worthwhile. In Plate 12 a view is given of an enclosed island in a nineteenth century quarter of Amsterdam, which looks treeless from the street.

SOME OTHER ASPECTS OF URBAN ECOLOGY

Plants and animals have to be seen primarily as essential members of urban ecosystems with material as well as psychological influences on human ecology. We mention here separately, as it refers to a different function, the use of 'bio-indicators' organisms which have specific reactions to certain environmental factors and can thus be used to give indications on certain kinds of environmental impact which are unfavourable for men. These indicators are, in general, specially selected kinds of plants on which the impacts may be directly seen and measured or counted. Plants as well as certain terrestrial and aquatic animals have indicator values. The best known are lichens which grow as epiphytes on trees and react strongly to the sulphur-dioxide (SO_2) content of the air. Due to this, they are in general now absent from urban centres. But even then, specially prepared cultures of lichens may be used to indicate the intensity of air pollution. These are prepared on glass plates and distributed in a regular network. Their reaction to the air is recorded by means of colour photography. Seedlings of conifers are very sensitive to the dust content of air. Grasses along the verges of motorways may be analysed with chemical methods in order to determine their contents of lead and other heavy metals. In special cases investigations on the composition of small communities of plants or animals have been found to have indicator value (UNESCO 1973).

Urban refuse is one of the problems which a town imposes on its peripheral area. This includes air, water and soil pollution as well as the special problems caused by the continuous extension and multiplication of refuse dumps. The problem of the peripheral zones of urban areas is a many-sided one (see Richter 1975). It has a large impact on the life of the areas surrounding the towns and on urban planning.

Many problems of urban ecology can only be studied, and at least partly solved, by an integrated multidisciplinary approach. A study of this kind was initiated some years ago for Hong Kong (UNESCO 1973). This area is very useful as a pilot research project due to its isolated position, mainly on an island and its very high population density. The following aspects are investigated: landscape, demography, settlement history, energy flow, material flow, population ecology, medical aspects, cultural aspects, interactions with plants, animals, protozoa, bacteria, pathogenic viruses, economic aspects. More of these investigations in other urban areas of the world are highly necessary.

7

Land degradation, land conservation and land improvement

LAND DEGRADATION

The decision to combine into one chapter the three subjects of land degradation, land conservation and land improvement is largely a result of the wish to keep this text as concise as possible. The impression must be avoided that land improvement is only relevant after some kind of land degradation has occurred. This is certainly not true. It is often possible and useful to initiate land conservation or land improvement or both when no land degradation has occurred: instead the aims are to ensure that land will not begin to be degraded and to improve an area for a specific land use.

A new term, which indicates land degradation due to human action as well as land improvement, is 'Land transformation', which is the title of an international project of SCOPE (Scientific Committee on Problems of the Environment of the ICSU: International Council of Scientific Unions, Paris). This has been initiated because the lands of the world, to which many water bodies may also be said to belong (see Chs 1 and 2), are undergoing increasingly rapid and extensive transformation as a result of various human activities. These activities include urban and industrial as well as various kinds of agricultural land uses. Pilot studies from many countries have been completed and the hope is that this project will promote a more comprehensive view than can be given here (Vink 1981b).

Land degradation, expressed as soil erosion is a well-known phenomenon against which, at least in some countries, farmers have taken the appropriate measures over many centuries. For example, in the former Netherlands East Indies (now Indonesia), laws were established during the nineteenth century in order to prevent deforestation and thus to combat erosion in hilly and mountainous areas (Vink 1963a). Soil erosion and soil conservation in a modern sense were brought to the attention of the USA and of the world, particularly by the activities of the late Hugh Hammond Bennett, the first Administrator of the US Soil Conservation Service, who started his work in the early 1930s (Bennett 1939). Today, a large library is necessary to hold the ever-increasing literature on soil erosion and soil conservation. Examples are found in the publications and bulletins of many national soil conservation services as well as in those of FAO and UNESCO and in many books by individual authors, such as Hudson (1971).

Today, land degradation has become a much more comprehensive subject which is seen as a part of the environmental crisis of the modern world (Eckholm 1976). Land degradation has the most serious impact in the poorest countries of the world and on the poorest peoples. It means, primarily, lack of food for the growing populations of most countries and this is a major and ever-increasing global problem.

Deforestation is one of the primary causes of land degradation. It is not possible, however, to conserve all forests: people have to have food as well as other agricultural and forestry products such as clothes, houses and the paper for newspapers, journals, books and other, often useful, purposes. Uncontrolled and unwarranted deforestation is perhaps the greatest of all ecological dangers. It is impossible to give general guide lines on the quantity and kind of deforestation which is still allowable under certain conditions. This has to be determined according to local or regional possibilities and requirements on the basis of landscape ecological maps of good quality and of other scientific, social and economic data within an integrated process of land evaluation (see also Ch. 8). One guideline, which has almost general significance, is that both from an ecological and from an economic point of view, there is a preference for concentrating agricultural land uses on those lands which are the best suited for these uses in each country or province. In order to meet the human requirements on these often rather limited areas a sufficiently high and sustained production has to be obtained on them. For this purpose suitable land utilization types have to be developed. Extension of food production over less suitable lands only gives a short-term solution with long-term deleterious effects. Those soils which are less suitable for agricultural land uses, which are in general also the lands most vulnerable for land degradation, should be put to extensive uses such as extensive grazing, forestry and nature conservation. Even then, sufficient control is necessary to conserve these lands within long-term stable ecosystems which require to be maintained within the social, economic and ecological context of the region, including the continuing processes of population growth and development.

In 1972 at Stockholm (Sweden) the United Nations Conference on the Human Environment took the initiative for the establishment of UNEP, the United Nations Environmental Programme (Nairobi, Kenya) and this new UN special agency has, among its many tasks, also a special care for the prevention and combation of land degradation, as was made clear by the UN Conference on Desertification held at Nairobi in 1977 (Conference 1977) and by many other activities. The Stockholm conference also stimulated a more integrated approach to land degradation by many other UN agencies and by many other national and international institutions. In a report published by FAO for the conference, Rauschkolb (1971) indicates the following subjects as belonging to land degradation: (1) erosion; (2) salinization and alkalinization; (3) organic refuse (mainly from urban areas); (4) plagues and diseases (for men, plants and animals) and the spreading of organisms transferring infections; (5) inorganic industrial waste (gaseous, fluid and solid); (6) pesticides; (7) radioactivity; (8) heavy metals (e.g. in rivers, of which the river Rhine is a notorious example); (9) in some cases chemical fertilizers (see Ch. 5); (10) detergents (e.g. from washing processes). The report also indicates that some deleterious impacts may be prevented by relatively simple applications of existing technology or by the development of new and feasible techniques.

The legislative aspects of land degradation and its prevention are often neglected. Still, a good legislative basis is essential for carrying out the necessary measures on a national or sub-national (provincial, local) scale. The legislative division of FAO is specially geared to the development of appropriate legislative systems for individual countries. It has for example some years ago drafted a law for the Republic of Colombia (Diario Official 1975). Also, a review of the legislative principles of soil conservation has been made (Christy 1971), a special study has been made on the water laws of moslem countries (Caponera 1973) and a review on the legal systems for environment protection in Japan, Sweden and the United States has been published (Sand 1972). Good legislation is essential for the prevention and control of land degradation, but it has to be accompanied by the appropriate institutional, ecological and technical measures and control systems, in a manner adapted to economic and social conditions. For this approach an overall strategy is required.

The World Conservation Strategy (IUCN 1980) to some extent fulfils the requirements of such a strategy, provided sufficient attention is paid to the different human requirements and land utilization types and to the various landscape ecological conditions in the different parts of the world (see also UNESCO: Nature and Resources XVI, 1: The World Conservation Strategy). Nature conservation is a very urgent and essential concern with regard to land conservation, but various other aspects with regard to human land use have to be taken into account. Foresters in all countries have always been, and still are, proponents of land conservation. Not all land conservation can be carried out within the context of forestry. But the forestry aspects are an essential part of all studies of land degradation and land conservation (see for example FAO Forestry Department 1977; Laban 1981).

Some mention has already been made of water in relation to land degradation. The degradation of water conditions and of water quality is as dangerous as land degradation itself. In many cases water degradation and land degradation go together and their combined impact is very serious. Some of the most important points of water degradation are:

1. Complete changes of the general water conditions which lead to major floods, serious drought, changes in microclimate and danger for human health.

2. Deterioration of water resources with regard to their quantity and quality due to insufficient water management and lack of soil conservation or water pollution.

3. Destruction of water resources due to excessive use (overexploitation) leading, for example, to the penetration of saline water into coastal areas, to compaction and subsidence of clay and peat areas, which again leads to poor drainage conditions.

4. Increase of soil erosion and of salinization due to insufficient water management in agriculture.

SOIL EROSION AND SOIL CONSERVATION

There are still major problems in many parts of the world although a large number of ecological and technical means of soil conservation have been available for some decades. Distinction must be made between the natural erosion of an area under natural vegetation and accelerated erosion due to human action, which is called here soil erosion. Natural erosion usually keeps pace with natural processes of weathering and soil formation. It is one of the processes in a condition of steady state, which result in soil profiles on slopes being shallower than soil profiles on flat areas. Natural erosion may be considerable, in particular in arid areas with a scarce vegetation. Even under natural vegetation, seen over some thousands of years, catastrophes may occur, for example due to land slides or to volcanic eruptions, but eventually a comparable new steady state is restored. Natural erosion is also called 'normal erosion'. Soil erosion, as induced by man, is a disruption of the steady state which increases with time unless special measures are taken. These measures have to establish a new steady state, in which erosion often is not completely avoided, but reduced to an intensity which does not differ too much from the normal erosion.

The most generally occurring kinds of soil erosion are water erosion and wind erosion, these being the most active agents on the surface of the earth. Streambank erosion, which is a special kind of water erosion, is sometimes treated separately. In some areas, denudative mass-movements such as soil creep and landslides are extremely important (see also Ch. 3), but these will not be treated here. The triggering-off of mass movements is often due to road construction and comparable works. We shall restrict the discussion to those kinds of soil erosion which are due to the use of land surfaces for agricultural and related land uses. An example of soil creep is given in Plate 13.

The most important kinds of soil erosion by water are: (1) sheet-erosion, (2) rill-erosion and (3) gully erosion. The universal soil loss equation of Wischmeyer is very useful for a general view of the various factors contributing to soil erosion. This equation reads (Hudson 1971):

$$A = R \times K \times L \times S \times C \times P,$$

where

A = soil loss in tons per acre,

Plate 13 Soil creep in clay soils on a slope in northern Tunisia

R = erosivity-index of the rain,
K = erodibility-index of the soil,
L = a length-factor: the quotient of the length of the tract of land which is considered to a standard length of 22.6 m,
S = a slope factor, the quotient to the standard slope of 9 per cent,

C = a crop treatment factor, which compares the crop considered, and its treatment, with a standard parcel of tilled bare fallow,

P = the soil conservation factor, the relation to a tract of land where no soil conservation is practised and where tillage is up and down the slope.

For some regions, in particular in the USA, the various factors have been determined and here the equation may be used in a quantitative sense. This kind of data requires to be related to permanent soil erosion experimental fields, where each parcel is treated in the same manner over a number of years and where the soil and water losses can be exactly determined. These experimental plots are usually established in small natural drainage basins with various kinds of slopes. A concrete construction of tanks and distributors for each parcel is used for the determination of soil loss and water flow. One of the oldest, and probably the oldest, of these soil erosion experimental centres is the centre of Coshocton (Ohio, USA) which was in operation in 1945. Plate 14 gives a view of part of the erosion experimental field of Vale Formoso (Alentejo, southern Portugal). Table 23 gives a summary of some data from the Coshocton centre (Harrold 1962).

The establishment of these nearly permanent experiments, which have to be of long duration to warrant their reliability under various weather conditions, requires large investments of land, instruments and personnel and is

Plate 14 View of a part of the permanent erosion experimental field at Vale Formoso (Alentejo, southern Portugal)

Table 23. Average soil loss under three different crops in a four year rotation (Maize – wheat – 2½ years pasture) with two kinds of land management at the erosion experimental centre of Coshocton (Ohio, USA), 1945–1956

Crop	Period on the land	Soil loss in tons/acre*	
		Treatment A	Treatment B
Maize	1 May to 10 October	7.70	2.03
Wheat	11 October to 30 April	0.88	0.14
Sown pasture	33 months	negligible	negligible

Source: Harrold, 1962.
* For tons/ha multiply by 2.2; A = without soil conservation, B = with soil conservation treatment.

therefore only rarely possible. In many countries the best way of obtaining information on soil erosion in its many forms and intensities is to map the various phenomena systematically on an appropriate scale, in general varying from 1 : 10 000 to 1 : 200 000. This gives not only an inventory, but is also enables the surveyors to obtain at least relative figures on the degree of erosion on the different kinds of slopes and with different soils and kinds of land use. If existing data on deforestation and land use are added, even some quantitative estimates may be obtained. To these may be added data on the flow and the sediment contents of streams and, where possible, field measurements of erosion over one or more years on well selected sites, based on soil, landscape ecological and erosion maps. For these investigations the systematic use of air photo-interpretation is nearly always indispensable. It facilitates the delineation and, to some extent, characterization of the different land units with differences in erodibility as well as the indication of their mutual relationships. In many cases it is also possible to indicate areas where a high probability of erosion exists. (Vink, in Rey 1968).

Nelson (in Laban 1981) discusses the conservation qualities of land under forest management. He describes a system for their determination depending on the nature of the land as well as on the forest land use objectives. The latter include such objectives as wood production, forage production, wildlife habitat, high water quality and even (tree-) age management. These have different requirements with regard to the land conditions: high tree growth rate, high grass growth rate, habitat diversity, minimal sediment load and various human activities (road building, log skidding, tree planting, etc.) respectively. The list of conservation qualities includes, for example, soil erosion hazard, fire hazard, insect hazard, windthrow hazard, plant community stability, landslide hazard, sediment delivery hazard, soil compaction hazard and soil fertility loss hazard. These may be established by various means of different intensity such as direct measure (mainly in trial plots and experimental areas), extrapolation and classification (transfer of experience from an area to another on the basis of soil maps or landscape ecological maps) single resource interpretation (based on either vegetation or soils or geologic information together with knowledge on climatic regimes) and synthesis of existing resource data. Data collection in extensive forests is expensive and often little money is available for this purpose. Therefore various kinds of interpretation, including the interpretation of aerial photographs and that of existing maps and documents, are in general essential. Conservation qualities have to be identified to determine the need to protect the site. These qualities, together with data on the site's productive capacity and its limitations to operational practices such as logging, have to be used together for making decisions on the kinds and intensities of forest land use.

Attention on soil erosion and soil conservation is often very much centred on the developing countries and in particular on the countries of Africa. Many kinds of nomadic and semi-nomadic land uses exist in this continent often under very extreme climates. The population increase under these poorly stabilized systems of land use leads to a strongly increased erosion hazard. This is perhaps greatest in the semi-arid savanna-zones, where humid periods of some months with heavy rainfall alternate with extremely dry seasons. In the forest savanna areas, a humid period of 5 to 7 months alternates with a dry period of some 3 to 8 months and here arable land agriculture as well as pastoral land use can easily be carried out if the appropriate conservation practices are applied. But this requires the establishment of land utilization types of a more stable nature than are now generally known in these areas. In the case of arable land farming, the hazard of soil erosion is in particular caused by rain falling on bare land at the end of the dry season. Under pastoral use, a great hazard is caused by the distribution of the wells for drinking water and by their use in various seasons. Use of drinking wells implies intensive grazing in their surroundings and when this is done too long, or in a too dry period on vulnerable vegetation, severe overgrazing may lead to a dangerous increase of soil erosion. To this must often be added the extensive forest fires, bush fires and grassland fires, which leave bare soils liable to erosion.

UNEP and FAO are trying together to arrive at an inventory of the actual and potential hazards of soil erosion in the various parts of the Third World. This would be a means for all countries concerned to cooperate in obtaining a better knowledge and to arrive at a means for stimulating and coordinating the necessary efforts. The *Soil Map of the World* on the scale of 1 : 5 million has proved to be very useful for a first general view and a *World Map of Desertification* has already been published as will be discussed below. Perhaps the largest benefits for the cooperating countries are not even found in the ultimate publication of these very generalized maps but in the experience obtained during their production.

In order to promote soil conservation under various circumstances, FAO have published several volumes of the FAO Conservation Guide (FAO 1976/1977) which include: guidelines for watershed management, hydrological techniques for upstream conservation, conservation practices for arid and semi-arid zones. These guides give up-to-date information in a form which can easily be digested and stimulates application of the various techniques and methods of land management.

In areas where in certain seasons high rainfall intensities and great quantities of rain are the norm, it is not sufficient to conserve the soils. It is also necessary to drain away excessive water in such a manner that no damage is caused. This has to be done with ditches of various sizes, even on rather steep slopes. The construction of these ditches needs great care in order to avoid their incision by erosion and this has to be done by giving the ditches a more gradual grade than that of the slope on which they are constructed. In addition, the ditches should be covered with plants: grassed waterways. In some cases, on rather steep slopes, the stream velocity in the ditches is reduced by including in the design several steps made of stones or concrete.

For the conservation of areas where already serious erosion gullies have been formed, small concrete or stone dams have to be constructed at critical points in the gullies and these dams have to be protected by stone or concrete floors against undercutting. In some tropical Asiatic countries, the planting of various species of bamboo has been found to be helpful. The planting of other plants, even well-known conservation plants such as 'kudzu' (*Pueraria triloba*) or 'tropical kudzu' (*Pueraria javanica*) in active gullies, is only possible if the stream velocity has been considerably reduced by the above-mentioned constructions.

Some special aspects of erosion can only be touched upon: (a) erosion of riverbanks caused by logging in rivers, (b) the influence of road construction on erosion and on landslides; (c) the planting of woods or of bamboo plantations to prevent the occurrence of landslides. A special kind of soil conservation is the terracing of slopes for irrigated rice ('paddy') production. The extensive paddy fields of many Asian countries such as Indonesia, Sri Lanka, Malaysia and India are good examples.

In forestry, in several European countries, there is a longstanding tradition of soil conservation. Good examples are found in Switzerland, Germany, Austria and Czechoslovakia. One of the measures frequently taken is the prohibition to clear-cut any forest area, thus preserving at least a minimum of vegetal soil coverage. In steep mountain streams under these systems, an elaborate network of small stone or concrete dams is built with distances adapted to the stream gradient ('Wildbachverbauung').

In relation to soil erosion, some attention must be paid to the serious effects of soil erosion in upstream areas on the increase of sedimentation in downstream areas. This sedimentation may be more serious than the erosion in the upper areas. Eroded sediments may mantle highly productive soils to make them far less productive, as would be the case with sands. Sedimentation of irrigation systems prohibits the proper functioning of the systems and, where salinity is a danger, may also increase salinization due to the silting up of the drainage systems. Where streams are dammed, sediment may, over a few decades, completely fill the reservoir above the dam and thus make the whole construction pointless. This is a danger for large dams, but periodic clearing of the reservoir should be foreseen in the design. Siltation is perhaps more serious in small systems of village tanks serving some tens of hectares; here the organization often fails to provide a systematic clearing of the tanks. Some regions of Sri Lanka which in the past had thousands of irrigated paddy fields are now reduced to a small surface area for this land use.

This section may be concluded by a summary of some important points with regard to soil conservation (see also Vink 1963a):

1. Agriculture is essential for human requirements of food, clothing and several other needs and therefore cannot be reduced in production; its production even has to be increased with a view of the rapidly growing population of the world. The ideal objective of soil conservation to conserve all forests and to plant all slopes with forests can therefore not be attained.

2. It is a generally accepted fact that most of the food has to be harvested as near as possible to the location where it is to be consumed. This means that in many regions of the world less than optimal lands have to some extent to be used for agriculture.

3. In order to arrive at the much needed reduction of soil erosion in each region (country, province, district) soil surveys, landscape ecological surveys and erosion surveys are required for indicating as precisely as possible those soils which are, relatively speaking, the best suitable for the kinds of land use and land management which are needed considering the existing social and economic conditions (see also Ch. 8: Land classification for land use planning). An old saying of the US Soil Conservation Service is that 'each soil has to be treated according to its needs and used according to its possibilities'.

4. Any soil which has some hazard of erosion has to be left bare only for the shortest period possible. This has to do with the various crops planted subsequently in a rotation as well as with each individual crop. A successful crop is the best means of soil conservation. In this respect good yielding crops with appropriate tillage and manuring, including the use of chemical fertilizers, are the best with respect to soil conservation. This is partly due to the activities of the roots but also to the interception of raindrops which prevents rainsplash erosion.

5. A proper tillage and a correct system of planting or sowing is often helpful for preventing or reducing soil erosion. This may, for example, be 'contour ploughing' and 'contour planting', i.e. working along the horizontal contour lines of a slope. By special systems of ploughing it is also possible to make small horizontal bunds and ditches along the slopes, or the soil surface may, on purpose, be left rough and irregular, thus improving the infiltration of rain water into the soil. 'Mulching', the covering of the soil surface with remnants of the previous crop such as straw, reduces the impact of raindrops and it also reduces surface flow.

6. Drainage and terracing with the use of permanent constructions in stone or concrete is necessary in those cases where the above-mentioned methods of land management are insufficient. A special form of these, where stone or concrete are only used for critical situations, is irrigated rice growing ('paddy') in tropical countries.

7. Soil improvement by deep ploughing is often a means of improving the infiltration of water into the soil.

8. In existing gullies, it is often possible to reduce the flow to below a critical point by the construction of small dams from local materials. The establishing of plant growth in waterways, often with herbaceous grasses and sometimes with bamboo bushes, is of great importance.

9. Soil conservation always has to be considered within the social and economic conditions of an area. In this context it has to be realized that a system of soil conservation which is appropriate from an ecological and technical viewpoint is not always feasible to the individual farmer. In addition, a good system of soil conservation is often only effective if it is established at the same time over rather large coherent areas such as drainage basins or 'watershed areas'. Both economic and organizational considerations therefore make it necessary that governmental bodies play an important role in soil conservation. This may for example, be done through the establishment of soil conservation districts. There exist for example in Bali and in some parts of Sri Lanka old cooperative village systems for irrigation and soil conservation. The modernization of society should reform and improve rather than abolish such systems.

10. Soil conservation has to be seen as a process in time. Farmers with safe and well-established rights on the soil often have, within the context of a stable society, the tendency to conserve the soil for their children and grandchildren. But wars and revolutions lead to the disruption of existing systems and these therefore tend to seriously increase soil erosion within a short duration. But sometimes under ostensibly stable conditions a gradual process of erosion may be active and this may suddenly become evident by a catastrophe. The best known example is the dust storm of 11 May 1934 in the USA, which was one of the major causes for developing soil conservation not only in the US but subsequently in many other parts of the world. A similar phenomenon with regard to water erosion is described by Louis Bromfield in his once famous book *The Rains Came*.

DESERTIFICATION AND SALINIZATION

The term 'desertification' has only come into use during the last decade. The most immediate cause was the great drought, and consecutive consequences, in the Sahel area of Africa in the years after 1970. The term 'desertization' was already in use before that, to indicate that certain areas had become similar to deserts, whereas desertification indicates that areas have been made (by men) into deserts (Latin: facere = to make). The latter term has been in general use in particular since the United Nations Conference on Desertification, which was held in Nairobi (Kenya) in 1977. The term desertification is defined as 'the intensification or extension of desert conditions; it is a process which induces a reduction of biological productivity with consequent reduction of the biomass of plants, of grazing capacity of the land for cattle, of the yields of crops and of human well-being'. In consequence, it is relevant to give a definition of deserts: 'Deserts are regions where vegetation is scarce or absent as a result of lack of precipitation or of edaphic drought.' (Conference 1977).

Basically, desertification may be seen as land degradation under arid conditions and by a purely scientific approach it might be argued that the term is unnecessary as the same processes also occur under less dry conditions, and also have very dangerous consequences. Seen in the broad context of the world as a whole, soil erosion in productive agricultural regions has a more dangerous impact on world food production than has desertification.

There are however a number of well-justified reasons for giving desertification a special treatment. These are of a social as well as of an ecological and an agronomic nature. Some of these are:

1. Men as well as plants and animals in arid regions are living near to an ecological as well as to a socio-economic minimum; each deterioration leads to catastrophes as has been clearly demonstrated in the Sahel.

2. Increasing population pressure, often connected with increasing herds of cattle, are more difficult to cope with in arid regions than in more humid areas as intensification of agriculture in arid regions has in general to be done within the scope of difficult and costly irrigation.

3. The consequences of weather conditions very different from the normal are greater in arid regions. The fluctuation of precipitation in arid regions is in general 40 per cent of the statistical average, whereas in humid areas this is often less than 20 per cent. This fluctuation may mean that under an annual average of 350 mm precipitation, not even a very low figure for arid regions, a dry year may have only some 200 mm; this is extremely low even for the most drought-resistant crops. The fluctuation of 20 per cent in a region with an average precipitation of 750 mm reduces precipitation to around 600 mm and this may even have some favourable effects due to more solar radiation. Two or three dry years of the kind indicated for arid regions may lead to a catastrophe.

4. The combination of the matters mentioned under 1, 2 and 3 means that the damage done in a number of consecutive years may almost be impossible to cure and this leads in one or more decades to a strong cumulative effect.

5. There is much less margin for variation of agricultural activities in arid regions than there is in humid areas, due to the marginal ecological conditions with regard to plant growth.

6. Wind erosion, which is a very wide-spread process in arid regions is, due to the nature of the process, much more difficult to combat than water ero-

sion. The difference is due to the fact that water is an essential nutrient for plants and animals, whereas wind is nothing but a deleterious factor, causing mechanical damage as well as drying out.

7. Salinization and alkalinization, the increasing contents of soluble salts in soils and in particular of the chlorides and sulphates of sodium and magnesium ($NaCl$, $MgCl_2$, Na_2SO_4, $MgSO_4$), is more preponderant under arid conditions and occurs in various very deleterious forms. These processes have to be halted and cured by means of large quantities of water, the most lacking matter in arid regions.

Although it is possible to discuss irrigation and drainage in the context of desertification and salinization, as both are indispensable for the improvement of the situation under approaching desertification, it is preferred, however, to treat these two subjects separately as they have a much wider importance (see also Kovda *et al.* 1973).

For the United Nations Conference on Desertification (1977), among other documents a *World Desertification Map* was produced (Conference 1977). This map was based on the *Soil Map of The World* (FAO/UNESCO 1971) and on various other data and criteria. In the legend of this map, which had to be produced on a very small scale (1 : 25 million), the following phenomena are shown:

- degree of desertification hazards (very high, high, moderate),
- vulnerability of land to desertification processes (sand movement, deflation, sheetwash, accelerated run-off, gully erosion, deposition, salinization, alkalinization),
- high human and animal pressure,
- bioclimatic zones (hyperarid, arid, semi-arid, subhumid).

Calculations in the attached report indicate that over 3 million km^2 of the world have a very high degree of desertification hazards, of which over 1 million are in the arid zone, over 2 million in the semi-arid and some 160 000 in the subhumid zones. High desertification hazards are estimated to exist over nearly 17 million km^2 of the world, of which by far the largest part is the arid zone. In the hyperarid zone only deserts are found with a total surface area of nearly 8 million km^2 of extreme deserts. In Africa nearly 17 million km^2 are affected by desertification of various degrees, including 6 million km^2 of extreme desert. For Asia these figures are over 15 million km^2 and 1½ million km^2 respectively. The areas affected by desertification for the other continents are: North and Central America over 4 million km^2, South America nearly 3½ million km^2, Australia nearly 6 million km^2 (all with relatively small surface areas of extreme desert) and Europe nearly nil. Some idea of the various problems arising from desertification may be studied in a publication edited by Tyrwhitt (1977). These include problems on housing with villages being totally covered by sand deposits. Various methods devised for restoration of productivity and for return of human well-being are given.

In discussing the means of combating desertification, some people (Le

Houérou, in FAO 1976/1977 no. 3) even ask the question whether it is at all possible to stop the various processes. Desertization, as this author prefers to call it, occurs predominantly along the borders of deserts, in areas where the average annual precipitation is in general between 100 to 200 mm per annum and rarely comes above 300 mm in any year. The main cause is found in the population increase which leads to: (1) rapid extension of arable lands over increasingly dry areas; (2) overgrazing; (3) destruction of woody plants for fuel; (4) increased establishment of groundwater wells for drinking water resulting in disturbance of the water balance over large areas.

Measures to be taken against desertification could be:

1. The planting of xerophyllous (drought-tolerant) plant species in pastoral areas; in general this is only possible with at least 300 to 400 mm annual precipitation, but some bushes which are used as forage crops may be grown under dryer conditions as has been shown in the USSR, Australia and Tunisia.

2. Systematic management of pastoral areas, including their protection against fires. The latter may be done by the establishment and maintenance of fire breaks, bare zones crossing the areas at regular intervals. The systematic management aims at giving a sufficient resting period to each part of the area at alternating periods (see also Thalen 1979).

3. Production of hay from the excessive biomass during the rainy season to provide forage during the long dry season, thus preventing overgrazing during the most critical period.

4. Temporary reservation of parts of the area in order to restore its vegetation.

5. Development of complementary systems of irrigated agriculture and dry pasturing, including the cultivating of forage on the irrigated lands, which is not a normal use in most regions as the irrigated land utilization types differ very much in their techniques and organization from the often semi-nomadic pastoral types.

6. Regular importation of forage into the arid regions from neighbouring semi-arid areas.

7. The extension of information to the people to use other fuels than woody plants; for example, paraffin; the destruction of woody plants is one of the crucial problems in all arid countries. In some countries (India, Iraq) cakes are made of animal manure with straw for fuel and these hand-made briquettes are satisfactory (Buringh 1960; Vink 1963a). The loss of organic manure under arid conditions has no serious repercussions.

8. Planting of windbreaks consisting of drought-resistant species and, on selected locations, of special woods for timber.

9. Fixation of dunes with suitable herbaceous plants, bushes and trees (Eucalyptus); a herbaceous plant used for this purpose in dune areas of the Netherlands, an ecological desert with some salinity, is bentgrass (marram, *Ammophila arenaria*).

10. Small water control constructions; for example, small dams in depressions (wadis), which improve the penetration of water at the times of occasional, but often very strong, floods.

The answer to the initial question posed above, whether something can be done against desertification, is therefore not a simple 'Yes' or 'No', but it should be put as 'Yes, if . . . the relevant measures applicable at a certain location can be taken.'

Of particular regional importance are often the windbreaks or shelter belts mentioned under 8. If these are planted in the right manner with appropriate species, they induce a local reduction of wind velocity. In order to arrive at this, the windbreaks should be penetrable to winds and should be of sufficient height. They have a favourable effect on land use and on cattle as well as on the human habitat and on wildlife. In semi-arid areas with snowfall in winter, snow accumulates in and behind these belts and leaves stored humidity in the soils.

Efficient water management in semi-arid regions includes the use of the precipitation which falls on bare rock areas. This water can be caught by a system of bunds and conducted towards arable lands for irrigation. These small-scale irrigation projects are in many semi-arid areas the only means of sustaining agriculture for food production. In some countries, for example in Australia, more artificial systems, using plastics, concrete or sheet-iron, are used (FAO 1976/1977 no. 3). More natural systems utilizing bare rock formations are, for example, applied in Tunisia.

Salinization of soils is a group of processes which induce a high concentration of water-soluble salts. The chlorides and sulphates of sodium (Na), magnesium (Mg) and calcium (Ca) are the most important of these, but also carbonates and, under extreme conditions, nitrates, are found. Seen in a large geochemical context (Kovda *et al.* 1973) the precipitation of salts in soils shows a zoning from subhumid to extreme arid which is correlated with the solubility in water of the different salts: from calcium carbonate ($CaCO_3$) via various sulphates and chlorides to magnesium chloride ($MgCl_2$), to sodium-chloride (NaCl) and finally to potassium-nitrate (KNO_3). The various kinds of saline soils were discussed in Chapter 3. The tolerance of some crops for salinity is indicated in Table 24. The salinity is indicated here as ECe, the electrical conductivity of the soil extract in millimhos, an international measure for conductivity as an indication of salts in solution (1 mho = 1 : 1 ohm) (see also Salinity Laboratory Staff 1954; Salinity Seminar 1971). The electrical conductivity is a very satisfactory indication for soils which have a relatively high sodium content. In soils which contain relatively large quantities of calcium and magnesium it can only be used when conversion diagrams are applied and here the actual proportion of the various kinds of cations and anions is often very important (Yahia 1971). Very high contents of sodium lead to alkalinity with very high pH values of the soils (pH more than 8.5). This causes additional damage to plants and has also a very unfavourable influence on soil structure and soil porosity due to peptization of clay particles by Na-ions. The sodium content is often

Table 24. Salt tolerance of some agricultural crops expressed as yield
depression at certain ECe values (in millimhos)

Crop	Yield depression	
	10–15%	50%
Barley	12	18
Cotton	10	16
Wheat	7	14
Beans	6	10
Sugarcane	4	9
Paddy-rice	5	8
Maize	5	7
Alfalfa (lucerne)	4	8
Datepalm	8	—

Source: Hulsbos 1968.

expressed as the sodium-adsorption-ratio, SAR, which indicates the proportion of Na-ions to the total of the cations adsorbed to a clay.

IRRIGATION, DRAINAGE AND DIKES

Irrigation and drainage were already mentioned in various previous sections.
In the present section some of the technical aspects will be indicated and
some other points will be briefly summarized.

To the broad technical aspects of water control and water management
belong the following kinds of major constructions: large dams, dikes, pumping stations and primary canals. These are mainly connected with major
landscape features and with the general nature of the water conditions. The
smaller scale technical aspects such as secondary and tertiary water courses
(small canals, ditches), the small dams and weirs associated with these, and
various other works which lead to optimum land use, are more directly connected with microrelief, soils and groundwater. The two kinds of technical
operations are in general managed by different kinds of engineers with different specializations. In many countries the former are educated at faculties
of engineering whereas the latter are educated at faculties of agronomy
(agricultural engineering).

The discussion in this book of the major technical works executed by civil
engineers is reduced to a very brief sketch of some salient points, although
its importance is very evident, in particular for an inhabitant of the Low
Countries. Flood control is, however, a major effort in many countries and
in particular in the large deltaic areas of Asia such as Bangladesh.

The kind and intensity of floods in deltas depends very much on the
nature of the drainage basins of the different rivers. The following points have
in particular to be distinguished: (a) the kind and duration of floods (gradual
or sudden rising, to a high or very high level), and (b) the river flow during
the dry season. In regions where sudden high floods occur, systematic land

use is impossible without a completely closed system of dikes. If on the other hand a river tends to rise gradually, stays at the same level for some weeks and then drops gradually as in tropical deltas, the cultivation of adapted paddy-varieties is possible; in other areas the floods have been used for many centuries as a natural system of irrigation as in the delta of the Nile for over five millennia. Low river flow in dry seasons brings in deltaic areas the hazard of penetration of seawater and therefore of salinization of groundwater and soils. Under these conditions the hazard of silting up of the streambeds is great as the river does not sufficiently transport the sediments into the sea. There is also the danger of floods by the sea caused by regularly occurring high tides and by exceptionally high seas under storm conditions. In Japan and in some other countries, the occurrence of typhoons is particularly dangerous.

In order to understand the working of *irrigation systems* the following points should be considered:

1. The intake of water. This may be done in different ways, for example: (a) direct flow from a river without a dam; (b) direct flow from a river upstream of a dam; (c) pumping from a river; (d) pumping from the subsoil, either shallow (some metres) or deep (some tens of metres or more).

2. The transport of water to the area to be irrigated, in general via primary canals but sometimes via pipelines. The first method gives a loss of approximately 30 per cent of the water taken in from the river or the pumping station, the second has fewer losses but is expensive. The losses are a result of evaporation and of seepage into the subsoil. The latter may be reduced by covering the canals with concrete or cement, but this is again costly.

3. The manner of application to the fields: gravity irrigation (basin-irrigation, furrow-irrigation), sprinkler irrigation, trickle- or drip-irrigation, subirrigation (infiltration by pipes through the subsoil) (see also Ch. 5).

4. Intake of water into the soil and its transport through the soil, which depends largely on the permeability of the soil and on the presence of poorly permeable layers, not only in the part of the soil profile normally considered but also in deeper layers (up to 50 m depth); and connected with these the intake and evapotranspiration by the plant which varies according to different plant species.

5. The drainage of the soil and from the field.

6. The transport of the drainage water to secondary and subsequently to primary canals.

7. The outlet from the primary canals, with or without locks or pumps, to downstream areas or rivers.

These points are not only essential for the water use itself but also in relation to possibly occurring salts.

Plate 15 shows a secondary drainage canal (from a complex of fields to the primary canal), in a project situated in the coastal area of the Nile Delta (Egypt). In Plate 16 the construction is shown of a small pumping station for a pilot project near the mouth River Tigris (the Shatt el Arab) near Basrah

Plate 15 Secondary drainage canal in the coastal area of the Nile Delta, Egypt

Plate 16 Construction in progress of a pumping station for drainage of a pilot project at Tanouma (near Basrah, Iraq)

Plate 17 Recently pruned vineyard in the coastal area of the Nile Delta, Egypt

(Iraq). Plate 17 illustrates the results of good land and water management, including irrigation, drainage and desalinization, in the shape of a vineyard in the coastal area of the Nile Delta (Egypt).

Irrigation for the purpose of soil improvement always has to be accompanied by systematic drainage. This is necessary for the removal of salts and in particular of sodium, magnesium and chloride ions. If this is done in soils which have a natural abundance of gypsum ($CaSO_4.H_2O$), as occurs in many areas of Iraq, an automatic substitution of the leached cations by calcium ions takes place. In those cases the soil structure is maintained and often even improved. If there is no natural abundance of gypsum, calcium carbonate may to some extent have this function, but there is a hazard of the formation of poorly permeable soils due to peptization. It is then advisable to give some tons of gypsum per hectare as a soil amendment during the leaching process, a system used on a large scale for the desalinization of the first of the Zuyderzee polders of the Netherlands, the Wieringermeer Polder. The same method was also used with success after the floods of seawater which inundated large coastal areas of the Netherlands in 1944/45 and in 1953. In some other countries calcium carbonate has been used for this purpose with comparable results.

The lack of water in many arid regions is very great and cannot be satisfied with the use of the available fresh water from the rivers. In those cases attempts are made, sometimes with good results, to use saline water for irrigation (Salinity Seminar 1971). The use of saline water is possible for the primary desalinization of very saline soils, which then is followed by a further desalinization with available fresh water. This system results in a longer desalinization process, but it has been found to be effective. Complete irrigation of crops with somewhat saline water is also practised. The results are quite satisfactory on very permeable soils and for crops which have some salt tolerance (see Table 24). Sprinkler irrigation with saline water is hazardous as the water may cause extensive leaf damage.

Drainage is to remove excess water from the soil surface and from the soils themselves. This may be accompanied by the removal of salts as indicated above. It may also be done for improving the possibilities of constructing roads or buildings and for creating an extra capacity of the soil to store excess water after heavy rainfall. Drainage of young sediments which were deposited in water leads to 'ripening', a complex of chemical, physical and biological processes which leads to the formation of a soil from the sediment (see also Ch. 4). During the ripening, in particular in clays and in peats, subsidence of the soil surface occurs. This may even be seen in polders which have already been reclaimed some centuries ago if, for purpose of modern land use, the groundwater table is lowered and the still unripened subsoil comes under the influence of these processes. In areas where sands, clays and peats occur in one pattern, differential subsidence occurs as peat subsides more than clays, which subside more than sands. This may lead to the development of microrelief features.

The most prominent role of drainage is, however, to provide more air to the roots of plants. A soil completely saturated with water can only be used by plants which have special adaptations to marshy conditions such as the ability to absorb oxygen in solution or to transport oxygen from the air taken up by the leaves, down to the roots. In Chapter 2 it was demonstrated that oxygen is indispensable for the root functions related to nutrient intake. Irrigated rice ('paddy') cultivated on lands which are purposely brought into a waterlogged condition ('sawahs', Indonesia, Malaysia) is an example of the second group of plants.

Drainage of a tract of land may be achieved by such natural means as (1) surface flow and (2) outflow through sufficiently permeable subsoils. In the first case, attention must be paid to the erosion hazard. In the second case, it must be understood that water flow through the soil does not go along straight lines but along curves (see Fig. 8). This means that the permeability of deep subsoil layers is still of considerable relevance to soil drainage (often down to 50 m below surface).

If natural drainage is insufficient for the kind of land use which is envisaged, it can be improved with various kinds of measures:
1. The digging of small canals or large ditches into which groundwater flows directly from the adjoining fields. In level areas with moderately permeable soils, the distance between these ditches may not be wider than 15 to 30 m and this causes a large loss of land surface, high maintenance cost and difficult accessibility of the land.
2. The construction of a more elaborate system of trenches, ditches and canals, the smallest trenches being not more than ½ m deep and having

distances of between 8 to 25 m depending on the nature of the terrain and the permeability of the soils. The trenches and ditches must have a slight gradient for surface flow to the canals and here again attention must be paid to the erosion hazard (see also the earlier section on land degradation). Connections between trenches, ditches and canals may often be made by short pieces of pipe, thus improving accessibility of the land, or by weirs for avoiding too steep gradients. Also these systems require a large amount of annual maintenance. In some cases, such as the newly reclaimed Zuyderzee polders in the Netherlands, the system is initially applied until the soils have attained sufficient ripening and stability, and is then replaced by tube-drainage.

3. Tube-drainage, the drainage of water through tubes in the subsoil; these 'drains' have in general a diameter of between 5 and 10 cm and are made either of brick or plastic materials. They may be laid out as a simple system of parallel drains at a distance varying between 5 to 50 m (depending on the permeability of the soils) or as a more complex system where several drains flow into a collector drain. The latter may, for example, be done in a her-ringbone pattern and it is often adapted to the shape of the relief; it is often applied in poorly drained pastoral areas in undulating or rolling terrain. The drains are often put into trenches surrounded with some permeable ma-terial: sand, gravel, brush, wood or peat dust. For some years, at more or less regular intervals, drains have to be cleaned and sometimes blocked portions have to be dug up and renewed. The intensity of regular maintenance de-pends very much on the nature of the soils.

4. Mole drainage, where drainage tubes are made in the subsoil by drawing a torpedo-shaped wedge through the subsoil leaving something not dissimi-lar to the tunnels of moles. This is only applicable in very stable subsoils. It has to be repeated every five or more years depending on the soil and the drainage requirements.

LAND IMPROVEMENT

Land improvement embraces all works which are aimed at an improvement of the land for a planned or existing land use and which have effects of permanent or at least long duration (10 or more years). Land improvement in this sense is a major investment, but the size of this depends very much on local needs and circumstances (see also Vink 1975a). Land may also be improved gradually by good land use and land management. These improve-ments, which may for example include the raising of the fertility level of the soil, are often extremely important, but they are not included in our defini-tion. Finally, there is also land use improvement; this is improvement not aimed at the permanent improvement of the land itself, but at the way in which it is used. Land use improvement may indirectly lead to improve-ments of the land or it may put a stop to land degradation. As such it is again very important, but, for clarity's sake, it is not included in our definition. Land improvement always implies a change in one or more attributes of the land itself. These may be changes of soil profile or of microrelief, both of which are also called soil improvement, or the construction of drainage systems, of irrigation systems or of permanent road systems which then belong to the artefactial attributes of the land (see Ch. 1). Land improvement is a kind of land transformation. It often differs from land transformation by degradation in that the biomass production is not diminished, but even this is not always the case as can be seen from the example of road construction, an activity which is often a very definite land improvement. This is achieved by improving the accessibility of certain tracts of land and thus their usefulness in agricultural production, in forest exploitation or for human habitation. Land improvement for a certain purpose may thus also result in land degradation for another purpose, e.g. for wildlife. More study has still to be made in this respect of the various implications of land transformation; some of this will hopefully be arrived at by the SCOPE project on land transformation as mentioned in a preceding section (see also Vink 1981b).

Soil improvement, as already indicated, is a much more limited subject than land improvement. This derives from the different definitions of land and of soil respectively (see Ch. 1). Soil improvement includes all those activities which aim at the changing of the physical and/or chemical characteristics of the soil profile and/or the microrelief for one or more planned or existing land uses and which have the effects of permanent or at least long duration (10 or more years). Microrelief is included, as this is an essential part of the three-dimensional soil profile (see also Ch. 3). In general, soil improvement is aimed at enhancing the biomass production of a soil, the habitat for specific crops, or the suitability for grazing or for arable land cultivation, the latter often with mechanized methods. In Fig. 22 some examples are given of soil profiles which may be improved such as occur in various parts of the Netherlands and in alluvial areas of many parts of the world. In most of these, physical improvement with a view to root development and tillage is the main object, but this is often accompanied by certain chemical improvements. This is very clearly so in profile d, where a calcareous sandy loam is mixed with a slightly alkaline clay and in profile f, where a calcareous sandy loam is brought on top of and partly mixed with an acid sulphate clay (pH between 2.5 and 4.5). It is also to some extent valid for profile a, where the C and B horizons of a podzol are brought on top of, and partly mixed with, the strongly leached and very poor A horizon. Typical examples of mainly chemical soil improvement are found in the various kinds of desalinization, as discussed in the preceding section, but these also imply certain other amendments; for example, the application of gypsum.

Soil improvement may be done in various manners. In some cases only the topsoil is improved; for example, by bringing a sandy layer on top of a rather weak peat soil in order to improve the suitability for human access (also for sports fields) and for grazing cattle. In addition, this is often useful for improving the accessibility with mechanized implements and tractors for hay mowing, manuring and other recurring activities. Improvement of a top-soil without changing the profile is also often done by liming, the application of some tons of calcium-carbonate (industrial products or ground limestone) to the topsoil and ploughing this into the top 30 to 50 cm. This may eventually have some influence on the lower parts of the profile by leaching. This liming of soils has to be repeated once every 7 to 20 years, depending on climatic and soil conditions. In soils which are not too stony, soil improvement, in this case expressed by major changes in the soil profile, is often done by mechanical means. The main ways of doing this are: (1) improvement of the subsoil by means of various kinds of subsoil – ploughs which leave the topsoil nearly undisturbed; this may for example be done in profiles c and d of Fig. 22, where in general it is preferred to keep the humic topsoil in its place; (2) complete changing of the whole profile – although in cases of long term manuring the very topmost part of the A horizon may be kept in its place by specially constructed ploughs. This deep ploughing,

Fig 22 Schematic representation of various soil profiles from the Netherlands which are often ameliorated by soil improvement (Krijger and Maris 1964)

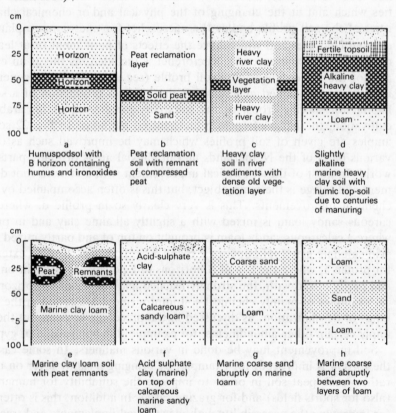

a
Humuspodsol with B horizon containing humus and ironoxides

b
Peat reclamation soil with remnant of compressed peat

c
Heavy clay soil in river sediments with dense old vegetation layer

d
Slightly alkaline marine heavy clay soil with humic top-soil due to centuries of manuring

e
Marine clay loam soil with peat remnants

f
Acid sulphate clay (marine) on top of calcareous marine sandy loam

g
Marine coarse sand abruptly on marine loam

h
Marine coarse sand abruptly between two layers of loam

which may easily go to over 1 m depth (a depth of up to 2 m is attainable in many Dutch polder soils) is applicable in the other profiles of Fig. 22. It is also done in the improvement of lands for modern vineyards in Tuscany (Italy), where deep ploughing of stony Tertiary clays with subsequent removal of the stones brought onto the surface is a common practice.

Changes in the microrelief of the soil surface are called levelling. It is the smoothing of the surface to a nearly level or gentle slope for irrigation and/ or drainage. It is often done with scrapers of a width of some metres drawn by heavy tractors. If this is done without proper care, the topsoil and sometimes most of the soil profile of the higher parts of the field may be lost and this may seriously diminish the productivity of these parts. Various kinds of machines have, therefore, been developed to keep a more or less even topsoil while bringing the suface to its preferred level condition.

Machines for soil improvement are in part the same as used in other engineering works such as bulldozers, graders and draglines. But special machines have also been developed for the various specialized activities. These include ploughs for deep-ploughing, which for example can keep the topsoil on the top while changing the whole lower profile, and special machines for thoroughly mixing the soils. Soil improvement was mostly done by hand, with only the assistance of transport such as narrow-gauge railways, until the end of the Second World War. After 1945 extensive mechanization has been started in many countries, including several developing countries. This was largely due to economic considerations, but various kinds of activities have proved to give better results with mechanized methods. Machines are better able to mix various soil horizons. Special sand-covering machines, which bring sand from deep subsoil and deposit the material on the surface, do work which even with cheap labour is nearly impossible to execute. Mechanization also allows for a better choice of time for executing the soil improvement, and the result depends very much on the moisture status of the soils and hence on weather conditions. In a relatively short time a large surface area can be improved when conditions are correct.

Soil survey produces essential data for determining the need for and the possibilities of soil improvement. In some cases, additional special maps have to be made within the framework of the soil survey in order to give sufficient data on the essential subsoil layers. In Fig. 23 a cross section is given of an area in the old peat reclamation areas of the north-eastern Netherlands (De Smet, 1968; see also Vink 1975a). These areas, which also occur in the adjoining parts of north-western Germany and analogous cases can be found to some extent in the British Isles, originally consisted of a layer of 2 to 4 m thickness of Holocene peat on top of late-Pleistocene aeolian coversands in which in early Holocene times a soil profile (mostly humuspodzols) had developed. In the Netherlands, past excavations for fuel, mainly in the sixteenth to eighteenth century, took off most of the peat but approximately 50 cm of the top peat was returned as a topsoil for use in agriculture ('bolster'). This topsoil was regularly manured and ploughed for

Fig. 23 Schematic cross-section of the soils in an area of the peat reclamation district of the province of Groningen (north-eastern Netherlands) (De Smet 1968)

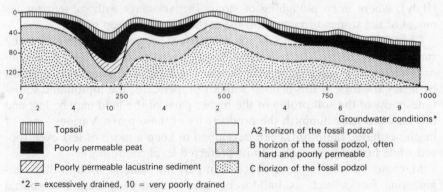

Topsoil

Poorly permeable peat

Poorly permeable lacustrine sediment

A2 horizon of the fossil podzol

B horizon of the fossil podzol, often hard and poorly permeable

C horizon of the fossil podzol

*2 = excessively drained, 10 = very poorly drained

arable land from the end of the excavation until the present time, a duration of some centuries during which most of the 'bolster' disappeared due to oxidation. As a result, land productivity declined, also the influence of some poorly permeable horizons of the old soil profile (B-horizon of the podsol, remnants of the bottom layer of the old peat, locally poorly permeable lacustrine sediments) had an increasing influence on land use together with the microrelief of the old eolian sands; the latter situation induced locally poor groundwater conditions.

In order to remedy this situation, soil surveys have been made and a series of measures has been developed for the restoration of the productivity of this region, which under good conditions has some of the highest potato yields of the world. A land classification based on the soil maps (see also Ch. 8) distinguished three major classes, and the required soil improvements for each of these are indicated in Table 25.

Table 25. Soil improvements to be applied on the three main land classes of the peat reclamation district of Groningen

Soil improvements	Classes		
	A	B	C*
Lowering of the soil by digging out part of the C horizon	X		
Raising the profile by adding C material and mixing soil			X
Covering the profile with sand on top			X
Breaking or mixing of peatlayers		X	X
Breaking or deep ploughing of B horizon	X	X	X
Breaking or removing of lacustrine loam layer			X
Levelling of undulating areas with retention of topsoil	X		X

* Class A corresponds with groundwater conditions 2 in Fig. 23;
  Class B corresponds with groundwater conditions 4 and 6 in Fig. 23;
  Class C corresponds with groundwater conditions 9 and 10 in Fig. 23.

Land consolidation, which includes land reallotment as well as several activities of land improvement, is carried out for making an area more suitable for the existing, as well as for new, land uses which are foreseen for the near future. Land development often embraces the same kinds of technical and institutional activities but is directly aimed at the increase and development of agricultural production and human habitat. Land consolidation as applied today in the Netherlands and in many other parts of Western Europe aims in particular at:

- rational and economically feasible farm management,
- a socially acceptable rural environment for living and working for all people concerned,
- a good use, and as many different uses as possible, of the rural areas by the whole non-agrarian population of the region, including those of the towns,
- the maintenance, and where possible re-establishment, of varied natural areas, in nature reserves and elsewhere.

The following objectives are relevant for these general purposes:

1. With regard to the natural environment:
   - maintenance and improvement of the natural components (plants, animals) in the cultural as well as in the (semi) natural ecosystems;
   - conservation of natural areas and nature reserves and of culturally significant (e.g. historical) areas and of monuments as well as the establishment of new kinds of attractive areas and features for the improvement of the human environment.

2. With regard to the visual aspects of rural areas and towns:
   - the promotion of visual aspects of landscapes and towns in such a manner, that historical significance and visual attractiveness are served;
   - conservation of significant landscapes of cultural importance and of monuments.

3. With regard to rural areas:
   - the conservation of open spaces by the maintenance of rural areas between urban zones, urban regions and inside these and by preventing the suburbanization of areas outside the established urban zones and regions;
   - promotion and maintenance of a sufficiently high standard of living for the farming population by developing feasible agricultural land utilization types;
   - promotion and maintenance of good living conditions for the rural population by maintenance of small rural centres with their various amenities for the functioning of the local communities;
   - maintenance and promotion of various possibilities for recreation by the conservation, and where necessary establishment, of good open

air spaces for the purpose (sports grounds, playing fields, walking areas, bathing facilities, etc.).

These various purposes and objectives need a whole framework of legal, institutional, technical and social activities. Their establishment depends very much on national and regional circumstances. In the Netherlands, the organization for land consolidation started after 1930 with relatively simple reallotment projects, where fields were reallotted and exchanged between farmers, for more efficient farming with increased production. Using basically the same methods and techniques in a more refined manner, it has now grown to a comprehensive system for modernizing the land for rural as well as urban populations and for conserving essential parts of the natural environment. The procedure has many phases for each land consolidation project which deal with areas of around 10 000 ha. The completion of each project takes approximately ten years. In Fig. 24 a diagram is given of the various stages. All projects are organized and coordinated by the Government Land Consolidation Service in cooperation with research institutes, provincial and local governments, societies concerned with special interests (farmers, conservationists, industrialists) and with other government services. The execution of a project is done by specialized engineering firms.

The cost of these projects is of the order of some thousands of guilders

Fig. 24 Phases and activities of land consolidation projects in the Netherlands

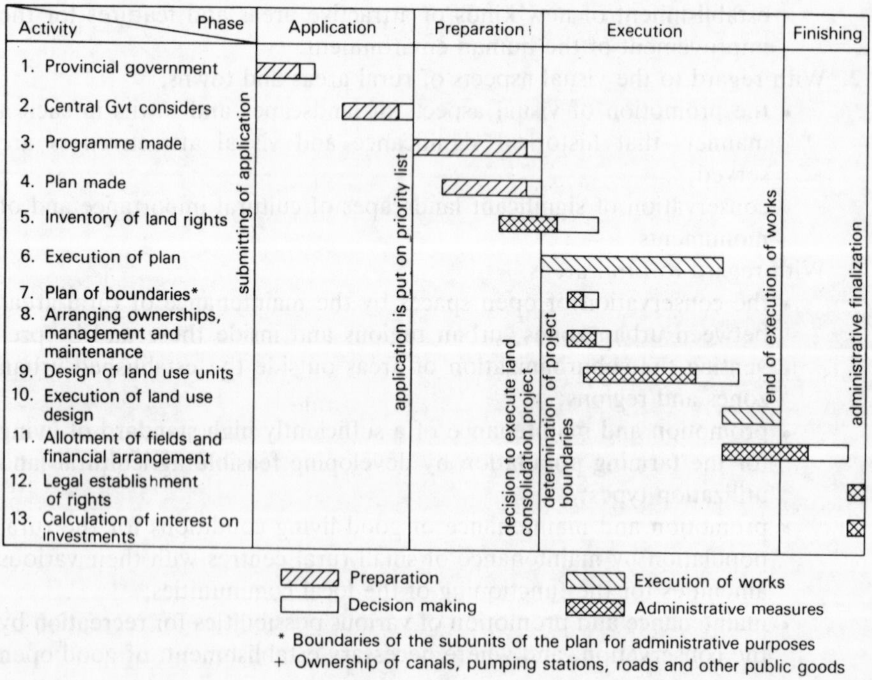
Activity
Phase
Application
Preparation
Execution
Finishing
1. Provincial government
2. Central Gvt considers
3. Programme made
4. Plan made
5. Inventory of land rights
6. Execution of plan
7. Plan of boundaries*
8. Arranging ownerships, management and maintenance
9. Design of land use units
10. Execution of land use design
11. Allotment of fields and financial arrangement
12. Legal establishment of rights
13. Calculation of interest on investments
submitting of application
application is put on priority list
decision to execute land consolidation project
determination of project boundaries
end of execution of works
administrative finalization
Preparation
Decision making
Execution of works
Administrative measures
* Boundaries of the subunits of the plan for administrative purposes
+ Ownership of canals, pumping stations, roads and other public goods

(US $1000 to 2000) per hectare for the total investment, of which approximately 65 per cent is carried by the central government on the annual budget of the Ministry of Agriculture and the remaining third paid by the landowners on a 30 years annuity. Each year some 40 000 ha of projects are started. Given the duration of each project, around 400 000 ha of projects are being managed in any year.

The following measures are carried out within a Dutch land consolidation project:

- construction and improvement of roads in such a manner that all farms and other enterprises have direct access to a public road of good quality;
- improvement of water conditions and of water management by the construction of new waterways and the improvement of existing ones as well as, where necessary, the construction of pumping stations, dams, etc.;
- combination of farmers' fields, often widely distributed over the area, so that each farmer obtains one or more larger fields near to his farm buildings, the new fields having often also an improved shape;
- relocation of farm buildings if these large investments are warranted by a much better distribution of land use over the whole project area, and establishment of electricity and water mains;
- planting of trees and bushes for the improvement of the visual character of the landscape and for compensating the loss of woods and plantations which had to be abandoned for the project;
- establishment of recreational amenities for the population living in the area as well as for visitors from neighbouring towns.

In areas where this is relevant may be added:

- the establishment of new nature reserves to be administered by the State Forest Service;
- the creation of industrial complexes near towns adjoining the project area.

In general some land in the project area can be obtained for allotment to farmers by establishing a pool of those lands from which the farmers have obtained new farms in the Zuyderzee polder area. Land from this pool may also be used for public purposes, depending on consultations with the local project commission. During phase 4 (the plan design, see Fig. 24) the owners of lands in the project area are called upon to vote in favour of or against the project. The contacts with local and other interests are maintained during most of the duration of the project and this allows some readjustments during the years of execution.

Other land use plans which often have some similarities to one or more phases of the land consolidation projects are the town and country planning projects of local and regional or provincial governments as well as the 'urban zoning' practised in various countries. Their importance and effectiveness depends very much on their legal status and on the institutional, financial and technical means available to the responsible authorities. In countries with a federal constitution, much depends on the willingness of the individual states and on the cooperation between these states and the federal government. In Switzerland the status of the federal 'Bundesdelegierte für Raumplanung', who is a member of the Federal Department of Justice, is gradually growing with the increasing needs for coordination of planning for land use and environmental management.

In land development, the emphasis put on the various activities often differs from that in land consolidation projects in industrialized countries. This is concurrent with differences in national, regional and individual (or family) interests. Some essential elements of development projects in the Third World are indicated in Fig. 25. It should be kept well in mind, however, that no two developing countries are alike and that there is an enormous diversity of needs and circumstances, not only between different countries but also between different regions within the same country. The decision on choice and priority of project within any country or region requires individual analyses. For this decision the following considerations have to be taken into account: (1) the choice between two projects belonging to different sectors of the economy of the country (for example, industry and agriculture); (2) the choice between competing projects of different kinds belonging to the same sector (for example, an irrigation project and a pastoral project; (3) the choice between two projects of the same kind; for example, two irrigation projects. For this choice, various economic and social reasons may be given but eventually the choice is always a political one and it also depends very much on the scarcity of available non-land resources, in particular financial resources. Another consideration relevant to the choice of projects is the different logistics of projects in various areas and the scarcity of suitable technical and administrative personnel for manning the project. These two may influence the primary choice to go to easily accessible areas; this is often very sound reasoning as the execution of any project for land development, especially in a developing country, is already a difficult problem.

A comparison between the rather well-known Zuyderzee Polder Project of the Netherlands and projects of comparable size in developing countries is justified in this respect. The Zuyderzee Polder Project was established by law and the technical activities started around the year 1926. The area, situated in an estuarine region in the centre of the country, is very easily accessible, in particular by boat, still a favourite means of transportation in the country. In 1981 a barrier dam and four polders with a total surface area of nearly 200 000 ha have been constructed and reclaimed using available modern machinery, sufficient financial means and many hundreds, if not thousands, of well-trained experienced technical personnel. After 55 years the project is still not completed as the last polder of some 20 000 ha has to be reclaimed.

Fig. 25 Elements to be distinguished in rural development projects in developing countries (after Mosher 1972)

A Basic data	B Project activities	C Types of land development projects

1. Research
2. Production and/or
   importation of inputs
   for farming enterprises
3. Rural activities for
   supporting agriculture
4. Activities for
   stimulating production
5. Land use planning
6. Instruction of people
   for obtaining schooled
   workers in agriculture
   and land development
	I Agriculture
	
	1. Markets for agricultural
	   produce
	2. Local selling points for
	   inputs
	3. Agricultural credit
	4. Extension, education
	5. Local pilot projects
	6. Roads from farm to
	   market
	
	II Other rural projects
	
	7. Rural industries
	8. Rural public works
	9. Socio-cultural projects
	10. Group activities
	    (recreation, cultural)
	11. Domestic extension
	12. Medical facilities
	13. Family planning
	    programmes
	14. Schools
	15. Local administration
	16. Religious activities
		1. Agricultural development
		   projects
		2. Rural development
		   projects with an
		   agricultural component
		3. Rural development
		   projects without
		   agricultural component

If this is compared with irrigation projects in developing countries, often of comparable surface area, it is clear that too much is often expected within a too short duration. In developing countries, given favourable conditions, perhaps some tens of well-trained technical personnel are available and these may be assisted by a team of some ten well-trained experienced people from a cooperating country or agency. Often only one moderate road gives access to the area and all machinery and materials have to be transported over long distances. It is, therefore, not surprising that results often seem to be unsatisfactory, in particular within the often stringent time limits imposed by financing agencies.

Land users and land use planners are always far apart, a situation specially marked in most developing countries (Franke 1969). The planner has to create, particularly in a developing country, such new conditions that it becomes attractive for the farmers to change and improve their way of farming. In this respect special attention has to be paid to the fact that farmers, and in particular small farmers, cannot afford to run large risks. The degree of risk associated with any kind of crop is often more important to the farmer than the possibly high yields which he may obtain in a good year under favourable conditions. This risk, as well as the lack of experience with new crops and new techniques, often leads to great hazards for the farmer, which is a major reason for poor response to the introduction of new crops. Another cause often lies in the need for the farmer to reduce his spare time that he has for social activities under the traditional systems. These social activities may be of a purely cultural nature, but often they are of import- ance to land use: harvest, maintenance of irrigation systems. In many Asian countries mutual help in this respect (Indonesia: tulung menulung) is of great importance.

Many investigations are needed to obtain an insight under given landscape ecological and cultural conditions into what will be sufficiently attractive to the farmers. To this must be added local demonstrations of suitable methods and techniques under the new conditions created by a project. The establish- ment of pilot projects at an early stage, with the inclusion of some ex- perimental and some practical demonstration farms, is often a very useful means, not only of reaching the farmers but of gaining experience on the impacts of various project activities under local conditions. It is still too often thought, although opinion on this subject is gradually changing, that the establishment of a large project with high investment guarantees success, but this is far from being the truth. Transfer of knowledge and experience on the basis of sound landscape ecological data is essential to any project and many projects have to be rather large to succeed at all. But the adap- tation of the data and knowledge transferred to the particular conditions of men and resources in the new area needs local modifications for which the proper place are pilot projects, assuming these are well selected and do not require too large investments of people and money.

Special attention has to be paid to the management and maintenance of the structures created in any project. This is often very much neglected by all concerned. An excellent project design may lead to poor results if no institutional and technical measures are taken for management and mainten- ance. Apart from various countries in Asia, organization and knowledge as well as the realization of this need are generally lacking in most countries. Even in these Asian countries, developments during the last decades have often led to the disappearance of this notion under the younger generation. Thus, in any project where small or large structures are installed, including irrigation and drainage canals, weirs, bunds for soil conservation and many others, continuous management and maintenance and supervision on their regular execution are essential. Preparation for these by continued guidance and demonstration, before as well as during and after the project execution by training of personnel and by the creation of appropriate social and insti- tutional arrangements, is necessary to achieve the long term objectives.

8
Land classification for land use planning

Land classification basically means the arrangement of land in classes. When the definition of land is considered (see Ch. 1) it is clear that this may be done in many different ways and for many different purposes. These purposes may be purely academic, e.g. for archaeology or for theoretical plant ecology, but often they are of a more directly practical nature. One of the latter kinds is land classification for land use planning, which gives a means for connecting the landscape ecological and the socio-economic aspects of land use. In the last decade, the term 'land evaluation' has come into use for the most essential aspect of this kind of land classification (Vink 1975; FAO 1976; Beek 1978). 'Land evaluation is the process of assessment of land use performance, involving the execution and interpretation of surveys and studies of landforms, soils, vegetation, climate and other aspects of land in order to identify and make a comparison of promising land uses in connection with specific land units in terms applicable to the objectives of the land evaluation' (FAO 1976; Beek 1978).

This definition includes all the different kinds of surveys and related investigations in land evaluation. There is some truth in this because there are indelible links between the various phases of research which start with the first surveys and end with the integration of land evaluation into land use planning. In general, however, emphasis with regard to land evaluation is put on the development of land suitability classifications for land use planning. In these classifications the suitability of certain tracts of land, mapped on landscape ecological and other maps, for one or more well-described land utilization types (see Ch. 5) is given. The selection of relevant and foreseeable land utilization types in a given region and for a given period is one of the crucial aspects as land evaluation and land use planning are very closely connected already at an early phase (see also Vink 1975a; Beek, 1978). Seen from the viewpoint of the planner, land evaluation, all parts of the above definition included, is part of the planning process. It is that part of the process which brings the substantial knowledge of the land into a shape which allows the integration of this knowledge into the other parts of the planning process (Faludi 1975).

Land classification is a more general term than land evaluation. Within the process of land use planning it embraces all the various ways of presenting the knowledge of the land in such a manner that they can be easily integrated. This is done with the help of maps and tables. The maps include landscape ecological or other maps indicating the basic scientific knowledge, and all other data, including various classifications, are given in tables and text related to the map units of the basic map: land qualities, land limitations, land suitabilities, etc. In many cases, however, it has proved to be more effective to also produce maps, largely based on and derived from the basic scientific maps, in order to present the interpretative data and classifications in a more easily readable manner. Various categories of these, and of related tables, will be discussed below. Seen from the viewpoint of the planner, the scientific base maps as well as the interpretative or 'derived' maps are called land classification maps (see also Davidson 1980).

Seen from the viewpoint of landscape ecology, land classification for land use planning is a part of applied landscape ecology. Land classification, land evaluation and land use planning all have to use landscape ecological maps as basic documents. They do this by extrapolating and predicting on the basis of certain assumptions. The assumptions are necessary with regard to the kind of land utilization types which are relevant and foreseeable with a view to current situations and expected future developments. Also included are the relevant socio-economic and institutional circumstances. The data and knowledge required for these assumptions are obtained from experts in these fields or from relevant literature. Preferably an integrated approach in which planners participate should be used for this purpose (Vink 1975a; FAO 1976; Beek 1978). In many cases it is useful to make various alternative classifications, based on different alternative assumptions, which show to the planners and decision makers the different possibilities in the various parts of a region.

Land classification has also been called 'Soil Survey Interpretation' (Kellogg 1961). This is a very appropriate term as the soil surveyor, or the landscape ecological surveyor, or the team which carried out an integrated survey of natural resources, has to interpret to the users, planners and decision makers, the basis scientific maps produced (see also Zonneveld 1979). Soil maps and landscape ecological maps have their own terminology based on the scientific methods used, and this is unavoidable for representing the nature of the surface of the earth. These terminologies are however unreadable for most non-experts in these sciences and they have therefore to be translated for the various practical purposes for which the maps are to be used. This translation may often also include a simplification to a smaller number of categories or classes than are represented on the basic maps. The basic landscape ecological maps or soil maps give as comprehensive a view as is conformable with the state of the art and the scale of the map. These maps therefore give basic information for many different practical purposes, each of which have their own requirements (see also Ch. 5) – for example, an urban extension project needs data different from a horticultural project – but still many of the basic data can be found on the same landscape ecological map. This map can, therefore, concurrent with its interpretation be summarized for one purpose and this makes for more easily readable and applicable land classification maps. The experts who have made the basic scientific maps have a special responsibility as they are the only people who fully know all the various intricacies of the mapped areas and they have to at least participate in their interpretation. The interpretation of soil and landscape ecological maps without the cooperation of at least one of the surveyors has already proved many times that insufficiently accurate interpretations are the result. The mapping of any area for one single purpose – for example, urban extension or horticulture – is too narrow an order for the survey since experience has shown that the maps, once made, are always used for other purposes.

The responsibility for the interpretation by the soil or landscape ecological surveyor has also the advantage that from the beginning of the survey he directs his attention not only to fundamental scientific aspects of the area, but also to those aspects which are perhaps negligible from a theoretical viewpoint but have great practical influence; for example, differences in topsoil texture, in groundwater regime, in subsoil characteristics or in slope classes. Sound land use planning has to use modern scientific knowledge together with the various empirical data which have proved to be effective for this purpose. An example of soil suitability classification for land use planning has been given by Vink and Van Zuilen (1967, 1974). In this case, the soil map of the Netherlands at a scale of 1 : 200 000 was interpreted for arable land and pastures. This included a classification in easily readable terminology as well as a reduction of the 150 units of the soil map to 20 land classes for this particular purpose. From the same soil map a suitability map for forestry was derived, with different classes and terminology (Sikkel et al 1971) indicating five different classes for broad land use planning for forestry in the Netherlands (see Table 37), based on a different grouping of the same soil map units with direct relevance to forestry.

Various different categories of land classification can be distinguished (see also Vink 1963b): land classification according to: (1) inherent characteristics of the land, (2) land qualities, (3) the responses of crops to management, (4) current land use, (5) potential land uses, (6) recommended land uses, (7) land use design, (8) decided land uses. These categories are fundamental to the identification of the various tasks and responsibilities in land use planning. Separation of these is essential for arriving at an integration where everybody contributes to the final result from his own particular position in the planning process.

Land classification according to inherent characteristics of the land is a broad category which embraces all the various ways in which land may be mapped for indicating its nature and particular aspects. It includes for example:

- topographic maps ('Ordnance Survey Maps').
- geomorphological maps,
- soil maps,
- landscape ecological maps,
- geological maps,
- vegetation maps,
- land use inventory maps (indicating present or current land uses),
- landscape climatological maps.

Each of these maps has its own legend and classification in terms of its basic science. This is unavoidable as otherwise no precise characterization of the scientifically determined features can be given.

The value of these maps may, however, be longer than the duration of the terminology of the science, in particular of a rapidly developing new science such as soil science or pedology. In principle, the validity of these maps, which have been called basic scientific maps, is equal to the stability of the phenomena mapped. But major developments in any particular science will often produce new methods for mapping and measuring, and therefore the 'state of the art' may make older maps at least partially obsolete. Often a period of 30 years, approximately one human generation, is taken as the valid period of use for such maps unless either natural developments (land degradation) or human interventions (land improvement) have caused significant changes in particular areas. In such a case these areas have to be remapped after some years for indicating the results of land transformation.

Land classification according to land qualities interprets and classes the mapping units of the basic scientific maps with regard to the physical, chemical and morphological requirements of any relevant land use, including the ecological requirements of various kinds of plants and animals as well as various technical aspects of land use, land improvement and constructions. Some examples are: erosion hazard, permeability, trafficability, water retention capacity. This category will be discussed in the next section.

Land classification according to the response of crops to management is a grouping of the inherent characteristics of the land with regard to the responses which crops and vegetations show due to various kinds of measures taken for land use purposes. These responses often differ considerably according to the various landscape ecological units. Different responses of the same crop on different soils to the application of chemical fertilizers and different responses to irrigation and drainage are well-known examples. The category might also be interpreted as indicating the responses to environmental management. A later section will examine this in greater detail.

Land classification according to current land use has also been labelled 'Present Land Use Classification' and even 'Land Use Classification'. The latter term has often caused misunderstanding because the next categories to be discussed are also called land use classifications. It is indispensable for land use planning to know the exact nature and location of the different current land uses in an area, as otherwise no sound measures for their improvement or change can be planned. The most famous of these classifications are those initiated and directed by the late Sir Dudley Stamp (1950, 1961) which include a land use survey of Britain during the Second World War as well as the World Land Use Survey under the aegis of the IGU (International Geographical Union.) These projects have introduced many sound principles on the mapping of current land use, although unwarranted extrapolations with regard to potential land uses have been made due to the lack of available basic data on land resources. Mapping of land use with aerial photographs and with satellite imagery is often very useful for following and studying land use developments (see also Vink 1975). Land utilization types (see Ch. 5) are today also used for the mapping of current land use.

Land classification according to potential land uses is more often indicated as 'land use capability classification', 'land suitability classification' or 'soil suitability classification'. As has been indicated above, it is the central objective of land evaluation (Beek 1978) and it is, therefore, a category of particular importance. In this category, the main aim is to designate the suitability of the various land units according to their inherent characteristics and qualities for various relevant and foreseeable land utilization types. As mentioned above, this has to be done under a number of assumptions, in particular with regard to socio-economic and institutional circumstances. In general, emphasis rests on the suitability of land for various kinds of land use, but land improvements may also be taken into account. This is called land suitability for improvement and, if this is considered, two different kinds of land suitabilities for use may be recognized: current land suitability for land use and potential suitability for land use. This often gives rise to misunderstanding as the 'current suitability for land use' is often different from the current land use. Current land use is a result of historical developments and reflects past socio-economic and technical conditions. Current suitability for land use may only develop after various measures for land use improvement have been taken; it is in many cases, as indicated above, a 'potential land use', but without improvement of the land itself. 'Potential suitability for land use' is suitability after land improvement, including various activities which bring permanent changes to the land (see Ch. 7). The difference between 'land use improvement' and 'land improvement' must be kept in mind.

Land suitability classification is the last category in this group which may still be considered as part of research. All the categories from 1 to 5 (inclusive) are fully amenable to scientific investigation, although for category 5 a number of assumptions have to be established, preferably based on the results of socio-economic and other investigations. If the assumptions are obtained from practical planners, they are, once established, still handled as objective data, together with possible alternatives. In categories 6 to 8 inclusive, many non-scientific considerations have to play a role, although they may be supported by data from social and other sciences. But financial considerations – available non-land resources – (Vink 1975a) as well as political and religious considerations are often essential. Priority decisions and logistics, as indicated in Chapter 7, often need to be taken into account. For example, in a certain area a decision may be taken to develop non-irrigated agriculture whereas the development of intensive irrigated agriculture might be eventually more relevant. The participation of people with scientific backgrounds may often be very useful for these categories, but their considerations will have to include many aspects which are not within scientific research.

Land classification according to recommended land uses considers the various alternative land uses as presented from land suitability classification and indicates to designers and decision makers which land use alternatives are thought to be the most feasible in a given area. Often the advice is accompanied by information on the associated socio-economic or environmental impacts involved. They may result in a report with a map of the kind illustrated in Fig. 26 from an area in East Africa.

Land classification according to land use design has thus far been little considered in describing the various kinds of land classification. Designing the lay-out and construction is a crucial activity in all projects where intensive modernization and improvement of rural and urban areas is planned. Once a line is drawn on a map for this design, it is very difficult to have it removed or changed. Only very small scale projects or projects based mainly on land use improvement by rural extension do not have this strong connection with a formal design. Project design is essential for the execution. It involves the use of various kinds of basic data, such as those provided by the above mentioned kinds of land classification, as well as the personal creativity of the designers. The designers have to take many decisions and have often to make a choice, in matters which within the context of the whole project look very small, but which may have an important impact on the future land use. There is finally only one design which is going to be executed although during the execution, which may take some years, often minor local adaptations may still be included. It is often useful to start with two or more alternative designs or with a very general primary design which is gradually completed during the various execution phases. The first phase may be based on a pilot project and subsequent phases can then be adapted according to the experience gained in all previous phases. If a project has a very long duration, for example 10 or more years, adaptation of increased general knowledge as well as to changed socio-economic conditions is necessary.

The use of landscape ecological data in project design may broadly speaking be approached in two different manners: (1) a very courageous standpoint saying: 'do not disturb me with data, because I know what I am doing', and (2) a very hesitating standpoint saying: 'Let's do nothing before all data are available'. Both these extremes lead to chaos – the first due to too much activity and not enough thought, the latter due to a lack of activ-

Fig. 26 Recommended land use for various land utilization types in an area
of East Africa (Van de Weg and Mbuvi 1975)

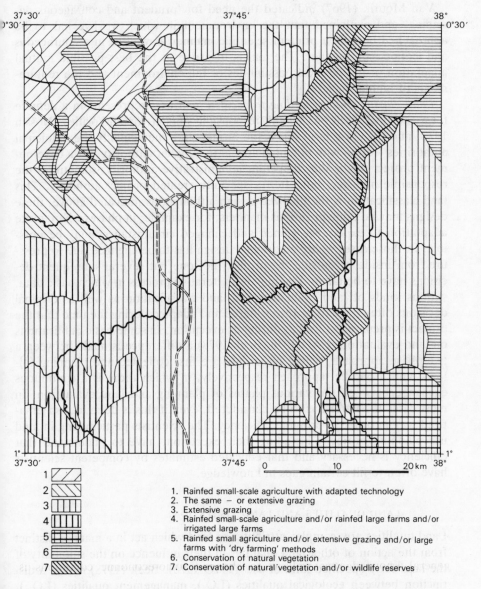

1. Rainfed small-scale agriculture with adapted technology
2. The same – or extensive grazing
3. Extensive grazing
4. Rainfed small-scale agriculture and/or rainfed large farms and/or irrigated large farms
5. Rainfed small agriculture and/or extensive grazing and/or large farms with 'dry farming' methods
6. Conservation of natural vegetation
7. Conservation of natural vegetation and/or wildlife reserves

ity, as it is impossible to have all data available. The first is comparable to
the way in which old-fashioned town planning has often proceeded; the latter to the viewpoint of the scientist who feels that he is unable to deliver the
necessary data within the time limits which are essential for the project.
During the last decade surveyors as well as planners and designers have tried
to find a solution to these problems, in particular in town and country plan-

ning. The problems have first to be indicated in order to find an appropriate solution under various circumstances.

Van Mourik (1967) indicated the need for 'prudent and courageous designing' and explained that the environment in which we live has to be approached both in a prudent scientific manner as well as in a courageous and iconoclastic manner. The aim is to arrive at the best possible mutual adaptation of the physical possibilities of the environment and the requirements of human society.

Land classification according to decided land uses represents in a definite form the final decisions by the responsible persons or authorities (Nossin 1977a and b). On a farm this is the farmer, in a municipality the municipal authorities – often with potential appeal to a higher authority, for a development project this is the competent administrative authority, sometimes the responsible minister, but often a specially created project authority. This land classification is the finalized design although, as indicated above, these designs may be done in various manners; for example, in phases where more adaptation to experience gained and changed circumstances may be possible. In those cases where an original design has to be changed due to pressure from inside or outside the project, not one but several subsequent decisions have to be taken. Planning is an iterative process in which basic data, various kinds of land evaluation and land classification as well as original decisions often have to be reconsidered and adapted during the time that the project is prepared as well as during its execution. In some basic publications on land evaluation (FAO 1976; Beek 1978) a difference is made between a two-phase approach, where basic data are first collected and planning follows, and a parallel approach respectively, in which there is a continuous exchange between the various phases of planning and land evaluation. In most cases the latter has to be considered, even if this is done in a schematized way in order to promote efficiency. The scientists participating in land use planning projects, including their execution, have to understand that efficiency is necessary and that educated estimates by competent scientists have often to fill certain gaps in knowledge.

LAND QUALITIES AND LAND LIMITATIONS

Land qualities are 'complex attributes of land which act in a manner distinct from the action of other land qualities in their influence on the suitability of the land for a specified kind of use' (FAO 1976). Beek (1978) makes a distinction between ecological qualities (LQ_s), management qualities (LQ_m), conservation qualities (LQ_c) and improvement qualities (IQ) which respectively have their influence on the growth of plants and animals, on human land management, on the suitability for soil conservation and on the suitability for land improvement. It is a means of expressing how a tract of land relates to certain ecological or land use functions without having to bring in too many outside assumptions and without implying in any way a value for

Table 26. Major land qualities and suggested symbols for agricultural land uses

A. Land qualities related to productivity from crops and other plant growth

Crop yields (a resultant of many qualities listed below) (c)
Moisture availability (the integrated moisture of climate and land) (w)
Nutrient availability (n)
Oxygen availability in the root zone (o)
Adequacy of foothold for roots (Fh)
Conditions of germination (s)
Workability of the land (ease of cultivation) (w)
Salinity and alkalinity (Sa)
Soil toxicity (To)
Resistance to soil erosion (Se)
Pests and diseases related to the land (d)
Flooding hazard (including frequency, periods of inundation) (In)
Temperature regime, (t)
Radiation energy and photoperiod (r)
Climatic hazards affecting plant growth (including hail, wind, frost) (h)
Air humidity as affecting plant growth (Ah)
Drying periods for ripening of crops (Hs)

B. Land qualities related to domestic animal productivity

Productivity of grazing land (resultant of many qualities listed under A) (g)
Climatic hardships affecting animals (Ch)
Endemic pests and diseases (De)
Nutritive value of grazing land (Ng)
Toxicity of grazing land (Pt)
Resistance to degradation of vegetation (Vd)
Resistance to soil erosion under grazing conditions (Eg)
Availability of drinking water (Wd)
Accessibility of the terrain (Ta)

C. Land qualities related to forest productivity

The qualities listed may refer to natural forests, forestry plantations, or both; see also
Laban (1981) for more extensive treatment.
Mean annual increments of timber species (a resultant of many qualities listed under
   A) (Fi)
Types and quantities of indigenous timber species (Ts)
Site factors affecting establishment of young trees (Tp)
Pests and diseases (Td)
Fire hazard (Tf)
Availability of plants, from which products may be harvested or extracted (medicinal,
   fruit, natural rubber) (Pm)
Availability of animals which may be harvested for meat or hides (Pg)
Accessibility of the terrain (Tb)

D. Land qualities related to management and inputs

The qualities listed may refer to arable use, animal production and forestry
Terrain factors affecting mechanization (m)
Terrain factors affecting construction and maintenance of access roads (Rc)
Size of potential management units (forest blocks, farms, fields) (Lo)
Location in relation to markets and to supplies of inputs (M)
Vegetation cover with restrictive effects on land use (Ve)

Source: After Beek and Bennema 1972; and FAO 1976; See also Vink 1975a; Beek 1978.

the tract of land. The relevance of land qualities for land use planning is that this approach focuses on various kinds of land characteristics in their ecological functions as interacting factors for plant growth and land use. Land qualities may in many cases be directly measured – for example, drainability (Bouma *et al.* 1979; see also Beatty *et al.* 1979) – and their interactions may be calculated by a computer (Bie *et al.* 1976; Kwakernaak 1982). Land qualities are often used as the basic data for suitability assessment, in which case they are also called 'assessment factors' (Bie *et al.* 1976). Beek and Bennema (1972) (see also Beek 1978; Vink 1975a) made the first comprehensive list of major land qualities for agriculture (see Table 26). The term 'soil qualities' has been used for a much longer time (Vink 1960; Kellogg 1961).

This list of major land qualities makes possible judging of the various degrees in which any tract of land corresponds with the various requirements of any land use. In the first instance, the tract of land must be characterized by means of a landscape ecological map, a soil map, or appropriate kinds of geomorphological maps. These maps provide the inherent characteristics on which the judgement, or measurement, of the land qualities is done. In the second place it is necessary to have as much knowledge as possible of the requirements of the various crops, animals or land utilization types. Where feasible, judgement of land qualities is made on a quantitative scale. Due to the complexity of ecological phenomena, complete scales for the world do not exist, although some good work has been done recently in the FAO Agroecological Zones Project (FAO 1978/1980). This project is a very generalized one, largely based on the *Soil Map of the World* on scale 1 : 5 million (FAO/UNESCO 1971). For more detailed investigations in individual areas, scales for judging land characteristics and land qualities have to be developed locally, as has been done for example by Haantjens (1966) for Papua-New Guinea; see Table 27.

These tables are partly based on general knowledge of the requirements of land use and of ecosystems and to this is added local knowledge largely gathered during the landscape ecological survey. The systematic comparison of actual field data offers a good opportunity for this. Where possible, additional quantitative measurements are made and the data of existing field experiments are used. Both, however, are always scarce and never give more than some benchmarks on which the judgements can be gauged. The example given in Table 27(a) contains only soil qualities which can be more easily quantified than land qualities (see also Vink 1975a).

As indicated above, land qualities, sometimes called assessment factors, are primarily used for arriving at a reasonable land suitability classification. But land qualities are also very useful as a classification for direct use, to be presented either as maps or tables, derived from the basic scientific maps. They give a translation and summary of these maps in ecological and technical terms and these aspects are in general dominant in the execution stage of land use planning. For this purpose the land qualities or soil qualities are often presented as land or soil limitations. Basically land limitations are the

Table 27. Examples of classification of soil qualities derived from soil characteristics in Papua New Guinea

(a) Soil permeability derived from soil texture and consistency

Permeability	Texture	Consistency and structure
Very good, more than 5 m/24 hrs	Gravel to coarse sand	
Good, 1.5 to 5.0 m/24 hrs	Fine sand to sandy loam sandy clay loam to clay	Non-swelling clays with high macroporosity or strong granular or crumb structure
Moderate, 0.3 to 1.5 m/24 hrs	Sandy clay loam to clay silty clay to heavy clay – porosity better than average	Moderate porosity and structure
Poor, 0.06 to 0.3 m/24 hrs	Silty clay to heavy clay Sandy clayloam to clayloam	Moderate porosity and structure Compacted and cemented no visible pores
Very poor, less than 0.06 m/24 hrs	Sandy clay to heavy clay	Dense, structureless, no visible pores, mostly swelling clays

(b) Hazards of flooding with freshwater

	Duration of the flood in days				
	less than 15	15–45	45–90	90–150	150–24	more than 240
Assessment class	0	1	2	3	4	5

Source: Haantjens 1966.

same as land qualities. The difference is that for land limitations a theoretically ideal condition is used for comparison with all land whose qualities are indicated as various degrees of limitations within this condition. In Table 28 an example is given of limitations which have been used in Western Europe; these were largely based on a system established by the soil and land use surveys of Portugal (Salgueiro *et al.* 1964). Similar systems are also used in other countries, such as Ireland (Gardiner and Ryan 1969).

In regions where processes of erosion and denudation (mass-movements) are of importance, a classification of the units of a landscape ecological map according to the nature and degree of these processes is very relevant. An example is given in Table 29 of the classification of soil erosion and slope stability of a part of the Mugello basin (east of Florence, Tuscany, Italy). This is based on the landscape ecological map of the area at a scale of 1 : 50 000.

Table 28. Land limitations in Western Europe, based on an enquiry of the European Soil Resources Committee of FAO, 1962

Land limitations	Relative significance in W. Europe for agriculture (1 = very significant)
(a) Altitude above sea level	1
(b) Relief (topography)	1
(c) Soil depth	1
(d) Rockiness of surface	2
(e) Stoniness of soil	3
(f) Hazard of water erosion	2
(g) Water deficiency	2
(h) Excess water, with or without artificial drainage	1
(i) Hazard of flooding	3
(j) Hazard of wind erosion	4
(k) Salinity/alkalinity	3
(l) Special problems related to the chemical or mineralogical characteristics of the soil	5
(m) Special problems of organic soils	6
(n) Special problems related to soil texture	7
(o) Special problems of soil structure	8

Source: Vink 1964.

Table 29. Classification of soil erosion and slope stability of the Northern part of the Mugello basin (Tuscany, Italy)

Composite land class	Soil erosion class	Slope stability class	Surface area (ha)
A	—	Stable	1000
B	Sheet	Stable	4250
C	Sheet	Potentially instable	250
D	Sheet	Instable	500
E	Sheet and rill	Stable	6700
F	Sheet and rill	Instable	3550
G	Sheet, rill, gully	Stable	5900
H	Sheet, rill, gully	Instable	400
I	Badlands	Stable	450

Source: Van Velthuizen 1975.

Table 30 gives an example of the way in which land limitations are used as assessment factors for the determination of land suitability. This is the regular system as used by the Netherlands Soil Survey Institute for its standard maps at a scale 1 : 50 000 (Stiboka 1975). A more general outline of the assessment procedure and of the classes is given in Fig. 27.

Table 30. Example of an assessment table attached to the soil map on scale 1 : 50 000 of the Netherlands: extracted from the table for sheet Venlo (52 East)

Land suitability land	Soil map unit and groundwater phase†	Limitations to soil suitability*				
		Excess water	Water deficit	Topsoil F §	Structural stability	Trafficability
Major class KB: Soils suitable for crops grown on clayey soils						
Soils with, in	BLH5-VI	1	1	1–2	1–2	1
general, many	BKd25-VII	1	1	1–2	1–2	1
possibilities	KRn1-VI	1	1	2	2	1
KB1						
Soils with, in	pKRn2-V	2–3	1	1–2	1–2	2–3
general, limited	Ln5-V	2–3	1	2	2	2–3
possibilities	AMm-V	2–3	1	2	2	2–3
KB3	KRN1-V	2–3	1	3	2	2–3
Major class ZB: Soils suitable for crops grown on sandy soils						
Soils with, in	bEZ21-VI	1	1	n.r.	n.r.	1
general, many	bEZ30-VI	1	1	n.r.	n.r.	1
possibilities	zEZ23-VI	1	1	n.r.	n.r.	1
ZB1	zEZ23-VII	1	1	n.r.	n.r.	1
Soils with, in	bEZ30-VII	1	1–2	n.r.	n.r.	1
general, good	Hh21-IV	1–2	1–2	n.r.	n.r.	1–2
possibilities	Hn21-IV	1–2	1–2	n.r.	n.r.	1–2
ZB2	Y23b-VI,VII	1	2	n.r.	n.r.	1
Soils with, in	Hn21-VI	1	2–3	n.r.	n.r.	1
general, limited	Hn30-VI	1	2–3	n.r.	n.r.	1
possibilities	Y23-VII	1	3	n.r.	n.r.	1
ZB3	bEZ30-VII	1	3	n.r.	n.r.	1

* 1 = little or no limitations, 3 = severe limitations
§ n.r. = not relevant for sandy soils
‡ With regard to the seedbed quality
† The soils may be briefly characterized as follows (see Ch. 3): BL and BK are fluvisols in sandy loam; KR and PKR are fluvisols in sandy loam; L are gleysols in sandy loam; AM are strongly gleyed fluvisols in heavy clay; EZ are deeply humic plaggen soils in loamy fine sand (23) and in coarse sand (30); Hn are humuspodzols in slightly loamy fine sand (21) and in coarse sand (30); Y are cambic arenosols in loamy fine sand, with gravelly subsoil; the Roman numerals IV to VII indicate the groundwater phase; from moderately well to excessively drained (see also Table 6).
Source: Stiboka 1975.

RESPONSE OF CROPS TO MANAGEMENT

Twenty years ago Kellogg (1962) pointed out in a paper which is still worthwhile to read that soil productivity results from a coordination of soil and land management and that the responses of different soils to various kinds of management, especially with intensive modern agriculture, are the most

Fig. 27 Assessment procedure and system of classes for land qualities (assessment factors) and land suitability of the Netherlands Soil Survey Institute (1979)
a. Procedure
b. Classes

a. Procedure

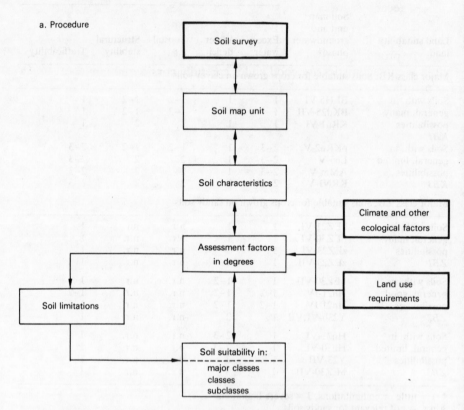

b. Classes *

Major class (total number: 3)	Class (number unlimited)	Subclass (number unlimited)
1. Soils with many possibilities for . . . (lut) †	1.1 1.2 1.3 etc.	1.3d ‡ 1.3n 1.3b
2. Soils with limited possibilities for . . . (lut)	2.1 2.2 etc.	
3. Soils with poor possibilities for . . . (lut)	3.1 3.2 etc	

* The classes given here are a more recent system than the classes given in table 30 as is seen from the description of classes 2 and 3
† lut = land utilization type;
‡ d, n and b are indications of the dominant limitations

crucial aspects of soil survey interpretation. He also indicated that the soil scientist must be highly resourceful in gathering and recording data from several sources including farms, ranch and plantation records, results of experimental fields, sampling of crops on well-known soils, and other possible sources. In practice the obtaining of sufficient data is always a problem.

More recently, attempts at systems analysis in land evaluation have also indicated the need for more data on crop response (Beek 1978). A soil which has an inherent low chemical fertility is in general under low inputs not very productive. It may however produce high yields, provided that its physical characteristics are good and if carefully considered inputs of chemical or other fertilizers are regularly given to suitable crops on this soil. A soil which has a higher original fertility may have lower responses to these inputs if either its physical characteristics are less favourable or the climatic regime is less suitable for high productions. But also measures to improve, either permanently, or by regular treatments, the physical conditions of soils meet with different responses due to the different other soil characteristics; this is very clearly experienced when drainage or irrigation is applied. These differences in responses of soil-plant systems to management are highly important in agriculture, where high net production is the eventual indicator of success, but the same approach also applies to all other land uses. In some cases a low environmental impact, in the form of low responses to outside inputs, may be preferred, but basically this is the same problem.

Most data on yield in relation to management have thus been collected for agriculture, but despite this it is often difficult to find suitable figures on the various kinds of soils under different ecological conditions. The collection of data on responses to management has to be done under different weather conditions and has thus to be carried out over a number of years. It is only rarely possible to run a number of comparable field experiments on different soils and under different well-described environmental conditions, over a sufficiently long number of years (7 to 15 years) to cover the annual weather variations. The American approach of using benchmark soils which are carefully selected soil taxonomic units under other clearly stated ecological conditions is basically sound, but it is only rarely applied in a sufficiently comprehensive manner (see for example Swindale 1978; Cady and Chan 1980).

A thorough examination of the extensive data from long-established experimental fields in West Java (Indonesia) gave a general indication of the responses to chemical fertilizers of tea on three different soils (Table 31). Some data from the Soviet Union are given in Table 32.

In several countries during the last few years, interesting data on responses of various crops to different landscape ecological conditions have been produced. Examples for Scotland are given by Burnham *et al.* (1970; grass yields) and by Jones and Tinsley (1980; herbage yields). Some interesting cases in Germany are given by Schlichting and Sunkel (1971). In Nigeria, Moormann *et al.* (1977) have studied rice growth on selected toposequences which presented a continuum of edaphic and hydrological conditions. A spe-

Table 31. Responses to fertilizers of tea on three different soils under
different landscape ecological conditions in West Java (Indonesia), based on
a summary of many field experiments; applications of N, P and K adapted
to the optimum requirements of each case

Soil and other landscape ecological conditions*	(1) Average yield without chemical fertilizers (kg/ha/yr)	(2) Average increase in yields with optimum application of fertilizers (% of column 1)	(kg/ha/yr)
Mollic Andosol in andesitic volcanic ash, sandy loam, well-drained, 1000–1500 m above sea level	2000	60	1200
Chromic Luvisol in andesitic volcanic ash, sandy clay-loam, well to moderately well-drained, 1000–1500 m above sea level	1400	70	1000
Dystric Nitosol in strongly weathered old andesitic tuffs, 250–800 m above sea level	1000	50	500

* All with approximately 3500 m annual precipitation, soils classified according to the
legend of the *Soil Map of the World*.
Source: Vink 1963.

Table 32. Relative data on the influence of complete chemical fertilizers
(N,P,K) on various soils in the Soviet Union

Soil*	Relative yield unfertilized	(soil 1 = 100) fertilized	Increase of yield
1. Podzoluvisols in siltloam	100	212	112
2. Phaeozems in siltloam	105	210	105
3. Luvic chernozems	118	231	113
4. Thick chernozems	150	214	64
5. Normal chernozems	143	218	75
6. Precaucasian chernozems	103	152	49

* As far as possible reclassified according to the legend of the *Soil Map of the World*.

Source: After Tyurin and Sokolov 1968.

cial study was also made of nitrogen behaviour and of iron deficiency. They
also included in their investigations the incidence of the 'blast' disease (*Pyri-
cularia orizae*) and found close correlations between this and the moisture
content of the surface layers of the soil as well as with depth of groundwater.
Severe nitrogen deficiency occurred in the intermediate zone between dry
and wet soils. Blast incidence was highest in the dry parts of the sequence.
More extensive results of these investigations have been published by
Veldkamp (1979).

If these and similar data are studied, the following tentative general conclusions may be given, although these should be critically studied for their relevance under any particular circumstance:

1. Physically good and chemically rich soils give in general a better response to management, as exemplified by fertilizer application.

2. Extremely good soil such as thick chernozem (no. 4 in Table 32) seems to give less response, but this might be due to the use of a cultivar with genetic restrictions; the use of a 'green revolution' wheat under these conditions might have produced more response.

3. Comparison of soils without giving additional data on climate may produce results which are not sufficiently indicative: nos. 5 and 6 have lower responses than would probably be possible and this might be due to the rather dry climate of southern Russia.

4. Different crops on the same soil sequences not illustrated here give varying responses.

5. In many cases chemical fertilizers result in clearer responses than organic manure.

6. The response to irrigation under various climates (semi-arid, subhumid, humid) is highest on soils which are both physically good and chemically rich.

Tolerance of crops to sub-optimal conditions is another means of expressing the response of soil–plant complexes. Tolerance to conditions of climatic hazard or of low-input agriculture may be more important than the effect of high inputs. In this case, crops and soils with a certain tolerance, which may not be optimal under high input conditions, have to be preferred. Some examples are given by Jung *et al.* (1978). The poor suitability of green revolution cultivars of rice and wheat under sub-optimal conditions is well known. Similarly, traditional agriculture often prefers soils high in nutrient status, even if they have rather poor physical conditions, to highly responsive poor soils (Vink 1963a).

LAND SUITABILITY IN GENERAL

From the preceding discussion, the following concepts have to be carefully separated:

1. The existing, current or present land use – the manner in which a tract of land is used at a given moment, which is to a large extent determined by social and technical conditions and processes in the past.

2. Current land suitability – the potential land use if no permanent improvements are made to the land; the land itself is not changed, but land use is improved to meet new or future requirements and to make better use of existing possibilities by introducing new crops, new management methods and new land utilization types.

3. Potential land suitability – the suitability of the land after the land itself has been improved in a permanent, or at least long lasting manner; in gen-

eral this also includes the introduction of new crops, management methods
and land utilization types.

In principle a survey of present land use gives nothing but the situation at
one moment in time. It may give some indication of the relative difference
in suitability of various land units in the area, if the (present) land use survey is compared on an analogous scale with the landscape ecological map of
the regions. If in a certain area wheat is extensively cultivated, its absence
on certain kinds of land usually gives an indication that under existing conditions of land use these other areas are not suitable for wheat. However,
present land use in many areas of the world is handicapped by a lack of
knowledge on possible crops and methods among farmers as well as by too
easy generalizations by scientific advisers. The lack of transfer of new results
from scientific experiments to practical cropping often seriously retards the
improvement of land use (Vink 1975a).

Current land suitability, which also is called land (use) capability, indicates how production may be increased by land use improvements or how by
some other use (for example, recreation) a better production of a different
kind may be obtained. It is the way of achieving a potential land use which
demands the lowest financial investments but may need large personnel investments, e.g. for agricultural extension and for overcoming social hin-
drances and barriers.

Potential land suitability indicates the possibilities of establishing better
kinds of land use after investments, often considerable, have been made for
land improvement. As is shown in Table 34, however, the quantity and intensity of these investments may differ. Permanent land improvements are
always needed for the establishment of potential land suitability, which is
the second category of potential land use.

There are differences between land suitability and soil suitability which, as
has already been indicated, derive from the different definitions. In practice
this difference becomes apparent when various artefactial land attributes are
considered – e.g. dikes and canals – and also when dense original vegetation, such as tropical marsh vegetations, are taken into account. The construction of polders with dikes and pumping stations creates new soils, but
the activity itself cannot be said to be soil improvement but land transformation or land improvement. The cutting of dense tropical vegetation for re-
claiming soils for agriculture is in general not seen as soil improvement;
from some points of view it might even be seen as soil degradation. From
the point of view of agriculture, it is definitely land improvement and it also
requires major investments as has been shown by Veldkamp (1979). In many
cases, only soil suitability is considered and even in cases where the FAO
(1976) terminology of land suitability and land evaluation is used, the differences are not always made clear. Consideration of soil suitability is often
easier as it is done under more normal conditions and is less easily influenced by local road construction and other land improvements. Even for the

Table 33. Assumptions indicated for the generalized soil suitability map for arable land and grassland of the Netherlands on scale 1 : 200 000

The classification of the soils, as made in this map, rests on a number of assumptions, the more important of which are indicated below (in particular in 1 and 2), together with some general directions for the use of the map:
1. The evaluation of the suitability was carried out under the economic and technical situation of agriculture prevailing in the Netherlands about 1960. As soon as the economic circumstances or the technical possibilities would change appreciably, a revision of the map will be necessary.
2. With a view to this situation the yardstick has been a rough estimate of what a good farmer can achieve under good conditions of parcellation and accessibility. In view of the great differences in water management of comparable soils in different parts of the country, an effort has been made to establish as a standard the most favorable water management prevailing in sufficiently large areas within each soil unit. For the latter it was found to be necessary in some cases to use within one soil unit two different standards in different parts of the country.
3. The classification supplies an ordinal arrangement only in so far as it indicates the range of use capabilities existing within the types of management current in the Netherlands about 1960 in arable land and grassland farming.
4. The numbering and the description of the classes do not indicate the financial value nor the suitability for improvement of the soils.
5. Owing to the small scale of the map an appreciable variation in the suitability for agriculture can be found within the soil units and consequently within the land classes. This has been taken into account as much as possible in the descriptions of the classes. This means among other things that the map must be regarded as a whole and that separate use of the individual sheets or parts of these is not recommended.

Source: Vink and Van Zuilen 1967, 1974.

consideration of soil suitability various assumptions have to be made in order to arrive at general predictions without undue influence of local variations. An example is given in Table 33.

The FAO framework for land evaluation (FAO 1976) gives a list of a large number of assumptions which usually have to be made, and which should be published together with the land evaluation itself. A change of assumptions, based for example on other expected economic conditions, may completely change the outcome of the land evaluation. This is necessary, as well as understandable, as land and land use are very intricate complexes of scientific and socio-economic variables. The list given includes: limitations of information used, reliability and applicability of the data, whether location is or is not taken into account (with regard to accessibility, roads), demography (population change), infrastructure and services, level of inputs, land tenure and other institutional conditions, demand and markets or prices, and various other technical and socio-economic data. The detail in which this has to be done depends very much on the level of generalization of the land suitability classification.

In addition to the three different kinds of classification mentioned at the beginning of this section, it is often very useful to develop a land suitability classification for land improvements. These classifications are often given as

Table 34. Different levels of land improvement as originally developed for
Iran and applied by Beek and Bennema (1972) to conditions in Latin
America around the year 1970

Level	Total cost per hectare	Examples	Technical implications for execution
A Low	Less than US$ 50, costs borne by farmer with occasional credit facilities	Special crop management Simple soil management Fertilizers in modest quantities, contour cultivation	May require some technical advisory service to the farmer
B Medium	US$ 50–100 cost borne by farmer with short term credit facilities	Intensive soil management (liming, soil amendments), simple engineering (land smoothing), ridge terraces, widely spaced open surface drains	Requires important advisory services to the farmer
C High	US$ 100–200 requires long-term credit facilities	Land grading, broad based terraces, mole drainage	Specialized engineering work, contractor services often with special equipment
D and E Very high	More than US$ 200, long-term credit facilities often through regional development projects, with a national priority	Reclamation work land levelling for irrigation, bench terraces, tile drainage, deep tile drainage, deep plouging	Execution is beyond farm development and implies regional planning and development

Source: Vink 1975a.

maps derived from the landscape ecological map and indicate the degree of
soil or land improvement which is possible under certain assumptions on the
different land units mapped. These may be for example deep ploughing as a
profile improvement, land levelling, desalinization, drainage and irrigation
construction (see also Ch. 7). These classifications indicate the way in
which it is possible to arrive at the potential suitability of the various land
units. Some examples with different investments are given in Table 34.

In addition to various classifications for land suitability in rural land utilization types, land suitabilities for various technical constructions can also
be made. An example for road construction is given in Table 35. In Fig. 28
an example of a land suitability map for natural gas pipeline construction is
given. Various methods of land suitability classification and of land (use)
capability classification have been used, and are still being used, in many
countries. The system of eight classes of the US Soil Conservation Service is
perhaps the best known in the world together with the six classes for irrigation established by the US Bureau of Reclamation. It is impossible within

Table 35. Ratings of soils for secondary roads

Item affecting use	Soil rating		
	Good	Moderate	Poor
Slope	0–8%	8–15%	>15%
Depth to bedrock*	>100 cm	50–100 cm	<50 cm
Unified soil group for sub-grade[†]	GW, GP, SW SP, GM, GC[‡] SM[§], SC[§]	CL with plasticity index <15	CL with plasticity index >15, CH, MH[§], OH, OL, Pt
Shrink-swell potential	Low	Moderate	High
Susceptibility to frost action[¶]	Low	Moderate	High
Stoniness class[‖]	0, 1 and 2	3	4 and 5
Rockiness class[‖]	0	1	2, 3, 4 and 5
Soil drainage class**	Excessively drained, somewhat excessively drained, well drained and moderately well drained	Somewhat poorly drained	Poorly drained and very poorly drained
Flooding	None	Soils flooded less than once in 5 years	Soils flooding more than once in 5 years

* If bedrock is soft enough so that it can be dug out with hand tools or light power equipment (such as backhoes), reduce ratings of moderate and poor by one category.
[†] If engineering test data are not available, estimate the unified soil groups from pedological data and Fig 1–2 and Tables 1–3.
[‡] Downgrade soil rating to moderate if content of fines is more than about 30 per cent.
[§] Upgrade soil rating to moderate if MH is largely kaolinitic, friable and free of mica.
[¶] Use this item only where frost penetrates below the paved or hardened surface layer and where moisture transportable by capillary movement is sufficient to form ice lenses at the freezing point.
[‖] Class definitions are given on pages 216–223 of the *Soil Survey Manual* (Soil Survey Staff 1951).
** Class definitions are given on pages 169–172 of the *Soil Survey Manual* (Soil Survey Staff 1951).
Source: Olson 1973.

the scope of this text to give them a thorough discussion. The reader is referred to the many good publications on these subjects and to Vink (1975a). A critical discussion of the differences between methods of land appraisal used in Victoria (Australia) and in the Netherlands was given by Gibbons and Haans (1976). An easily readable discussion of various systems

Fig. 28 Lay-out for a gas pipeline, made with and without the aid of a soil map (Haans and Westerveld 1970)

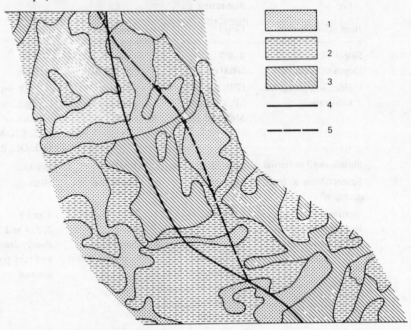

1 = High, excessively drained, sandy soils
2 = Medium-high, well-drained to moderately well-drained sandy soils
3 = Low, poorly to very poorly drained, sandy soils
4 = Pipeline route marked out before soil mapping
5 = Pipeline route marked out after soil mapping

of soil and land use capability assessment has been published by Davidson (1980). Emphasis is placed in the following section on examples drawn from the author's own experience.

LAND SUITABILITY IN AGRICULTURE

Given a certain land utilization type and other general assumptions, the suitability of a tract of land for agriculture depends on the following five factors (Vink 1963a and b):

1. Gross yields in kg/ha.

2. The physical costs which have to be made to arrive at that yield (in hours of labour, kilograms fertilizers, litres of fuel, etc.) also called the input level.

3. The variability of the yields in relation to the variable weather conditions in different years.

4. The quality of the harvested products.

5. The relative surface area of the various land units within the farm or enterprise, also called the 'soil pattern'.

These factors result from the soil and land characteristics together with the influences of the weather, and the annual climatic variations. Some additional factors have often to be considered; for example, irrigation and drainage works and their annual maintenance, running cost and accessibility. In the following, only the above mentioned five factors will be discussed. On each soil and in each land utilization type the average gross yields per hectare show many fluctuations. To characterize a land suitability class according to average gross yields gives only a very general idea, even under rather stable temperate climates.

In intensive industrial agriculture the physical cost, or input level, for agricultural production is often the most critical of the soil suitability factors. We have found that within the same small area of alluvial soils, with ostensibly only minor soil differences, the inputs may differ by 50 per cent of the net income of the farmer and even then the general level of yields on the soils with high inputs tends to be lower than that on the good soil. If areas with soil conservation problems are considered, the differences may be even greater on different slopes. Land suitability always presupposes a maintenance of soil productivity and therefore soil conservation. When different regions are compared, the drainage cost in low lying areas may be very high and this may result in the net income of the farmers on the best young alluvial soils being lower than that of farmers on somewhat better than average hill soils.

Variability of yields which highlights the hazard of poor yields in years with unfavourable weather conditions, is often for good farmers the most direct yardstick of suitability. An example of the variations which occur is given in Table 36. This table, based on field investigations in the sandy areas of the Netherlands with a very drought-resistant crop, rye, indicates that the best soils (O) showed 27 per cent good, 57 per cent mediocre and 16 per cent poor yields over a number of years, whereas the poorest soil (S) had only 3 per cent good, 42 per cent mediocre and 55 per cent poor yields, all

Table 36. Yield variations of rye on seven soil types in the Netherlands during three consecutive years

Percentages of yields considered good (more than 3200 kg per ha per year), normal (2500 to 3200 kg ha year) and poor (less than 2500/kg/year) Soil type	Good	Mediocre	Poor
Q = deeply humic loamy sand	27	57	16
B = deeply humic sand	6	71	23
H = podzol in sand (excessively drained)	8	37	55
M = podzol in sand (well drained)	13	66	21
L = hydromorphic soil in sand (poorly drained)	33	50	17
A = acid brown soil in loamy sand (well drained)	29	47	24
S = regosol in sand (excessively drained)	3	42	55

Source: Vink 1975a.

within the same land utilization type and under the same mild Dutch climate.

In interpreting this table, it should be understood that a sequence of two or three dry, and therefore unfavourable, years is common even in the Dutch climate. This leads to a sequence of poor yields on the driest soils and it would make farming on these soils nearly impossible if the farmer did not also have some better fields. The example shows that in regions with more extreme climates, this effect must be considerably greater, but no data are available to the author.

The quality of a product is often closely correlated with specific soil and landscape characteristics. These also include climatic characteristics in certain areas; for example, the cultivation of flax and of barley for breweries in Belgium and the Netherlands is to some extent correlated with the maritime, specially mild, climate of the coastal provinces. In climatic zones near the border of the northern limit of wine production, the possibility of producing wine of suitable quality is strongly associated with southern aspects of slopes and to some extent also to excessively drained soils. The latter, because of a certain drought incidence, promotes the development of the grapes through slowing the growth of the vines. For special products, such as port-wine, similar effects are observed even in areas in Portugal. An example of quality differences correlated with soil characteristics is given by potatoes in the Netherlands; in soils with acid and dispersed humus the quality of the product is often not considered suitable for human consumption, whereas soils in the same areas with milder humus yield potatoes suitable for human use. Variations in soil pattern also can have an influence, in particular if the quality of the product demands homogeneity: an example of this is flax. In the Netherlands this crop may give high yields on rather heterogeneous alluvial soils but the product is unacceptable for processing because of its heterogeneity.

The relevance of soil pattern has been introduced in relation to the quality of flax. However, it has a much larger meaning. An example is demonstrated in Fig. 29 for two farms in the Zuyderzee polder area of the Netherlands, which both have basically the same soils. However, farm A has a large coherent surface of fine-sandy loam with only some patches of heavier soils and of some coarser textured soils. Farm B has mainly the same soils but in an erratic pattern with, in addition, some narrow areas of heavy clay. As a result farm A has very good yields, both gross and net, whereas farm B has to undertake more and costly methods of soil management in order to have at least satisfactory yields. As these special methods of soil management cannot be taken in an efficient manner due to the intricate soil pattern, the net results are very much lower than those of farm A, also considering that the gross yields of B are already on a lower level (Haans and Westerveld, 1970). Similar observations were made for American farms by Kellogg (1941). He indicated that the simple presence or absence of one soil type on

Fig. 29 Differences in soil pattern of two arable land farms in the Wieringermeer Polder, an area of the Zuyderzee polders in the Netherlands (Haans and Westerveld 1970)

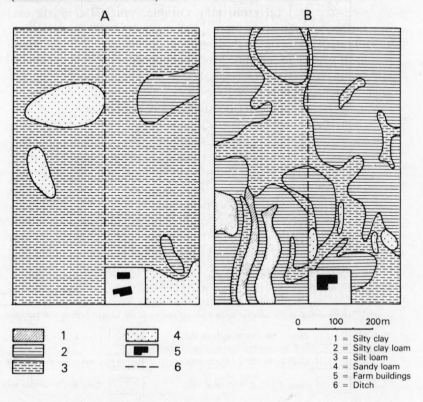

1 = Silty clay
2 = Silty clay loam
3 = Silt loam
4 = Sandy loam
5 = Farm buildings
6 = Ditch

a farm with a number of different soil types can have a decisive influence on the management of the whole farm.

As has been indicated above, land suitability and soil suitability differ for different land utilization types, which each have their own requirements. As a general rule it can be said that those soils which meet the requirements of the widest range of crops are the most suitable in a general sense. There are, however, exceptions to this rule if the land utilization type preferred predominantly includes a crop with very special requirements; for example, several kinds of horticultural crops and also irrigated rice. If a special crop also commands a high price over a rather long number of years, the special requirements of this crop may dominate the suitability judgement. Prices and other economic and social conditions play an important role in the determination of soil suitability. To some extent this may be standardized, and a physical land suitability calculated mainly on ecological consideration if the socio-economic conditions are incorporated into assumptions (Beek 1978). For more quantitative calculations of land suitability, however, more precise

Fig. 30 Land classification map of a part of the Mayaga area in Rwanda (Central Africa) (Vink 1968)

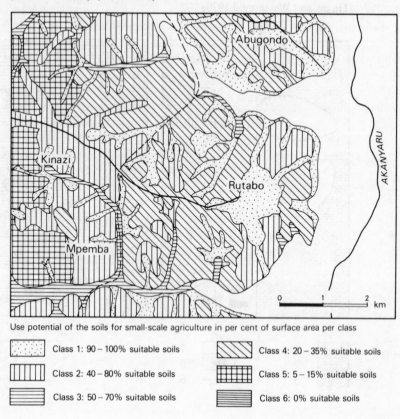

Use potential of the soils for small-scale agriculture in per cent of surface area per class

Class 1: 90 – 100% suitable soils   Class 4: 20 – 35% suitable soils

Class 2: 40 – 80% suitable soils   Class 5: 5 – 15% suitable soils

Class 3: 50 – 70% suitable soils   Class 6: 0% suitable soils

data are necessary. The prices taken for these calculations should not be the prices of one or two years, but average prices over at least 10 consecutive years or price expectancies estimated by economists. Fully quantitative land evaluation in agriculture is only possible by multidisciplinary work, including at least landscape ecologists (or soil surveyors) with a good knowledge of land evaluation methods, as well as farm economists. Often crop experts and experts on drainage and irrigation are also required (see also Vink 1960; Beek 1978). Land suitability classification and land evaluation therefore produce results of shorter validity than that of the base scientific maps. Recourse is made to these basic maps if the need arises for the development of new classifications and evaluations.

It is often difficult to find standards for land evaluation, if only as an example on which local standards for a particular region may be based. Some good examples have been published, for example by FAO (1978, 1980). Various guidelines and examples from many countries are given for rainfed agriculture and for irrigated agriculture. The application of similar principles to the *Soil Map of the World* may be studied in the reports of the Agroecological Zones Project of FAO (1978, 1980). Some very good data for tropical areas are given by Young (1976).

In some cases it is less important to indicate different degrees of land suitability and more urgent to give an estimate of the surface areas of suitable soils within the various mapping units of a landscape ecological map. An example of this is given for Rwanda (Central Africa). The reason for this, especially in strongly dissected areas, is that it is not possible even at a semi-detailed map scale of 1 : 50 000 to indicate sufficiently homogeneous land units for land evaluation. In addition, project specifications for settlements with rather traditional land utilization types do not require great detail in degrees of suitability, but rather need to know how large a surface area each settler has to have for obtaining an acceptable standard of living. In this case the above approach has been found to be a suitable basis for land use planning. There is, in fact, also a correlation between the percentage of suitable soils and the degree of suitability of the soils in the Rwanda area. Broadly outlined, these are, in terms of ecological productivity, estimated to be in relative figures (the best soil at 100):

- class 1: 70–100
- class 2: 50–80
- class 3: 40–70
- class 4: 35–55
- class 5: 20–35
- class 6: nil.

If these productivity estimates are combined with the areas of suitable soils, a more refined estimate of required farm size is possible.

Reference has already been made to the FAO Framework for Land Evaluation (FAO 1976). This framework is not meant to replace all existing land suitability and land use capability classifications. It may be used as a framework for general reference to facilitate comparison of the results of different regions and to stimulate the use of sound methods in land evaluation. Within the framework, a system of classification was also developed for overall comparison. This method has since been found to be very useful as a national system in various developing countries. The general outline of the system is given in Fig. 31.

During the last few years, people in several countries have become aware that there is a danger of the best agricultural lands being transformed into urban areas. This led in the USA to the discussion on 'Prime Lands', which may be said in general to be those lands which have a special suitability for particular kinds of land use, and often this is emphasized for agricultural lands, although this is not necessarily the only case (USDA 1975; Mark *et al.* 1977). There are in fact not only prime lands, but even unique lands for certain kinds of land use, and these embrace various kinds of nature conservation as well as several kinds of agricultural land use. In Canada, the term used is 'Special Resource Lands' and in this respect six different major

Fig. 31 FAO Framework for Land Evaluation; Structure of the Suitability Classification (FAO 1976)

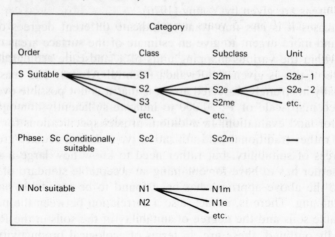

land uses are specially considered: agriculture, recreation, wildlife, forestry, urban growth and energy development (Simpson-Lewis *et al*. 1979). No general rules can be given for this selection and it is even difficult in many cases to decide on which lands in any area are to be considered prime lands for a selected use and which are not. The need for this approach is essential and the methodology will have to be developed in the next decade, as continuous population growth in the world and explosive urban growth in many countries demand special measures for conserving natural resources for the future.

It is not just a question of the replacement of one land use by another, but also the compatibility or incompatibility of adjoining land uses. Even at some distance, one land use may have an effect on another by means of hydrological processes. This may be the case of intensive agriculture having an effect on nature reserves, of urban land uses having influence on rural land uses, of industrial land uses having impacts on urban and rural land uses, and various other similar impacts. A thorough examination of this problem is done by McHarg (1969), whose conclusions have been proved to be valid in many cases of land classification for land use planning.

FORESTRY LAND EVALUATION

Land evaluation, using a number of approaches, has always been high on the priority of foresters and their organizations. Natural forests have to be evaluated for the useful timber which they contain and for the manner in which this can be harvested. The planting of forests is always of long-term significance and is usually done in large areas at the same time, thus binding future generations to the decisions of today. Forest investments only provide returns after many years, starting with the first thinnings of low commercial value and gradually giving more yields as the forests grow. This also means that investments in forests are normally low as they have to be capitalized over a long period (from 25 years for poplars to over 100 years for various hardwood species such as beech and oak). Forests therefore depend very much on natural land conditions such as vegetation, soil, topography, altitude and aspect. Landscape ecological surveys, often executed as vegetation surveys but also as soil surveys and terrain surveys, have therefore a regular position in forestry even in countries where soil surveys for agriculture have made little headway. For long, foresters have also recognized the need for soil conservation and the role of forests in this respect (see for example FAO Forestry Department 1977). The natural forests as well as the ecological management of planted forests have always been important for landscape and for natural ecosystems (see for example Buchwald and Engelhardt, 1968/9). More recently foresters have also directed their attention to the functions of small forests in local community development in developing countries (FAO Forestry Department 1978).

An example of forest site evaluation based on several landscape ecological factors has been given by Cook *et al*. (1977) for an area in Scotland. Site variables were assessed, partly from available maps and from aerial photographs and also from field work. These factors were: rainfall, altitude, slope, aspect, geomorphic shelter, soil parent material, major soil group, vegetation type and topographic position. The evaluation was done for Scots Pine (*Pinus silvestris*). Some of their results were that growth decreased with altitude, but that there were marked differences between the two studied regions (Ballater and Strathdon in West Aberdeenshire). Growth increased with increasing geomorphic shelter which gives a measure of the lee aspects of the slopes, and there was also a clear influence of aspect, the south slope being significantly more favourable than the north one. Apart from those quantitative results which were established using statistical methods, there were also clear trends of some qualitative variables such as soil parent material. Basic rock materials were better than materials derived from acid rocks, which were correspondingly better than serpentines. Also relevant to timber yields were major soil group, original vegetation and topographic position (valley floors, middle slopes, lower slopes).

In Table 37 a suitability classification is given of the soils of the Netherlands for forestry. This is based on the soil map of the country at a scale of 1 : 200 000 and on collected data and experience from more detailed investigations in various parts of the country.

At a recent international workshop on land evaluation for forestry (Laban 1981), a first attempt was made to arrive at a systematic approach to the various problems and possibilities of land evaluation for forestry in the world. The great variation existing between various national and regional systems is largely due to the many aspects of forests as well as to the many different manners in which forests can be used. Natural forests as well as

Table 37. Legend for the *Generalized Soil Suitability Map* (scale
1 : 600 000) for forestry in the Netherlands

Soil suitability classes
1. Deciduous woods with high timber yields
2. Deciduous woods with low timber yields
3. Coniferous woods with high timber yields
4. Coniferous woods with low timber yields
5. Not suitable for productive woods
The classes are indicated singly for homogenous areas and are used as follows for
heterogeneous areas.*

Areas where variation is possible

Classes 1 and and 2:	suitable for deciduous woods with high yields in some areas and low yields in others
Classes 2 and 3:	suitable for deciduous woods with low timber yields as well as for coniferous woods with high timber yields
Classes 3 and 4:	suitable for coniferous woods with high yields in some areas and low yields in others

Areas where variation is necessary

Classes 2 and 3:	suitable for deciduous woods with low timber yields or for coniferous woods with high timber yields
Classes 4 and 5:	suitable for coniferous woods with low timber yields but partly not suitable for productive woods
Classes 1, 2 and 3:	suitable for deciduous woods with partly high and partly low timber yields or for coniferous woods with high timber yields
Classes 1, 2, 3, and 4:	suitable for deciduous or coniferous woods with high yields in some areas and low yields in others

---

* Indicated in this way because of the small scale of the land evaluation
Source: Sikkel *et al.* 1971.

long-established planted forests have always been recognized as ecosystems
and in general a more or less ecological management has prevailed, often
simply because of the lack of means for industrial inputs. According to the
definition given in this book, it is more correct to speak of true natural
forests as being natural ecosystems and forests, either natural or planted
which are strongly influenced by man, as cultural ecosystems in varying degrees. Land evaluation for forestry, therefore, more than for agriculture,
implies evaluation for not one crop but for intricate ecosystems. Bearing in
mind the definition of land as given in this book (see Ch. 1 and FAO 1976),
forests have to be considered as part of the land, and this is more directly
relevant in this case than with regard to agricultural crops. When timber is
harvested from a natural forest, the timber harvest plus some facilities for
transport (logging roads, cable transport systems) are the only human activities in the ecosystem and these remove part of the forest as a land component. In those cases the nature of, for example, the soils may be less directly
relevant than in those cases where the soils are manipulated for planting and
other human activities. As soon as natural rejuvenation of forests is considered, however, various biotic and abiotic landscape factors, apart from the
nature of the forest itself, have to be taken into account.

Land use objectives in forestry are much more diverse than is often understood. Some examples are:

- storage of genes and/or development of knowledge,
- environmental protection,
- foraging,
- recreation and tourism,
- wood production,
- production of other forest products (including game harvesting),
- agroforestry production. (Andel *et al*. in Laban 1981)

Within each of these categories many variations are found depending on land conditions and on human requirements.

Forests are often poorly accessible and survey costs for landscape ecological surveys have to be kept within reasonable limits. This also leads to special methods for site evaluation, terrain analysis and for more comprehensive landscape ecological surveys, and these again have their impact on the manner in which land evaluation is carried out. Finally, the purpose of land evaluation is land use planning, and the way the results are to be presented depends therefore very much on the nature of the planning authorities and the decision makers in forestry areas. This also applies to the areas where reafforestation is planned (see also Interdepartmental Task Force 1980).

LAND USE DESIGNS, TOWN AND COUNTRY PLANNING

For land use plans to be executed, at a certain stage one or more designs have to be made showing how the planned land uses will be established as well as the methods to be used to arrive at these, often including land improvement of various kinds. These designs include one or more maps of the project area as well as plans for the construction of such works as dams, sluices, weirs, canals, bunds, etc. These maps and plans are accompanied by a report which gives additional information. In many cases these designs are made by civil engineers, architects or by land reclamation or land conservation experts. In those cases where the current land use is essentially maintained but modified and modernized, the designs are made by agronomists or foresters. In all cases, these people do not participate in the basic investigations such as landscape ecological surveys. However, they have to be able to use the results of these investigations if the results are presented to them in a suitable manner. Their designs are not only based on these results but also on various other considerations as described in Chapters 7 and 8, including financial aspects ('non-land resources'), logistics for the execution of the project and timing of the various phases. For the Lower Medjerda Project in Tunisia, the primary consultants, Grontmy of the Netherlands, designed two projects for the same area: a minimum plan and a maximum one. The minimum plan included all those land units which were the most suitable for irrigated agriculture. The maximum plan added all other land units which might eventually be included. Within each of these plans, the land units were indicated with regard to their suitability for different irrigated crops.

This strategy has the advantage that the easiest part of the plan is done first whilst later additions may be made on the basis of accumulated knowledge and experience and according to the growing needs in the decade or more in which the project is established.

It is a major problem to find suitable methods for the effective use of basic research data and their interpretations in the designs. The designer has to use his creative ability to arrive at any design at all, and to include in these efforts an optimum evaluation of the data requires special knowledge and techniques. An integrated approach at an early stage, which has been called the 'intersector approach' in Canadian land use planning (McCormack, cited by Vink 1975a), is often very useful. The various sectors included in land use planning, from basic research workers to decision makers, are then included in one team and have a more or less continuous interchange of data and ideas. But this approach is not always possible and therefore, particularly in town and country planning, various methods have been developed to facilitate the work of the designers while optimizing the use of basic data. Some of these are:

1. Sieve analysis, which sieves the basic data on the various parts of the region in order to find the restrictions induced by landscape factors and by other considerations.

2. Sieve analyses with a system of points, the points being used for a normative gradation of the degree of impact of the various restricting factors.

3. Threshold analysis, in which the thresholds formed by the need to make various kinds and amounts of investments in the various parts of the region are estimated and compared.

4. Analysis of interconnecting decision areas (AIDA) which aims at the elucidation of the consequences of various decisions with regard to the area as a whole as well as of its parts.

5. Potential surface analysis (PSA), in which the various parts of an area are evaluated according to their use potentials for the various kinds of land use.

6. Land use competition models (LCM), in which the results of the PSA with regard to the various land utilization types are integrated in one or more models.

7. Planning balance sheet analysis (PBSA), in which alternative area designs are evaluated in order to arrive at an optimum choice, including the financial analyses of costs versus benefit.

In addition, there are various ways of arriving at an optimization of costs for a project, either on the basis of invested money versus the benefits to be expected (cost-benefit analysis), or of the cash-flow during the establishment of the project as well as for the subsequent operational periods. Some interesting data and calculations have been published by a Dutch Agricultural Investment Commission (1960) in A Priority Scheme (1960), by Smits and Wiggers (1959); a review on land settlement projects has been published by Takes (1975) and a treatise on irrigation efficiencies has been given by Bos and Nugteren (1974). A framework for regional planning in developing countries was edited by Van Staveren and Van Dusseldorp (1980). In the latter publication checklists on various land resources are also given. A broad review on land reclamation and water management has been published by Schulze *et al.* (1980).

There has in general not been enough systematic study on the integration of land classification with the design stage of planning. It seems that the sieve analyses mentioned above as nos. 1 and 2 provide suitable methods for linking these with land limitation and land quality maps. Threshold analyses seem to have to be connected with potential land suitability classification where investments on land improvement are considered. The analyses mentioned under nos. 4 to 6 have distinct connections with land suitability classification. The PBSA (no. 7) has to be connected with quantitative land suitability evaluations.

In some cases soil maps have been used for town planning. This was easier some decades ago as some soil maps at that time were less complicated and therefore easier to comprehend by non-soil scientists, than are most soil maps and landscape ecological maps of today. The use of the soil series as mapping units with some local name used as a symbol, for example Miami siltloam, does have some advantages in this respect, as experience in the USA has shown. The name-symbol gives to field officers within a restricted area a comprehensive impression of the kinds of land units it stands for. However, the growth of scientific knowledge on soils and land makes it less easy to interpret directly the practical aspects of the basic scientific maps for any specific practical purpose. To require soil scientists or landscape ecologists to make more simple basic maps is a negation of the growth of science; rather they should be requested to produce, on the basis of their complicated maps, the relevant land classification maps. The computerized collection of mapping data in databanks is in some cases effective for later application, but this is still in an experimental stage.

The production of a design has various attributes and objectives: (1) communication and coordination; (2) the determination of the quality of the plans to be executed; (3) the assimilation of information; (4) designing as a creative process; (5) designing as a decision-making process. The contact with land classification as described above is indicated as no. 3; the assimilation of information. A document produced by the Technical University at Delft (the Netherlands) describes this as follows (Studiecomissie C4, 1975): the designer starts from information (knowledge, literature, archives, documentation); he digests this and produces his own synthesis in the form of drawings, text, figures and models. If he wants to have the relevant information available at the right moment and wants also to transfer his information in a clear and comprehensive manner, he will have to manage, arrange and systematize the flow of information. The degree and the way in which he succeeds depends on his own ability, and this depends primarily on the problems he has to cope with in a given project. Land classification for land use planning in this view is the management, arrangement and systemization of the flow of information.

The same Dutch report also indicates the following phases in the evolution of designing:

1. The algorithmic approach, in which the designer "knows" that his way of handling the design will be correct.

2. The participation approach, in which people with divergent kinds of experience and knowledge cooperate and produce equally valuable contributions to the design.

3. The 'hunch-and-check' approach, which in essence means the generation of hypotheses and their testing; this means that everybody including the designer has the opportunity to indicate possible solutions which are either accepted, modified or refused.

Some figures may illustrate the importance of this kind of work for land use planning in the Netherlands, a very densely populated and highly industrialized country. For town and country planning only, in 1976 some 400 000 ha of planning areas were studied, partly on the basis of specially made soil maps and partly on the basis of existing soil maps to which additional data were sometimes collected in the field. In a country with a total surface area of some 3 million ha, this amounts to over 12 per cent of the total surface area in one year. It included planning on the various levels from large-scale national projects (on small-scale maps) to very small-scale municipal projects (on very large-scale maps).

LAND CLASSIFICATION FOR ENVIRONMENTAL MANAGEMENT

Land classification results in areal differentiation and this becomes of increasing importance in environmental management. The following reasons may be given for this:

1. The regional and local differences between different environmental factors in the various kinds of land mean that the same human activities have different impacts on different land units.

2. The various kinds and intensities of human activities in different regions and localities enhance the effects as indicated in para 1.

3. Environmental criteria differ for the various communities of men, animals and plants and this again enhances the differentiating effect.

4. In particular human criteria for environmental management differ considerably, as can be demonstrated by the differences in requirement with regard to, for example, air quality, noise and botanical variability as between a town centre, a recreation area and a nature reserve.

5. The various differentiating factors mentioned above have very complex interactions and this makes the ultimate local and regional differentiation of environmental management an absolute necessity.

It should be understood that various people discussing 'the environment' have different things in mind. These may for example be (Vink 1975a):

(a) The disturbance of human 'ways of life' by different forms of pollution, including the incidence of noise and the disturbance of different ecosystems; this is often indicated as 'environmental hygiene'.

(b) The decreasing attractiveness of daily life, particularly in urban areas, sometimes indicated as the 'spatial environment'.

(c) The predictable exhaustion of some natural resources, e.g. fossil fuels and some other resources termed the 'limits to growth' or 'Club of Rome' approach.

(d) The destruction of natural or semi-natural ecosystems, which may be called the 'biological environment'.

(e) The existence of unsatisfactory structures in society, leading to 'estrangement' (or alienation) between human beings and their societal and other environments, which were noted by Karl Marx during the industrial revolution of the nineteenth century and are perhaps even more valid today, and which may be indicated as the 'societal environment'.

(f) The tensions between developing human societies and the legislative and administrative structures and institutions which have to cope with the changes in society, to be indicated as the 'governmental environment'.

One or more of these aspects may be included in any kind of land use planning, including town and country planning. They have to be compared with the suitabilities and vulnerabilities of the various kinds of land and thus a spatial differentiation of activities may lead to acceptable results.

But land classification for various applications of modern technology to rural and urban areas should also be executed with a view to indirect and often unforeseen environmental impacts. Good land use planning implies the avoidance, and where necessary improvement, of land degradation in its many different forms. This has to be considered in the various phases of land evaluation such as:

1. Identification and judgement of land qualities and limitations with regard to land degradation.

2. The formulating of relevant and foreseeable land utilization types (LUT) which often has to include various land conservation practices.

3. The indication of land suitability classes for these LUTs.

4. The identification and judgement of the needs for land improvement on the different land units, including constructions or other permanent improvements for land conservation.

In this respect it must be understood that many land qualities or land limitations are not static data, but instead give an indication of variables of natural and cultural ecosystems, which should preferably be studied as processes. These processes include various kinds of degradation (see also Ch. 4). In addition, the various state variables of ecosystems are not independent in their effects; their interactions and the interactions of the processes with which they are connected often induce the gravest dangers. This is perhaps best exemplified by the processes leading to desertification (see Ch. 7). Finally, the effect of processes connected with land limitations is not only of impact on the lands directly considered, but it may have a much wider meaning as has been discussed in Chapter 7; for example, siltation reservoirs and salinization. Destruction of vegetation in one part of a continent may even have impact on the climate of adjoining parts (see Ch. 3); (Zonneveld 1980). The need to consider various environmental aspects in land evaluation necessitates a certain amount of study of these problems during the initial phases of the basic surveys.

Land evaluation for environmental purposes may be done with a very definite purpose in mind. An example of this is the Californian Early Warning report (Patri *et al.* 1970). This report gives a model for long-range planning of an American county with a view to the prediction of the location and definition of conflicts and of potentially degrading impacts in some naturally dynamic landscapes. Basic data on landscapes and land uses were used for the production of maps indicating natural dynamics and development potentials. This includes, for example, sewerage availability and fire hazards as well as seismic response in this very earthquake-prone region. The report aims at encouraging development of the community as a whole, preserving the county's physical beauty, improving the spatial organization for economic and social development, maintaining and strengthening interrelations between communities and maximizing individual freedom of choice.

Schreiber (1977) gives a number of good examples on the relationships between landscape planning and the protection of the environment. He calls for simple and rapid methods with which to apply basic landscape ecological data in land use planning with a view to the increasing ecological burdens being put on many of the landscapes of the world. Fabos and his colleagues of the University of Massachusetts at Amherst have developed a Metropolitan Landscape Planning Model, named 'METLAND' (Fabos and Caswell 1977; Fabos *et al.* 1978). They developed a planning process which includes composite landscape assessment, alternative plan formulation and plan evaluation. Their findings include the assessment of special resources, of hazards, of development suitability and of ecological stability. Geological hazards, soils, wildlife, air and water pollution and many other factors are considered. They distinguish in their ecological concept protective land uses, productive land uses, urban–industrial land uses and compromise land uses. The various factors are judged by means of rating and these are based as much as possible on quantitative data. The results are obtained by computerized procedures and these give, for example, composite hazards, visual development suitability, ecological compatibility, a combined composite landscape value and an ecological land use classification. On the basis of these, various plans are formulated. The methods are worthy of study as the system is one of the most comprehensive which has been published.

Nature conservation may be considered as a special aspect of environmental management. In particular in highly industrialized countries, nature conservation, which includes the management of nature reserves ('nature management'), is most necessary to protect the politically weakest kind of land use, the (semi)-natural landscapes, against further degradation and hopefully to mprove them wherever possible. These land uses are weak in ecological as well as in social and economic aspects as in general they have a low priority in land use planning. It should be realized that basically nature conservation, or nature management, is a group of land uses as is any other land use. They are maintained and managed by men, often with extensive but sometimes with intensive methods, to achieve specific human purposes (see also Ch. 1 and Vink 1981a).

Regional differentiation, and therefore land classification, is almost automatically done in nature conservation. It often lacks a systematic approach, due to the urgency of protecting as many areas as possible with little money, few trained personnel and hence a lack of long-term planning. A systematic approach based on landscape ecological maps and on a characterization of the many different land utilization types to be distinguished in nature management will eventually improve the possibilities for incorporating nature conservation as an equal component together with other major kinds of land use. This approach will have to take into account the uniqueness of many natural ecosystems and the impossibility of replacing them once they have been destroyed.

At present, four different kinds of landscapes are recognized in nature conservation:

1. Natural landscapes where vegetation and fauna are the original indigenous ones and have not been influenced by men (Plate 18).

2. Relatively natural landscapes, 'almost' or 'ostensibly' natural landscapes where vegetation and fauna are predominantly indigenous with some exceptions; the vegetation has undergone some human influence but is largely similar to the natural vegetation.

3. Semi-natural landscapes where vegetation and fauna are mainly indigenous, but structure and visual characteristics of the vegetation have undergone intensive human influence.

4. Cultural landscapes in their strict sense, where the composition of both vegetation and fauna have been essentially changed by men; in many extreme cases the dominant species have been imported by men (arable lands, woods of exotic species).

This range of different main landscape types, or ecosystem groups, is superimposed on a wide range of different landscape ecological conditions, and nature management has to be adapted to the complexes consisting of these combinations. It has furthermore to be adapted to combined purposes; for example, of nature management combined with the need for harvesting timber, or combined with outdoor recreation facilities, or for watershed pro-

Plate 18 A special kind of natural landscape: tree ferns on a volcanic slope in Indonesia

tection (Laban 1981). In addition it has to protect the reserves against external influences which may be catastrophic for the ecosystems in the reserve. Nature management therefore consists of both internal management, the extensive or intensive guiding of ecosystems with a view to the established objectives, and external management, the protection of the nature reserves against deleterious external impacts. The objectives of internal management may be different in different reserves due to human preferences. For example, in some areas it may be preferred to conserve certain heather moors, which is the artificial fixation of one stage in the natural succession, by cutting down trees or burning grass covers. Another purpose is the promotion of a natural succession, which often needs a careful restriction of grazing animals by artificial means.

Nature conservation may also require certain kinds of land improvement. An example is provided by the drying out of the originally wet valleys in the coastal dunes of the Netherlands. Some of these valleys may be restored by excavating some parts of the valley floors (Bakker *et al.* 1981). It may also contain full systems of land use planning, of which an example is shown in Fig. 32. The new polder areas of the Zuyderzee Project in the Netherlands, originally planned for extension of agriculture and for new towns, are now partly reserved for the establishment of nature and wildfowl reserves. With regard to nature conservation, reference is also made to Riney (1972),

Fig. 32 Land use as planned and executed in the wildfowl reserve 'Kievitslanden' in eastern Flevoland (Netherlands) (Van Duin 1978)

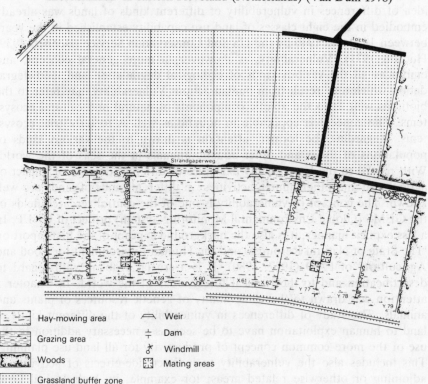

Hay-mowing area		Weir
Grazing area		Dam
Woods		Windmill
Grassland buffer zone		Mating areas

Kramer (1973), UNESCO/UNEP (1974), Fuentes (1979), Lasserre (1979) and to many reports and publications of the MAB project no. 8. See also Chapter 5.

For various Environmental Impact Statements (EIS), a careful land classification according to nature and degree of the vulnerability of different land units in a region will become of increasing importance. This starts with the procedure of 'scoping' for the delineation of the actual investigations to be done for these statements. It may include the delimitation of the areas to be considered for chemical pollution of water resources, but also for various changes of land use; for example, irrigation and drainage projects. A research project carried out for the US Bureau of Reclamation provides a good example (Dee *et al.* 1972, 1973; see also Vink 1975a). The 'Environmental Evaluation System' evolved in this project does not yet give direct cartographic or chorological information, but it gives indications on many interrelationships in the investigated area with regard to a planned irrigation project. In connection with the land classification mapping of the USBR, it will certainly be possible to consolidate the results in one or more ecological land classifications.

The vulnerability of lands to environmental impacts of various kinds is often a crucial subject for land-classification with ecological objectives. The idea of differences in vulnerability of different kinds of lands was already embodied in the eight classes of land use capability established in the years between 1930 and 1940 by the US Soil Conservation Service (Bennett 1939; Hudson 1971). Vulnerability, is, however, a more general concept, and embraces all the various kinds of ecological degradation and land degradation which may result from human action. Vulnerability may refer to the biotic as well as to the abiotic components of natural and cultural ecosystems. The concept is applicable to aquatic as well as to terrestrial ecosystems. Regarding the former, attention is drawn to the various kinds of populations of fishes and other aquatic animals in the seas of the world. With regard to the latter, many examples of different degrees of impact of agricultural and other human activities on different kinds of lands are well known. The concept of vulnerability is one of the central research fields of the GEMS (Global Environmental Monitoring System) project of UNEP. In a less explicit manner, it is also the background concept of the first report on 'The State of Natural Resources and the Human Environment for Food and Agriculture' of FAO (1977, 1980). It is a crucial problem with regard to desertification and to the tropical forest areas of the world. In Chapter 5 attention was drawn to the vulnerability of genetic resources of plants and animals. The study of differences in vulnerability of the different kinds of land to human exploitation have to be seen as a necessary addition to the use of the more common concept of productivity for all land use planning. This includes also the vulnerability to indirect side-effects of activities in adjoining or otherwise related areas; for example, by hydrological flow-systems. In industrialized countries and in all rural areas adjoining large urban concentrations, the vulnerability of lands to recreation activities is of great direct importance. Some years ago, studies on this were done in the coastal dune areas of the Netherlands (Van der Werf 1970; Van Ittersum and Kwakernaak 1977). These showed large differences in vulnerability of the different kinds of vegetation and of various geomorphological units to the effects of regular walking in the areas and in particular of the regular visiting of adjoining beaches by people staying in the lands behind the dunes.

The development of ecological models for planning of national and of regional and local activities is a means of embodying the essential ecological concepts in land use planning. In the Netherlands attempts have recently been made to arrive at a generalized ecological model for this purpose (GEM: Van der Maarel and Dauvellier 1978). This model is having increasing impact on planning activities in the country. Some of its basic ideas are represented in Fig. 33 and 34. They provide a means for integrating the interactions between nature and human society in a manner which may be made operational.

Fig. 33 Generalized ecological model (Van der Maarel and Dauvellier 1978)

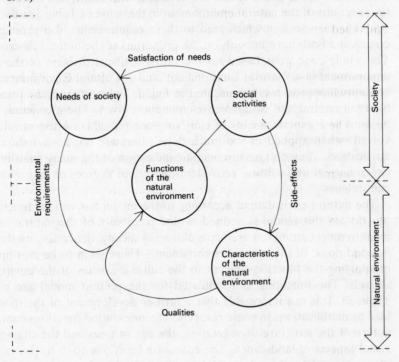

Fig. 34 The concept of 'Natural Environment' within the framework of the GEM (Van der Maarel and Dauvellier 1978)

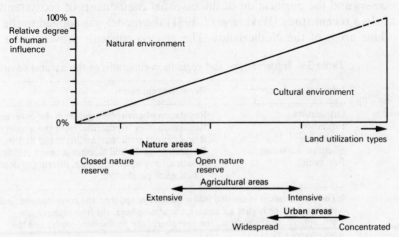

In Fig. 33 the primary relationships between the requirements of human society lead to the needs to use the natural environment, and this reflects on the functions of the natural environment in the sense of Table 38. The activities of human society which lead to these requirements also produce side-effects and both have impacts on the properties of the natural environment. The whole concept is based on the rather artificial division of the human environment in a 'Natural Environment' and a 'Cultural Environment'. This conceptual approach is represented in Fig. 34, where the gradual transition between natural and cultural environments is given. These concepts should be seen as a general means of clarifying our thoughts on the problems involved; when applied in too much detail, they are not always suitable for application: They do give a schematic indication of the many transitions between natural and cultural ecosystems in various degrees of naturalness and culturalness.

The natural environment according to the model has various functions. A function in this model is defined as 'the possibility of the natural environment to meet certain requirements of human society, depending on the specific conditions, of the natural environment'. There seem to be no objections in applying the function-concept to the cultural aspects of the environment as well. The functions as formulated for the present model are given in Table 38. It is not impossible that a further development of the model will lead to modifications in some respects. The orientation functions contain the nature of the structure of vegetation, the age of trees and the characteristic visual aspects of landscapes. The education functions point to the variety of plants, animals, soils and ecosystems. The indication functions are related to the indicator values of biota. The scientific activities have to do with all the variables of ecosystems and their variability. The reservoir functions indicate the availability of various genetic resources. The regulation functions indicate the possibilities for stabilizing external and internal variations and processes and the purification of the essential components of ecosystems.

In a recent study (Bakker *et al.* 1981) the model was applied to the coastal dune areas of the Netherlands. The general concepts proved to be a good

Table 38. Information- and regulation-functions of the natural environment

Information-functions	Regulation-functions
Orientation	Regulation of environmental from the cosmosphere*
Education	Regulation of environmental from the atmosphere
Indication	Regulation of environmental from the hydrosphere
Scientific activities	Regulation by the soil biotic regulation purification,
Reservoir	such as: absorption of noise, filtering of dust, biological purification

* The environment is divided into a number of spheres: the cosmosphere (including the sun and the higher air zones), the atmosphere, the hydrosphere, the lithosphere, the biosphere, the geosphere, the pedosphere (soils) and the noösphere (men).

Source: Van der Maarel and Dauvellier 1978.

starting point but various parts of the model had to be modified, in particular with regard to the various human effects on the various spheres of the model. In a regional model where more detailed data are available, it was also possible to apply various aspects of systems analysis in more detail.

POPULATION GROWTH, DEVELOPING COUNTRIES

In this book reference has often been made to various conditions and problems of developing countries. In this final section a few aspects of the studies of landscape ecology and land use for these areas of the world will be indicated. In particular, land classification for land use planning provides a crucial link between landscape ecology and land use. The following aspects will be briefly discussed:

- population growth as food scarcity,
- the refugee problem,
- some ecological problems,
- evaluation of development projects.

At present the largest concentrations of population are found in Western Europe, China and South Asia. Data published by FAO (1973) indicate that the largest growth of population is taking place in developing countries. This growth is distributed as follows:

1. A growth of less than 1.5 per cent per year is found in the USSR, Eastern Europe, Western Europe and North America, which together now have 25.6 per cent of the global population.

2. A growth of between 1.5 and 2.5 per cent is found in the complex consisting of China and Oceania, in some parts of Asia, in central Africa, in Southern Africa and in the Caribbean area, now together having 27.6 per cent of the global population.

3. A population growth of more than 2.5 per cent per year exists in South America, Central America, south-western Asia, eastern, southern and south-eastern Asia and in north-western, western and eastern Africa, which together have 46.8 per cent of the population of the world.

This population increase has to be accompanied by at least the same increase of food production in the countries concerned. Food is difficult to conserve, and in fact very large production losses occur during the storage of harvested foods. It is also difficult to transport in large quantities over long distances. This transport is expensive and the availability of foods to be transported is uncertain as these depend from season to season on the existence of food surpluses in other parts of the world. These depend strongly on weather conditions in the region of their production at any given season.

During the last years, several attempts are being made to predict the availability of food in the world and in the various continents and countries. A very general study, under various assumptions of inputs and other production conditions, is being done by a Dutch multidisciplinary team using fully computerized models. Thus far some estimates have been published on the absolute maximum food production of the world, with 40 different kinds of landscape ecological conditions (Buringh, *et al.* 1975) and on world food production based on labour-oriented agriculture (Buringh and Van Heemst 1977). Gradually, when more results become available, these data will provide a basis for better land use policies for food production for long-term planning.

A project which is aimed at a more direct applicability in global and national planning is the FAO/UNFPA project on Land Resources for Populations of the Future. This project is a cooperative effort of FAO and the United Nations Fund for Population Activities (New York). It is aimed at providing useful data for the next two or three decades (FAO/UNFPA 1980). It uses data from the *Soil Map of the World*, from the FAO Agroecological Zones Project (FAO 1978, 1980) and from an internal research project of FAO on 'Agriculture towards the year 2000'. Its models are also fully computerized with the help of IIASA (International Institute for Applied Systems Analysis, Laxenburg, near Vienna, Austria), but in contrast to the Dutch research project, it aims at results which are more directly applicable by incorporating data and assumptions derived from the present situation and from development trends which can be observed today. The comparison of the food production potential of the various regions with their expected population growth gives indications for predicting critical situations and critical areas with regard to food scarcity in the coming decades with more accuracy than was possible so far. Implementation of measures to be taken and projects to be established will rest largely on the initiatives to be taken by the governments concerned, but international cooperative research can, by delivering the data and the predictions, point out the dangers and stimulate the undertaking of action at the earliest possible moment.

The refugee problem is not only a problem of the developing countries, but the largest numbers of refugees in general are found in these areas and the solution of their problems is the most difficult. The growth of the number of officially known refugees in the world was indicated in the FAO-journal *Ceres* of May/June 1981: the number has risen to 16 million refugees in 1979. The last figure may be compared with the total population of the Netherlands: 14 million. Solutions to this problem, which in fact has to be separated into a number of regional problems, each involving some millions of people, will at least partly have to be found by resettlement, of the kind provided by the UNHCR (United Nations High Commissioner for Refugees, Geneva, Switzerland) at Ulyankulu in Tanzania (UNHCR 1976). This will have to be done by the investigation of landscape ecology and present as well as potential land use in various countries and regions which are thought to be relevant for the purpose. UNHCR will have to cooperate with various national and international agencies for solving the problems involved after they have given the first relief to the refugees, in order to avoid the existence of a continuously growing population of poorly-settled refugees in many parts of the world. The settlement of refugees in areas with an existing population will demand even more careful investigations than the modernization of settled areas. These investigations will have to be very efficient and their resulting land classifications for land use planning will have to be geared to effective and rapid application.

Some ecological problems connected with landscape ecology and land use have to be mentioned with regard to the situation in developing countries, where often other aspects need emphasis than the ones dominating the situation in industrialized regions. In developing countries, pollution problems, if they exist, are in general much more localized than they are in industrialized countries. Here, as in most other respects, it should be understood that the differences between various developing countries are very great and often greater than the differences between some developing countries and comparable countries which are considered to be industrialized on the basis of generalized normative figures.

Wiener (1972) distinguishes four different levels of environmental relevance which may be distinguished for each person:

1. The metabolism of the body and mind of the individual.

2. The physical habitat of the individual and his close family, his home.

3. The communal habitat – the vital services supplied within the community framework.

4. The wider environment, as we generally consider in the developed world.

In actual practice the interests of any individual will often be closely connected with those related to the well-being of his nearest and dearest family, but under extreme circumstances his first concern is for himself. Cannibalism, sometimes even including members of the same community, existed less than 20 years ago in some parts of tropical Africa, probably due to extreme protein-deficiency. In many areas with serious food deficits, the interests of most people will not proceed beyond the second of the indicated levels. Ecological considerations related to land use may then, due to age-old experience, still be included in traditional agricultural methods, which are often very well adapted to the prevailing landscape ecological conditions.

The maintenance without any changes of traditional land utilization types however is impossible due to the growing populations and consequent needs for food. This problem will, as indicated above, become more serious within the next decades. To this has to be added the very justified wish of all people in all developing countries for a higher standard of living, the means for which will have at least partly to be found in agriculture. This stresses the need for modernization of traditional agriculture, the need for more agricultural output and the need for higher standards of living from the same source; the consequences are a possible series of potential ecological disturbances. The environmental impacts of land development have therefore to be considered more specifically.

In this respect it is possible to differentiate between land management and land development (Mahler 1972). Land management consists of the periodic recurring activities (per season, per year) for regular agricultural production.

Land development demands changes in the land itself and, therefore, some kinds of land transformation (see Ch. 7). Changes in land management as well as land development are often considered to be necessary for increasing agricultural production. The following problems result from the processes involved:

1. Problems resulting from the existing situation of underdevelopment in which primitive activities for enhancing production may induce degradation.
2. Problems related to the activities needed for land development which, even if they ultimately result in better land conservation, may temporarily produce vulnerable situations due to the time needed for the various constructions and for the growth of protective vegetation.
3. Problems which result from unavoidable ill-balanced conditions during the development process, which are often due to changes in land management, either without or with land development. An example of the latter is the frequent situation where sound new irrigation projects are not well managed because the knowledge and organization for this are still lacking.

It is therefore necessary that at an early stage of land use planning in developing countries the following questions should be raised and subsequently answered by land use surveys, landscape ecological surveys and land evaluation:

1. Which are the present important problems and limiting factors for development in the area?
2. Is the solution of these problems to be found by the reclamation of new lands and/or the resettlement of the population or by developing the already existing land uses in their present areas?
3. Has this development to be arrived at either by (a) changing the characteristics and properties of the land itself (land development), or by (b) changing the land utilization types, perhaps including the reallocation of the various lands to the various land utilization types, or (c) by changing the land management within the existing land utilization types, thus causing an evolution of land use without any sudden and drastic changes and the ill-balanced situations resulting from these?

In considering these questions, an open mind should be kept for the various possibilities; also that currently prevailing and increasing needs have in many parts of the world already destroyed the equilibria existing in the traditional land uses; large forest areas have also been destroyed by irrational land reclamation. Various alternative solutions will have to be considered on the basis of good scientific basic data and their evaluations. Land classification and land evaluation therefore provide a challenge to many scientists in all developing countries.

There is one kind of evaluation, quite different in character from land classification and land evaluation, which is only rarely done in a systematic and quantitative manner and even more rarely published. This is the evaluation of the results of development projects. This evaluation is completely different from the various kinds of land evaluation embodied in the various

Table 39. Plan and accomplishment; project: Mohammad Bazar agriculture (India)

Activity	Targets for years 1953–54	Accomplishments April to September 1953
Distribution of improved seeds		
Aus paddy (in maunds)*	20	20
Aman paddy (in maunds)	150	151
Wheat (in maunds)	50	
Potato (in maunds)	300	
Distribution of fertilizers and manures		
Sulphate of ammonia (in tonnes)	100	59
Paddy fertilizer mixture (in tonnes)	100	531
Bonemeal (in tonnes)	90	20
Village compost (in maunds)	1 000	420
Sann hemp (in maunds)	100	38
Short term loans (rupees)	50 000	—
Storage godowns (rupees)	8 000	—
Afforestation (acres)	500	—

* 1 maund = 100 lb troy or 82.30 lb avoirdupois = 37.3 kg
Source: Hayes from a report of the Planning Commission of the Government of
   India, 1954.

stages of a project. The project evaluation, as this final evaluation is properly named, provides, together with the evaluation of various other project activities, a means of testing the validity of the predictions made in the original land evaluations and the result should be of benefit to subsequent projects in comparable areas.

In Table 39 an illustration is given of one method used for project evaluation by means of a comparison between the original objectives and the results at a specific target date. This example shows that ultimately the results depend on the activities of the people working within the project area. In this case, these people have on some points done much better than the original objective. On some other points they have remained far below the targets set in the plans, which may be a result from essential limitations which were not understood during the preparation and execution of the project. This is a further illustration of the fact, indicated in Chapter 7, that where planners and farmers have to cooperate for development, ultimately the farmers decide the results (Franke 1969). This is reasonable, as the farmers are the people who risk their well-being and often their lives.

A more general pronouncement on development strategy was given some time ago by Dr J. Hrabovsky of FAO (Rome) that in land development 'one must keep striving for the best while living with feasible compromises'. This is indeed the way our effort in landscape ecology and land use has to be made. Without striving for the best, we shall not be able to meet the critical situation of today and the even more critical conditions to be expected in the near future, but in any given situation we shall have to arrive at acceptable compromises.

References

Alberda, T. *et al.* (1966) De groene aarde, biologie en ecologie van de plant, *Het.* *Spectrum* Utrecht/Antwerpen.

Algemene Milieustatistiek (1974–1975/76) Centraal Bureau voor de Statistiek. Staatsuitgeverij, 's-Gravenhage.

A Priority Scheme (1960), 'for Dutch land consolidation projects', Publ. 6, Intern. Inst. Land Reclamation and Improvement, ILRI, Wageningen.

Baas Becking, L. G. M. (1934) *Geobiologie, of inleiding tot de milieukunde.* van Stockum, 's-Gravenhage.

Bailey, R. G. (1981) *Integrated approaches to classifying land as ecosystems, Forestry Land Evaluation*, in: Laban (1981) pp. 95–109.

Bakker, T. W. M., Klijn, J. A. and **Van Zadelhoff, F. J.**, (1979) Duinen en Dunivalleien, PUDOC, Wageningen, 201 pp + maps

Bakker, T. W. M., Klijn, J. A. and **Van Zadelhoff F. J.** (1981) *Nederlandse Kustduinen: Landschapsecologie.* PUDOC, Wageningen.

Barner, J. (1981) *Landschaftstechnik.* Enke Verlag, Stuttgart (GFR)

Barnes, R. S. K. and **Mann, K. H.** (1980) *Fundamentals of aquatic ecosystems.* Blackwell, Oxford, 264 pp.

Barsch, H., Fromm, W., Knothe, D. and **Richter, H.** (1979) Naturraumtypen in der DDR und naturräumliches Nutzungs-potential im Bezirk Potsdam, *Potsdamer Forschungen*, Reihe B, Heft 13. Pädagog. Hochsch. 'Karl Liebknecht', Potsdam, GDR, 159 pp. + maps.

Bavappa, K. V. A. and **Jacobs, V. J.** (1981) A model for mixed cropping, *Ceres,* FAO, Rome, **14**, 44–6.

Beatty, M. T., Petersen, G. W., Swindale, L. D. (eds) (1979) Planning the uses and management of land, *Agronomy Series no.* **21**, Amer. Soc. Agron., Crop Sci. Soc. Amer., Soil Sci. Soc. Amer., Madison, Wisc., 1028 pp.

Beek, K. J. (1978) *Land evaluation for agricultural development*, Publ. *23* ILRI, Wageningen.

Beek, K. J. and **Bennema, J.** (1972) *Land evaluation for agricultural land use planning: an ecological methodology. Collegedictaat* Landbouwhogeschool, Wageningen.

Bennema, J. *et al.* (1980) Landevaluatie, *Landbouwk. Tijdschr.* **92**; 34–70.

Bennett, H. H. (1939) *Soil Conservation.* McGraw-Hill, New York.

Bernatzky, A. (1975) In: P. Duvigneaud and S. Denaeyer-De Smet (eds) *L'écosystème urbain.* Colloque international, Brussel, Agglomération de Bruxelles.

Bie, S. W., Lieftinck, J. R. E., Van Lynden, K. R. and Waenink, A. W. (1976) Computer-aided soil suitability classification – a simple Bayesian approach, *Neth. Journ. Agric. Sci.* **24**, 79–186.

Biersteker, K. and Zielhuis, R. L. (1975) *Inleiding tot de milieuhygiëne.* Stafleu, Leiden.

Birse, E. L. (1971) *Assessment of climatic conditions in Scotland.* Soil Survey of Scotland, Aberdeen.

Birse, E. L. and Dry, F. T. (1970) *Assessment of climatic conditions in Scotland* 1. Soil Survey of Scotland, Aberdeen.

Birse, E. L. and Robertson, L. (1970) *Assessment of climatic conditions in Scotland* 2. Soil Survey of Scotland, Aberdeen.

Blumenthal, K. P. (1977) Waterverdeling in Nederland, *Landbouwkundig Tijdschr.* **89**: 292.

Boone, F. R. *et al.* (1976) Some influences of zero-tillage on the structure and stability of a fine-textured river level soil, *Neth. Journ. Agric. Sci.* **24**: 105.

Bos, M. G. and Nugteren, J. (1974) *On irrigation efficiencies,* Publ. 19. ILRI, Wageningen, 89 pp.

Bouma, J. (1971) Evaluation of the field percolation test and an alternative procedure to test soil potential for disposal of septic tank effluent, *Soil Sci. Soc. Amer. Proceed.*, **35**, 871–5.

Bouma, J. *et al.* (1972) Soil absorption of septic tank effluent, a field study of some major soils in Wisconsin, *Inform. Circ.* **20**. University of Wisconsin-Extension, Madison, Wisc.

Bouma, J., Dekker, L. W. and Haans, J. C. F. M. (1979) Drainability of some Dutch clay soils: a case study of soil survey interpretations, *Geoderma* **22**, 193–203.

Boyden, S. (1980) Ecological study of human settlements, *Nature and Resources,* UNESCO, **16**, no. 3, 2–9.

Bradford, J. (1957) *Ancient Landscapes. Studies in fields archeology.* Bell, London.

Brady, N. C. (1974) *The Nature and Properties of Soils* (8th edn). Macmillan, New York.

Broek, J. O. M. and Webb, J. W. (1973) *A Geography of Mankind* (2nd edn). McGraw-Hill, New York.

Buchwald, K. and Engelhardt, W. (eds) (1968/1969) *Handbuch für Landschaftspflege und Naturschutz,* Vol. 1/4, 245 + 502 + 271 + 252 pp.

Buringh, P. (1960) *Soils and Soil Conditions of Iraq.* Min. of Agric., Baghdad.

Buringh, P., Van Heemst, H. D. J. and Staring, G. J. (1975) *Computation of the Absolute Maximum Food Production of the World.* Agric. Univ., Wageningen, 59 pp.

Buringh, P. and Van Heemst, H. D. J. (1977) *An Estimation of World Food Production Based on Labour-Oriented Agriculture.* Centre for World Food Market Research, Amsterdam/The Hague/Wageningen, 46 pp.

Burnham, C. P., Court, M. N., Jones, R. J. A. and Tinsley, J. (1970) Effect of soil parent material, elevation, aspect and fertilizer treatment on upland grass yields, *Journ. Brit. Grassland Soc.* **25**, 272–7.

Cady, F. B. and Chan, P. Y. (1980) Development and evaluation of a soil family transfer model, *Benchmark Soils News* (Honolulu), **4**, no. **4**, 1–8.

Calhoun, J. W. and Wood, G. J. (1969) *Soil Survey of Ben Hill and Irwin Counties, Georgia.* Soil Conserv. Service, US Dept. Agric., Washington, DC.

Caponera, D. A. (1973) Water laws in Moslem countries, *Irrigation and Drainage Paper* 20/1. FAO, Rome, 223 pp.

Capper, P. L., Cassie, W. F. and Geddes, J. D. (1971) *Problems in Engineering Soils.* Spors Ltd, London.

Canada Committee (on Ecological (Bio-physical) Land Classification) (1980). Newsletter no. 9: *Wetlands.*

Carson, M. A. and Kirkby, M. J. (1972) *Hillslope, Form and Process.* Cambridge Univ. Press, Cambridge.

CGIAR (Consultative Group on International Agricultural Research) (1974) *International Research in Agriculture.* New York, 70 pp.

Chorley, R. J. and Kennedy, B. A. (1971) *Physical Geography: A Systems Approach.* Prentice Hall, London.

Christian, C. S. and **Stewart, G. A.** (1968) "Methodology of Integrated Surveys, in: Rey (1968), pp. 233–280.

Christy, L. C. (1971) Legislative principles of soil conservation, *Soils Bulletin* (FAO, Rome) **15**, 68 pp.

Clapham, W. B. (1973) *Natural Ecosystems.* Macmillan, New York.

Colinvaux, P. (1973) *Introduction to Ecology.* Wiley & Sons, New York, 621 pp.

Commissie Onderzoek Biologische Landbouwmethoden (1977) *Alternatieve landbouwmethoden.* PUDOC, Wageningen.

Conference (1977) (UN – on Desertification), *World Map of Desertification*, scale 1 : 25 million, Nairobi.

Cook, A., Court, M. N. and Macleod, D. A. (1977) The prediction of Scots Pine growth in North-East Scotland using readily assessable site characteristics, *Journ. Royal Scot. Forestry Soc.* **31**, 251–64.

Correll, D. L. and Dixon, D. (1980) Relationships of nitrogen discharge to land use on Rhode River watersheds, *Agro-Ecosystems*, **6**, 147–59.

Davidson, D. A. (1980) Soils and land use planning. *Topics in Applied Geography.* Longman, London/New York, 129 pp.

Dauvellier, P. L. and Littel, A. (1977) Toepassing van het globaal ecologisch model en de landelijke milieukartering in de ruimtelijke planning, *Meded. Werkgem. Landschapsecol. Ond.* **4**, no. **2** : **3**.

De Bakker, H. en Schelling, J. (1966) Systeem voor bodem-classificatie voor Nederland. PUDOC, Wageningen.

De Boer, Th. A. (1956) Der Zusammenhang zwischen Grünland-vegetation und Bodeneinheiten, *Int. Symp. Pflanzensoz.*, Bodenk. Stolzenau.

Dee, N. *et al.* (1972) Final report on environmental evaluation system for water resource planning. US Bur. Reclamation. Columbus Laboratories, Batelle, Columbus, Ohio.

Dee, N. *et al.* (1973) An environmental evaluation system for water resource planning. *Water Resource Research* **9**, 523.

De Groot, A. J. (1969) Geochemisch onderzoek in deltagebieden. Voordracht Kon. Mij. Diligentia, 's-Gravenhage (reprint), p. 61.

De Smet, L. A. H. (1968) Grondverbeteringsmogelijkheden en hun betekenis in de Groningse Veenkoloniën. *Cultuurtechn. Tijdschr.* **7**: 252, 2–28.

De Veer, A. A., Buitenhuis, A. en Van het Loo, H. (1977) Vergelijking van Nederlandse methoden van landschapsbeeldkartering. PUDOC, Wageningen.

De Wit, C. T. (1966) Overbevolking zonder ondervoeding, in: *De Groene Aarde*, Th. Alberda et al., 1966. Aulaboeken, Utrecht, pp. 425–36.

De C. T. Wit, (1975) Substitution of labour and energy in agriculture and options for growth, *Neth. Journ. Agric. Sci.* **23**: 145.

Diario Official (Republica de Colombia) (1975) Decreto numero 2811 de 1974 (Codigo Nacional de Recursos Naturales Renovables y de Proteción al Medio Ambiente). Diario Official Ano CXI no. 34243, Bogota.

Di Castri, F. and Mooney, H. A. (Eds.) (1973) Mediterranean Type Ecosystems, origin and structure. *Ecological Studies* **7**, Springer Verlag, Berlin/Heidelberg/New York, 405 pp.

Diemont, W. H. and Van Wijngaarden, W. (1974) Sedimentation patterns, soils, mangrove vegetation and land use in the tidal areas of West-Malaysia, *Proceed. Int. Symp. Biol. Manag. Mangroves Honolulu (Hawaii)*, vol. **II**, p. 513.

Doorenbos, J. and Pruitt, W. D. (1977) Crop water requirements. *Irrigation and Drainage Paper* **24** (revised). FAO, Rome.

Durwen, K. J., Thöle, R. and Schreiber, K. F. (1979) Einsatzmöglichkeiten landschaftsökologischer Informationssysteme in der räumlichen Planung, *Verhandl. Ges. f. Oekologie*, **7**, 187–90.

Dutch Agricultural Investment Commission (1960) An assessment of investments in land reclamation. Publ. 7, Intern. Inst. Land Reclam. and Improvement, Wageningen.

Duvigneaud, P. (1974) *La synthèse écologique*. Doin, Paris.

Duvigneaud, P. *et al.* (1975). In: P. Duvigneaud and S. Denaeyer-De Smet (eds). *L'écosystème urbain*. Colloque international. Brussel, Agglomération de Bruxelles.

Eckholm, E. P. (1976) *Losing ground*, environmental stress and world food prospects. Norton & Co., New York 223 pp.

Ecological Land Survey Task Force (1980) Ecological land survey guidelines for environmental impact analysis. Environment Canada, Ottawa, 40 pp.

Edelman, C. H., (1950) *Soils of the Netherlands*, North-Holland Publ. Cy., Amsterdam, 188 pp + map

Edelman, C. H. (1960a) Podzols forestiers et podzols de bruyère. *Pédologie* **10**: 229, 2–32.

Edelman, C. H. (1960b) *Inleiding tot de bodemkunde van Nederland* (2nd edn). Amsterdam, Noordholl. Uitg. Mij.

Edelman, C. H. and Eeuwens, B. E. P. (1959) Sporen van een Romeinse landindeling in Zuid-Limburg. *Ber. Rijksd. Oudheidk. Bodemond.* **9**: 40, 1–35.

Eyre, S. R. (1968) (Repr. 1970) *Vegetation and soils*. Arnold, London, 328 pp.

Fabos, J. G. and Caswell, S. J. (1977) Composite landscape assessment. College of Food and Natur. Res. Univ. of Massachusetts at Amherst, Mass.

Fabos, J. G., Greene, C. M. and Joyner, S. A. (1978) The METLAND landscape planning process, part **3** of the *Metropolitan Landscape Planning Model*, Massachusetts Agric. Exper. Sta. Univ. of Massachusetts, Amherst, Mass.

Falcon, L. A. and Smith, R. F. (1973) Guidelines for integrated control of cotton insect pests. FAO, Rome, 92 pp.

Faludi, A. (1975) Planningtheorie en planningonderwijs. Oratie T. H. Delft, Univ. Press, Delft.

FAO (1972) *Atlas of the Living Resources of the Sea.* Dept. of Fisheries, FAO, Rome.

FAO (1973) The world and its inhabitants, *Ceres,* **6** (Population Special), FAO, Rome.

FAO (1974) Shifting cultivation and soil conservation in Africa. *Soil Bulletin* **24**. FAO, Rome.

FAO (1976) A framework for land evaluation. *Soil Bulletin* **32**. FAO, Rome

FAO (Kimble, S. H. and Thames, J. L., eds.) (1976/1977) *FAO Conservation Guide,* no. 1, Guidelines for watershed management. 293 pp., no. 2, Hydrological techniques, no. 3, Conservation in arid and semi-arid zones, 125 pp. FAO, Rome.

FAO (1978/1979) *Report on the Agro-ecological Zones Project.* Vol. 1, Methodology and results for Africa; vol. 2, Southwest Asia; vol. 3, Southeast Asia. *World Soil Resources Report* 48, FAO, Rome.

FAO (1977 and 1980) The state of food and agriculture (1977). Chapter 3: The state of natural resources and the human environment for food and agriculture, *FAO Environment Paper* no. **1**. FAO, Rome, 62 pp.

FAO (1978) Land evaluation standards for rainfed agriculture, *World Soil Resources Report* **49**, FAO, Rome, 116 pp.

FAO (1979 seq.) Land and water, *Technical Newsletter* of the Land and Water Development Division. FAO, Rome.

FAO (1980) Land evaluation criteria for irrigation. *World Soil Resources Report* no. **5**, ± 120 pp.

FAO Forestry Department (1977) Guidelines for watershed management (Forest Conservation and Wildlife Branch, Forest Resources Division), *FAO Conservation Guide* **1**, FAO, Rome, 293 pp.

FAO Forestry Department (1978) Forestry for local community development. *FAO Forestry Paper* 7 (with the assistance of the Swedish International Development Authority) FAO, Rome, 114 pp.

FAO/UNESCO (1971) *Soil Map of the World,* 1 : 5.000,000, vol. IV, South America. UNESCO, Paris.

FAO/UNESCO (1974) Soil Map of the World, 1 : 5 000 000, Volume I, Legend, UNESCO, Paris

FAO/UNFPA (1980) *Report of the Second FAO/UNFPA Expert Consultation on Land Resources for Populations of the Future.* FAO, Rome, 369 pp.

Feis, N. (1970) Kunnen singels, hagen en bosschages de hoogbouwstormen keren? *Landbouwk. Tijdschr.* **82**, 269–77.

Flawn, P. T. (1970) *Environmental Geology.* Harper and Row, New York.

Flint, R. F. (1971) *Glacial and Quaternary Geology.* Wiley, New York/London, 892 pp.

Franke, A. (1969) *Boeren en plannenmakers in ontwikkelingslanden.* Oratie, Wageningen.

Frankel, O. H. (1972) *The Significance, Utilization and Origin of Crop Genetic Resources.* FAO, Rome, 29 pp.

Frankel, O. H. (Ed.) (1973) Survey of crop genetic resources in their centres of diversity, *First Report.* FAO, Rome, 164 pp.

Freedman, S. M. (1980) Modification of traditional rice production practices in the Developing World: an energy efficiency analysis, *Agro-Ecosystems* **6**, 129–46.

Frissel, M. J. (1977) De stikstofkringloop in landbouwsystemen. *Landbouwk. Tijdschr.* **89**: 380.

Frissel, M. J. (ed.) (1977) Cycling of numeral nutrients in agricultural ecosystems *Agro-Ecosystems* **4**, 1–354.

Fuentes, E. R. (1979) Integrated research on the southern Andes, *Bulletin MAB, Nature and Resources* UNESCO **15**/3, 23–4.

Gardiner, M. J. and Ryan, P. (1969) A new generalised soil map of Ireland and its land-use interpretation, *Irish Journ. agric. res.* **8**, 95–109.

General Environmental Statistics – Algemene Milieustatistiek, (1975/76), Centraal Bureau voor Statistiek. Government Publ. Office, The Hague, 1978.

Gibbons, F. R. and Haans, J. C. F. M. (1976) Dutch and Victorian approaches to land appraisal. *Soil Survey Papers* no. 11. Soil Survey Institute, Wageningen, 40 pp.

Golterman, H. L. (1970) De invloed van het menselijk handelen op de biocoenosen in het water, in Quispel *et al.* (Eds), *Biosfeer en mens.* PUDOC, Wageningen, p. 80.

Grant, K., Finlayson, A. A., Spate, A. P. and Ferguson, T. G. (1979) Terrain analysis and classification for engineering and conservation purposes of the Port Clinton Area, Qld., including the Shoalwater Bay Military Training Area. *Div. Applied Geomechanics Tech. Paper* no. 29. CSIRO, Melbourne, 185 pp.

Grice, D. G. *et al.* (1971) Soil Survey of Mercer County, Pennsylvania. Soil Conserv. Service, US Dept. Agric., Washington, DC.

Grontmij (1968) De ontwikkeling van de Medjerda Vallei, OVVM-Grontmij N.V., Tunis. *Excursieprogramma.*

Gulland, J. A. (Ed.) (1971) *The Fish Resources of the Ocean.* FAO, Rome.

Haans, J. C. F. M. and Westerveld, G. J. W. (1970) The application of Soil Survey in the Netherlands, *Geoderma* **4**, 279–309.

Haantjens, H. A. (1966) Agricultural land classification for New Guinea land resources surveys. *CSIRO Techn. Mem.* no. 8. Canberra.

Haase, G. (1968) Inhalt und Methodik einer umfassenden Standortkartierung auf der Grundlage landschafts-ökologischer Erlündung. *Wiss. Veröff. deutsch. Inst. f. Landesk. (G.D.R.), neue Folge* 25/26 (5–81)

Harley, J. L. and Scott Russell, R. (Eds.) (1979). *The Soil–Root Interface.* Academic Press, London.

Harrold, L. L. (1962) Hydrology of agricultural watersheds, *Journ. Soil and Water Cons.* (1962), p. 1–17.

Hayes Jr., S. P. (1969) *Evaluating Development Projects.* UNESCO, Paris.

Hill, I. D. (Ed.), (1979), Land resources of Central Nigeria, Land Resources Study 29, Land Res. Dev. Centre, Min. Overseas Dev., Surbiton (Surrey), 6 Vols + maps

Hill Farming Research Organization (1979) *Science and Hill Farming.* HFRO, Penicuik (Midlothian), 184 pp.

Hudig, J., (1937), Chemisch onderzoek van tropische gronden, in: *Landbouwkundig Tijdschrift* 49, pp. 378–401

Hudson, N. (1971) *Soil Conservation.* Cornell University Press, Ithaca, NY.

Huggett, R. (1980) *Systems Analysis in Geography.* Oxford University Press.

Hulsbos, W. C. (1968) The determination of the drainage factor as a criterion for the soils of the Indus plains, *Netherl. Journ. Agric. Sci.* **16**, 25–35.

Hulsbos, W. C. and Boumans, J. H. (1960) Leaching of saline soils in Iraq, *Neth. Journ. Agric. Sci.* **8**: 1 (1–32)

Institute of Natural Resources Research. Abu Ghraib, Iraq (1975) Contributions on natural research. UNDP/UNESCO, Paris.

Imeson, A. C. and Jungerius, P. D. (1976) Aggregate stability and colluviation in the Luxembourg Ardennes; an experimental and micromorphological study, *Earth Surface Processes* **1**, 259–71.

Imeson, A. C. and Jungerius, P. D. (1977) The widening of valley incisions by soil fall in a forested Keuper area, Luxembourg, *Earth Surface Processes* **2**, 141–52.

Interdepartmental Task Force (1980) Land use in Canada, Report of the Lands Directorate, Environment Canada, Ottawa, 51 pp.

Irrinews (1979 seq.) Newsletter of the International Irrigation Information Center, Ottawa (Canada)/Bet Dagan (Israel).

ITC-UNESCO Centre for Integrated Surveys (1968) Integrated Surveys of Natural Grazing areas. ITC-UNESCO Centre, Delft (Enschede), Publ. S15/S28.

IUCN (International Union for the Conservation of Nature and Natural Resources) (1980) World Conservation Strategy, living resource conservations for sustainable development. IUCN, Gland, Switzerland, 40 pp + maps.

Jankowsky, W. (1975) Land use mapping, development and methods, *Geographical Studies* **111**. Polish Academy of Sciences, Warsaw, 103 pp.

Janse, A. R. P. (1970). Bomen en het lawaai in de straat, *Landbouwk. Tijdschr.* **82**: 227, 5–51.

Jones, R. J. A. and Tinsley, J. (1980) Hill land studies in the Grampian region of Scotland. 1, Effects of soil parent material, altitude and aspect on the herbage yields, composition and responses to fertilizer treatments in the Upper Don Basin, *Journ. Soil Sci.* **31**, 343–70.

Journaux, A. (ed.) (1978) *Carte de l'environnement et de sa dynamique, échelle 1 : 50,000, feuille Caen.* Centre de Géomorphologie CNRS, Caen (France).

Jung, G. A., Stelly, M., Krol, D. M. and Nauseef, J. H. (Eds.) (1978) *Crop Tolerance to Suboptimal Land Conditions.* Amer. Soc. Agron., Crop Sci. Soc. Amer., Soil Sci. Soc. Amer., Madison, Wisconsin, 343 pp.

Jungerius, P. D., Koster, E. A. and Kwaad, F. J. P. M. (1973) *Fysische Geografie, aspecten van het landschapsonderzoek.* Oosthoek, Utrecht.

Jurdant, M., Belair, J. L., Gerardin, V. and Duruc, J. P. (1977) *L'inventaire du capital-nature.* Environnement Canada.

Kassam, A. H., Kowal, J. M. and Sarraf, S. (1977) *Climatic Adaptability of Crops.* FAO, Rome.

Kellogg, Ch. E. (1941) Climate and soil, *Climate and Man, Yearbook of Agriculture*, US Dept. Agric., Washington, pp. 265–91.

Kellogg, Ch. E. (1961) *Soil Interpretation in the Soil Survey.* Soil Conservation Service, US Dept. Agric., Washington DC.

Kellogg, Ch. E. (1962) Soil surveys for use, *Trans. Intern. Soils Conf.* Wellington, New Zealand, pp. 529–35.

Kovda, V. A. *et al.* (1973) *Irrigation, Drainage, Salinity.* Hutchinson/FAO/UNESCO. Paris/London.

Kramer, P. (1973) Wildlife conservation in the Galapagos Islands (Ecuador), *Nature and Resources* UNESCO **9/4**, 3–10.

Krijger, P. D. and Maris, R. (1964) *Cultuurtechniek* (3rd edn). Wolters, Groningen.

Kuenen, D. J. (Ed.) (1976) *Inleiding in de Milieukunde*, Van Gorcum, Assen/Amsterdam, 335 pp.

Kwakernaak, C. (1977) Gevolgen van de recreatie voor de Wadden-eilanden. *Recreatievoorzieningen* ANWB **9**: 468.

Kwakernaak, C. (1982) An iterative method for ecological land classification, developed in a case-study in the Prealps of Switzerland. Ph.D. thesis Univ. of Amsterdam. Publ. Lab. Phys. Geogr. and Soil Science, University of Amsterdam.

Kwakernaak, C., Bolt, A. J. J., Levelt, Th. W. M. and **Vink, A. P. A.** (1979) "Voorne-Putten, een landschapsecologisch onderzoek", in: Geografisch Tijdschrift NR 13, p. 116–141

Laban, P. (Ed.) (1981) *Proceedings of the workshop on land evaluation for forestry*, Publ. no. **28**, ILRI, Wageningen, 350 pp.

Lacate, D. S. (1969) *Guidelines for bio-physical land classification*, Publ. **1264**, Dept. Fisheries and Forestry, Ottawa.

Lasserre, P. (1979) Coastal lagoons, sanctuary ecosystems, cradles of culture, targets for economic growth, *Nature and Resources* UNESCO **15/4**, 2–20.

Lee Ling, Whitmore, F. W. and **Turtle, E. E.** (1972) *Persistent insecticides in relation to the environment and their unintended effect.* FAO, Rome, 46 pp.

Leser, H. (1976) *Landschaftsökologie.* Ulmer, Stuttgart.

Lopoukhine, N., Pront, N. A. and **Hirvonen, H. E.** (1978) Ecological land classification of Labrador, *Ecol. Land Class. Series* no. **4**, Environment Canada, Ottawa, Ontario, 85 pp.

Mass, F. M. (1971) *Toekomstmodel voor natuur en landschap.* Wereldvenster, Baarn.

Macan, T. T. and **Worthington, E. B.** (1968) *Life in Lakes and Rivers.* Collins, London.

Mahler, P. J. (1972) Integrated surveys and environmental problems associated with land development in developing countries, *ITC Journal* 1973–2: **256** (5–85).

Maletic, J. T. and **Hutchings, T. B.** (1967) Selection and classification of irrigable land, in Hagan, R. M. c.s. (ed.), 1967: *Irrigation of Agricultural Lands. Agronomy* **11**, Amer. Soc. Agron. Madison, Wisc.

Mark, S. M. et al. (1977) *Land use: tough choices in today's world.* Special Publ. no. **22**, Soil Conserv. Soc. Amer., Ankeny, Iowa, 434 pp.

McCormack, D. E., Hartung, R. E. and **Larson, K. N.** (1981) *Evaluations of forest lands in the United States.* in Laban (1981), p. 167–179.

McHarg, I. L. (1969) *Design with Nature.* Natural History Press, New York.

Melvyn Howe, G. (Ed.) (1977) *A World Geography of Human Diseases.* Academic Press, London.

Melvyn Howe, G. and **Lorraine, J. A.** (eds.) (1973), Repr. 1976, *Environmental Medicine.* Heinemann, London, 271 pp.

Meyer, F. et al. (1978). *Bäume in der Stadt.* Verlag Eugen Ulmer, Stuttgart, 327 pp.

Minderhoud, G. et al. (1956) *Veenman's agrarische Winkler Prins.* 3 dln. Veenman/Elsevier, Wageningen/Amsterdam.

Moormann, F. R., Veldkamp, W. J. and **Ballaux, J. C.** (1977) The growth of rice on a toposequence – a methodology, *Plant and Soil* **48**, 565–80.

Moormann, F. R. and **Van Breemen, N.** (1978) *Rice: Soil, Water, Land.* Intern. Rice Research Inst., Los Banos, Philippines.

Mosher, A. (1972) Custom-made systems, *Ceres* FAO, Aug. 1972: **33**.

Neef, E. (1967) *Die theoretischen Grundlagen der Landschaftslehre.* Haack, Gotha, GDR, 152 pp.

Nelson, J. G. and Chambers, M. J. (1969) *Vegetation, Soils and Wildlife.* Methuen, Toronto/London/Sydney/Wellington, 372 pp.

Nossin, J. J. et al. (1977a) Surveys for development, *ITC Journal* 1977–**2**: 251.

Nossin, J. J. et al. (1977b) *Surveys for Development.* Elsevier, Amsterdam.

Nossin, J. J. (1980) Land resources in regionaal verband, *Geografisch Tijdschrift* **14**, 388–405.

Odum, E. (1963, 1975) *Ecology.* Holt, Rinehart and Winston, New York.

Olson, G. W. (1973) Soil survey interpretation for engineering purposes, *Soil Bulletin* **19**, FAO Rome.

Papadakis, J. S. (1938) *Ecologic Agricole.* Duculot, Gembloux.

Pape, J. C. (1970) Plaggen soils in the Netherlands, *Geoderma* **4**, 229–56.

Patri, T. et al. (1970) The Santa Cruz Mountains Regional Pilot Study, Early Warning System. Dept. Landscape Architecture. *College Environm. Design* Univ. of California, Berkeley, Cal., 293 pp.

Pedroli, B. (1980) Report of a landscape ecological survey on scale 1 : 50,000 of the region Talla and Capolona, Arezzo, Italy. M.Sc. thesis, Univ. of Amsterdam, Dept. of Phys. Geography and Soil Science.

Pimentel, D. and Pimentel, M. (1977) Counting the kilocalories, *Ceres* FAO, Rome **10** (No. 59): 17.

Pimentel, D., Hurd, L. E., Bellotti, A. C., Forster, M. J., Oka, I. N., Scholls, O. D. and Whitman, R. J. (1973) *Workshop on research methodologies for studies of energy, food, man and environment*, Phase I. Cornell Univ., Ithaca, New York.

Policard, A. (1963) Essay on the psychology of team work in science, *Impact* **18** (No. 2), 71 (5–88).

Pons, L. J. (1964) Pyrites as a factor controlling chemical 'ripening' and formation of 'cat clay', with special reference to the coastal plain of Surinam, *Bull. Agric. Exp. Sta. Paramaribo*, 141 (1–19).

Pons, L. J. and Zonneveld, I. S. (1965) *Soil ripening and soil classification.* Publ. **13**, ILRI, Wageningen, 128 pp.

Purnell, M. F. and Venema, J. H. (1976) Agricultural potential regions of the Sudan, *Techn. Bull.* no. **28**, Soil Survey Admin., Wad Medani.

Rappaport (1971) The flow of energy in an agrocultural society, *Scientific American* **224**(3), 116–32.

Rasmussen, J. J. (1971) *Soil Survey of Benton County Area, Washington.* Soil Conserv. Service, U.S. Dept. Agric., Washington, DC.

Rattray, J. M. (1960) The Grass Cover of Africa. *FAO Plant Production and Protection Series* no. **9**, FAO, Rome, 168 pp.

Rauschkolb, R. S. (1971) Land Degradation. *Soils Bulletin* **13**, FAO, Rome.

Rey, P. (ed.) (1968) *Aerial surveys and integrated studies.* Natural Resources Research VI, UNESCO, Paris, 575 pp.

Richter, H. (1975) Changes in land development within the peripheral zone. Case study of the Halle-Leipzig agglomeration, *Geographica Polonica* **30**, 95–103.

Riemer, W. and Rozestraten, C. J. A. (1978) Greater Bandung planning and water resources management, *Masalah Bangunan* (Indonesia). UN Regional Housing Centre, Bandung, **23**, 17–26.

Riney, P. A. (1972) *Wildlife, national parks and recreational resources.* UN Confer. Human Environment, Stockholm, 26 pp.

Ringelberg, J. (1976) *Inleiding tot de aquatische oecologie.* Bohn, Scheltema and Holkema, Utrecht.

Rubec, C. D. A. (ed.) (1979) Application of ecological (biophysical) land classification, *Ecol. Land Class. Series*, no. **7**, Environment Canada, Ottawa, Ontario, 396 pp.

Ruthenberg, H. (1976) *Farming Systems in the Tropics* (2nd edn). Clarendon Press, Oxford, 366 pp.

Ruting, J. (1977) Vogels in de binnenstad, *De Lepelaar*, no. **52**, 18–21.

Salgueiro, T. A. *et al.* (1964) The land capability map of Portugal, *Trans. 8th Intern. Congr. Soil Sci.*, Bucharest, V, pp. 837–45.

Salinity Laboratory Staff (1954) Diagnosis and improvement of saline and alkali soils. *Agriculture Handbook* no. **60**. US Dept. of Agric., Washington, DC.

Salinity Seminar (1971) *Baghdad, Irrigation and Drainage Paper.* FAO of the UN, Rome.

Sand, P. H. (1972) Legal systems for environment protection. Japan, Sweden, United States, *Legislative Studies* no. **4**, FAO, Rome, 60 pp.

Schlichting, E. (1972) Pseudogleye und Gleye-Genese und Nutzung hydromorpher Böden, *Pseudogley & Gley*, Verlag Chemie, Winheim, pp. 1–6.

Schlichting, E. (1975a) Stoffhaushalt von Bodenlandschaften in Südwestdeutschland als landschaftökologische Planungsgrundlage, *Daten und Dokumente zum Umweltschutz*, **14**, 103–11.

Schlichting, E. (1975b) Bedingungen und Bedeutung landschaftsökologischer Umsatz- und Bilanzuntersuchungen, *Forstwissenschaftliches Zentralblatt*, **94**, 273–80.

Schlichting, E. and Sunkel, R. (1971) Nährstoffgehalte und Düngewirkung in einigen Böden Württembergs, *Landwirtschaftliche Forschung* (Frankfurt a.M.), **24/2**, 170–92.

Schreiber, K. F. (1970) Trennung von Wald und Weide und Intensivierung der Weidenutzung in Berggebieten, *Symp. Anw. Landsch. Okol. in Praxis*, Smolenice, pp. 5–104.

Schreiber, K. F. (1977) Landscape planning and protection of the environment, *Applied Sciences and Development*, Inst. f. Sci. Coöp., Tübingen, FRG, pp. 128–39.

Schreiber, K. F. (1980) Brachflächen in der Kulturlandschaft, *Daten u. Dok. z. Umweltschutz*, **30**, Oekol. Agrarlandsch., Univ. Hohenheim, Stuttgart-Hohenheim, FRG, pp. 61–93.

Schreiber, K. F. (1980) *Entstehung von Oekosystemen und ihre Beeinflüssung durch menschliche Eingriffe.* Publ. Minist. Umwelt, Raumordnung und Bauwesen Saarland, Saarbrücken, FRG.

Schulze, F. E. (ed.) (1980) *Land reclamation and water management.* Publ. **27**, ILRI, Wageningen, 191 pp.

Sekiguti, T. *et al.* (1980) Japanese Progress in Climatology, 1979: Agro-Bio-environmental maps, *Japan Climatology Seminar*, Min. Education, Science and Culture, Tokyo, 101 pp.

Serno, G. (1975) Verslag van een landschapsecologisch onderzoek in een gebied ten noorden van het Val d'Arno, Italië. M.Sc. thesis Fys. Geogr. Bodemk. Lab., Univ. of Amsterdam.

Sevink, J., Remmelzwaal, A. and Spaargaren, O. C. (1982) *Soil Map of Southern Lazio and adjacent Campania (Italy)*. Lab. f. Phys. Geogr. Soil Sci., Univ. of Amsterdam.

Sikkel, D. *et al.* (1971) Nieuwe bossen in Nederland. *Extra nummer Ned. Bosouw Tijdschr.* Wageningen. Kon. Ned. Bosbouw Ver.

Simpson-Lewis, W., Moore, J. E., Pocock, N. J., Taylor, M. C. and Swan, H. (1979) Canada's Special Resource Lands, a natural perspective of selected land uses, *Map Folio* no. **4**, Lands Directorate, Environment Canada, Ottawa, 232 pp.

Sissingh, G. and Tideman, P. (1960) De plantengemeenschappen uit de omgeving van Didam en Zevenaar, *Mededelingen Landbouwhogeschool* Wageningen **60** (13): 1.

Smith, K. and Tobin, G. A. (1979) Human adjustment to the flood hazard, *Topics in Applied Geography*. Longman, London/New York, 130 pp.

Smits, H. and Wiggers, A. J. (1959) *Soil survey and land classification as applied to reclamation of sea bottom land in the Netherlands*. Intern. Inst. Land-reclam. Improvement Publ. 4, ILRI, Wageningen.

Soemarwoto, O. (1977) Ecological aspects of development, *Surveys for development*, Int. Symp. ITC, Enschede, pp. 5–123.

Soil Survey Staff (1951, 1963) (repr. 1963) *Soil Survey Manual*, US Dept. Agric., Washington, DC.

Soil Survey Staff (1975) Soil Taxonomy. Soil Cons. Serv. US Dept. Agric., *Agric. Handbook* no. 436, Washington, DC, 754 pp.

Somasiri, S., (1980) Map of the Agroecological Zones of Sri Lanka, Department of Land and Water Use, Kandy

Somasiri, S., Tinsley, R. L., Panabokke, C. R. and Moormann, F. R. (1978) Evaluation of rice lands in Mid-Country Kandy district, Sri Lanka, *Soil Resource Inventories and Development Planning*, Cornell Univ., Ithaca, New York, p. 122.

Stamp, L. Dudley (1950) *The Land of Britain, Its Use and Misuse* (2nd edn). Longman Green, London.

Stamp, L. Dudley (1961) *Applied Geography*. Pelican A 449 (2nd edn).

Starr, C. *et al.* (1971) Energy and power, *Scientific American*, **225**(3), 37–224.

Stearns, F. W. and Montag, T. (1974) *The Urban Ecosystem: a holistic approach*. Dowden, Hutchinson and Ross, Stroudsburg, Pa.

Stiboka (1975) *Kaartblad 52 Oost (Venlo) van de bodemkaart van Nederland op schaal 1 : 50,000*. Stichting voor Bodemkartering, Wageningen.

Studiecommissie C4 (1975) *Kennismaking met methodisch ontwerpen ACCIS/SBR*. Rapport C4–1. Stichting Bouwresearch, Delft.

Swindale, L. D. (Ed.) (1978) *Soil resources data for agricultural development*. Hawaii Agric. Exp. Sta. College of Tropic Agric. Univ. of Hawaii, Honolulu, 306 pp.

Takes, C. A. P. (1975) Land settlement and resettlement projects. *Bulletin 14*, ILRI, Wageningen, 44 pp.

Ten Cate, J. A. M. and Maarleveld, G. C. (1977). *Geomorfologische kaart van*

Nederland, schaal 1 : 50,000. Stichting voor Bodemkunde/Rijks Geologische Dienst, Wageningen/Haarlem.

Terwindt, J. H. J. and Walther, A. W. (1976) Current trends of coastal research in the Netherlands, *Geoscience and Man 14*: 73.

Teune, P. J. (1976) *Fysische Geografie en Milieu*, 's-Hertogenbosch, Malmberg.

Thalen, D. C. P. (1979) *Ecology and Utilization of Desert Shrub Rangelands in Iraq*. Junk, The Hague, 428 pp.

Traill, J. C. M. *et al.* (1979) *Trypanotolerant livestock in West and Central Africa*. ILCA (International Livestock Centre for Africa), Addis Ababa, 2 vols., pp. 147–303.

Tricart, J. (1965) *Principes et Méthodes de la géomorphologie*. Edn Masson, Paris, 496 pp.

Tsutsin, H. and Ohta, S. (1977) *Irrigation aspects – global target of irrigation development by 1990 in developing countries*. FAO, Rome, 9 pp.

Tyrwhitt, J. (ed.) (1977) Living with the desert, *Ekistics* (Athens, Greece) **43**, no. **258**, pp. 242–324.

Tyurin, I. V. and Sokolov, A. V. (1958) Soil types and efficiency of fertilizers, *Trans. Comm. II and IV*, Intern. Soc. Soil Sci., Hamburg, pp. 60–72.

UNESCO (1963) Bioclimatic map of the mediterranean zone. *Arid Zone Research XXI*. Unesco, Paris.

UNESCO (1973) Ecological effects of utilization in urban and industrial systems, *Exp. Panel Project II, MAB report series* no. 13, Unesco, Paris.

UNESCO/UNEP (1974) Task force on criteria and guidelines for the choice and establishment of biosphere reserves, *MAB report series* no. **22** Unesco, Paris, 61 pp.

UNHCR (1976) *Habitat, refugees in human settlements*. United Nations High Commissioner for Refugees, Geneva, Switzerland, 23 pp.

USDA (1975) *Perspectives on prime lands*. US Department of Agriculture, Washington, DC, 257 pp.

US Geological Survey (1980) *Ground Water*. US Govt. Printing Office, Washington, DC.

Van Amstel, A. (1981) Landschapsecologisch onderzoek in Montevarchi en omstreken (Valdarno Superiore, Prov. Arezzo, Italy). M.Sc. thesis, Univ. of Amsterdam.

Van Dam, J. G. C. and Wopereis, F. A. (1978) Grond en groen in Haarlem, *Groen* **34**(I): 1.

Van den Broek, M., Van Amstel, A., Verbakel, A., Pedroli, B. (1981) Variability of soil properties in a landscape ecological survey in the Tuscan Apennines, Italy, *Catena* **8**, 155–70.

Van der Drift, J. (1970) Terrestrische ecosystemen, *Contactblad voor Oecologen* **6**: 43, 5–95.

Van der Maarel, E. and Dauvellier, P. L. (1978) *Naar een Globaal Ecologisch Model voor de ruimtelijke ontwikkeling van Nederland*. Staatsuitgeverij, 's-Gravenhage.

Van der Werf, S. (1970) Recreatie-invloeden in Meyendel, *Meded. Landbouwhogeschool*, **70**, no. 17, Wageningen.

Van de Weg, R. F. and Mbuvi, J. P. (1975) Soils of the Kindaruma area; *Recomm. Soil Surv. Rept*. No. **1**. Soil Survey, Min. Agric.

Van Dobben, W. H. (1970) De terrestrische oecosystemen: de genese en de gevolgen van de menselijke technologie, Quispel *et al.* (eds) *Biosfeer en mens.* PUDOC, Wageningen, pp. 104.

Van Duin, R. H. A. (1978) Natuurbouw, een nieuwe loot aan de cultuurtechniek, *Landbouwk. Tijdschr.* **90**: 77,

Van Dyne, G. M. *et al.* (1969) *The Ecosystem Concept in Natural Resource Management.* Academic Press, New York/London.

Van Heesen, H. C. (1970) Presentation of the seasonal fluctuation of the water table on soil maps, *Geoderma* **4**: 257, 1–53.

Van Ittersum, G. and Kwakernaak, C. (1977) Gevolgen van de recreatie voor het natuurlijk milieu, *Eilanden onder de voet.* Landel. Ver. Behoud Waddenzee, pp. 59–103.

Van Leeuwen, C. G. (1966) A relation theoretical approach to pattern and process in vegetation, *Wentia* **15**: 25, *RIVON-meded.* **219**, 2–42.

Van Mourik, W. J. G. (1967) *Planologie, voorzichtige vermetele vormgeving.* Oratie Landbouwhogeschool Wageningen.

Van Mourik, W. J. G. *et al.* (1970) *Bodem en Planologie.* Extra nummer, Stedebouw en Volkshuisvesting.

Van Rijn, H. T. U. *et al.* (1976) Geintegreerd milieu-onderzoek, *Rapport*, 6 dln. Openbaar Lichaam Rijnmond, Rotterdam.

Van Staveren, J. M. and Van Dusseldorp, D. B. W. M. (1980) *Framework for regional planning in developing countries.* Publ. **26**, ILRI, Wageningen, 345 pp.

Van Velthuizen, H. T. (1975) Verslag van een landschapsecologisch onderzoek in het Mugello-bekken (Italië). M.Sc. thesis Wubfac. Fys. Geogr. en Bodemk., Univ. of Amsterdam.

Van Wambeke, A. (1974) Management properties of ferralsols, *Soils Bulletin* no. **23**, FAO, Rome, 129 pp.

Van Zuidam, R. A. and Van Zuidam-Cancellado, F. I. (1978) Terrain analysis and classification using aerial photographs, a geomorphological approach, *ITC Textbook of Photo-interpretation*, vol. I, ch. 6, ITC, Enschede, Netherlands, 310 pp. app.

Van Zuylen, G. F. A. (1971) Stadsklimaat, *Akademiedagen* **22**, Kon.Ned. Akad. Wetensch. Noord-Holl. Uitgevers Mij., Amsterdam, p. 21.

Van Zuylen, G. F. A. (1973) Stadsklimaten, in: P. D. Jungerius, E. A. Koster and F. J. P. M. Kwaad (eds) *Aspecten van het landschapsonderzoek.* Oosthoek, Utrecht, pp. 62–73.

Vavilov, N. I. (1951) Phytogeographic basis of plant breeding; the origin, variation, immunity and breeding of cultivated plants, *Chronica Botanica*, **13**, 1–366 (cited by Frankel, 1972).

Veldkamp, W. J. (1979) Land evaluation of valleys in a tropical rain area – a case study. Ph.D. Thesis, Agric. Univ. Wageningen, 265 pp.

Verbakel, A., Van Amstel, A., Van der Broek, M., Pedroli, B. (1982) Simulation study based on quantitative field information and ecological survey of part of the province of Arezzo (Italy), (in prep.).

Verboom, W. C. (1977) Lines of weakness in forests and early human settlements, *ITC Journal* 1977–3: 531.

Verstappen, H. Th. and Van Zuidam, R. A. (1968) ITC System of Geomorphological Survey, Ch. VII, **2**. ITC Delft-Enschede, 49 pp.

Vink, A. P. A. (1953) Proeven en problemen met betrekking tot bemesting en schaduw in de theecultuur, *Archief voor de Theecultuur*, Bogor, Indonesia, 1953, 33–91.

Vink, A. P. A. (1960) Quantitative aspects of land classification, *Transactions 7th Int. Soil Sci. Congr.*, Madison, Wisc., Section 5.

Vink, A. P. A. (1962) Observations and experiences with some soils in Indonesia, *Boor en Spade* **XII**, pp. 33–48. Stichting voor Bodemkartering, Wageningen.

Vink, A. P. A. (1963a) *Aspects de Pédologie appliquée*. La Baconnière. Neuchatel, Switzerland.

Vink, A. P. A. (1963b) *Planning of Soil Surveys in Land Development*. Publ. **10**, Intern. Inst. Landrecl. and Improvement. ILRI, Wageningen.

Vink, A. P. A. (1964) De natuurlijke gesteldheid als factor in de agrarisch-geografische situatie in Nederland, *Tijdschrift KNAG* **81**: 20.

Vink, A. P. A. (1968) The role of physical geography in integrated surveys in developing countries, *Tijdschr. Econ. Soc. Geogr.* **294**, 5–68.

Vink, A. P. A. (1973) Ricerche sui suoli e i paesaggi nel Lazio e in Toscane, *Rivista Geografica Italiana* **80**, 3, 261–77.

Vink, A. P. A. (1975a) *Land Use in Advancing Agriculture. Advances in Agriculture* 1. Springer, Berlin/Heidelberg.

Vink, A. P. A. (1975b) Cartographie de sols et de paysages en Suisse occidentale, *Geographica Helvetica* (1975), **4**, 169–78.

Vink, A. P. A., (1975c) Les sols urbains, in: P. Duvigneaud and S. Denayer-De Smet (Ed.): *L'écosystème urbain*, Bruxelles, p. 58–61

Vink, A. P. A. (1980) *Landschapsecologie en Landgebruik*. Bohn, Scheltema en Holkema, Utrecht, 160 pp.

Vink, A. P. A. (1981a) Antropocentric landscape ecology in rural areas *Perspectives in Landscape Ecology*, PUDOC, Wageningen.

Vink, A. P. A. (ed.) (1981b) *Land transformation in the Netherlands*. SCOPE, Netherlands National Committee, Wageningen.

Vink, A. P. A. and Van Zuilen, E. J. (1967) De geschiktheid van de bodem van Nederland voor akker- en weidebouw, *Bodemk. Studies* **6**, Stichting voor Bodemkartering. Wageningen.

Vink, A. P. A. and Van Zuilen, E. J. (1974) The suitability of the soils of the Netherlands for arable land and grassland. *Soil Survey Papers* no. **8**, Netherl. Soil Survey Inst., Wageningen, 58 pp.

Vink, A. P. A. and Van de Weg, R. F. (1982) Land and land use in eastern Tuscany, *Rivista Geografica Italiana* (in press).

Wamukoya, O. K. H. (ed.) (1977) Proceedings of a seminar on land evaluation for rangeland use. *Miscellaneous Paper* no. **M 11**, Kenya Soil Survey, Min. Agric. Nairobi, 75 pp.

Welch, D. M. (1978) Land/Water Classification. *Ecol. Land Class. Series*, no. **5**, Environment Canada, Ottawa, Ontario, 54 pp.

Westhoff, V. (1970) New criteria for nature reserves, *New Scientist* (1970), pp. 111–13.

Westhoff, V. (1971) Quelques aspects de la conservation de la nature aux Pays Bas, *Natura Mosana* (Liège), **24**, 33–55.

Wiener, A. (1972) Water resources development and environmental management in developing countries, *Transactions ITC-UNESCO. Symposium on*

Environmental Management and Integrated Surveys. ITC, Enschede.

Williams, P. J. (1979) Pipelines and permafrost: physical geography and development in the circumpolar North. *Topics in Applied Geography*. Longman, London/New York, 98 pp.

Wolff, W. J. (ed.) (1979) *Flora and vegetation of the Wadden Sea*. Leiden State University.

Workshop (1978) *Soil Resource Inventories and Development Planning*, Proceedings of a workshop, held at Cornell Univ., Ithaca, New York.

World Map of Desertification (1977) World Desertification Conference, Nairobi, Doc. A/Conf. 74/2.

Worthington, E. B. (ed.) (1977) *Arid Land Irrigation in Developing Countries*. Pergamon Press, Oxford.

Yahia, H. M. (1971) *Soils and soil conditions in sediments of the Ramadi Province*, Iraq. Ph.D. thesis, Univ. of Amsterdam, 227 pp.

Young, A. (1976) Tropical soils and soil survey. *Cambridge Geogr. Studies* no. **9** Cambridge Univ. Press, 468 pp.

Zonneveld, I. S. (1979) Land evaluation and land(scape) science, *ITC Textbook*, Ch. **VII.4**, ITC Enschede, Netherlands.

Zonneveld, I. S. (1980) Some consequences of the mutual relationship between climate and vegetation in the Sahel and Sudan, *ITC Journal*, Enschede, Netherlands, 1980/2, pp. 255–96.

Zuber, R. *et al.* (1970) Le plomb comme facteur de pollution atmosphérique et son accumulation sur les plantes croissant en bordure des artères à forte densité de circulation. *Publ. no. 849*. Stat. Fédédr. de rech. agronom. de Lausanne. Recherche agronom. en Suisse **9**: 83.

Index